Prentice Hall

MATHEMATICS
Course 2

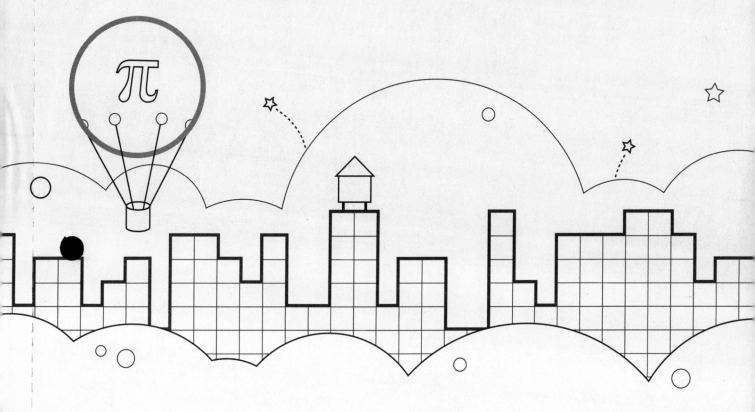

ALL-IN-ONE
Teaching Resources

CHAPTERS 1–4

Boston, Massachusetts • Chandler, Arizona • Glenview, Illinois • Upper Saddle River, New Jersey

ISBN-13: 978-0-13-372127-0
ISBN-10:   0-13-372127-2

PEARSON

3 4 5 6 7 8 9 10 V012 13 12 11 10

All-In-One Teaching Resources

To the Teacher:

During the school year, you use several sources to help create your daily lesson plans. In Prentice Hall's *All-In-One Teaching Resources*, these lesson and chapter based sources are organized for you so that you can plan easily and effectively.

The *All-In-One Teaching Resources* are split into 3 volumes — Chapters 1–4, Chapters 5–8, and Chapters 9–12 — in the same order as the student edition chapters. Inside, you'll find several resources to support and extend every lesson:

- Practice (regular and adapted)
- Guided Problem Solving
- Reteaching
- Enrichment
- Activity Labs
- Daily Puzzles

Additional resources have been designed to support and assess every chapter:

- Vocabulary and Study Skills support
- Checkpoint Quizzes
- Chapter Projects
- Chapter Tests (regular and below level)
- Alternative Assessment
- Cumulative Review

To assist you in effective lesson planning, a special 2-page detail showing each resource page is included in each volume. All resources have been aligned either to a particular lesson, as review, or as assessment material.

At the end of each book, you will also find all of the answers for the chapters in that volume.

How To Read

Chapter

Lessons

Chapter 1: Whole Numbers and Decimals

Lesson	1-1	1-2	1-3	1-4	1-5	1-6	1-7	1-8	1-9		Review	Assess
For Each Lesson												
Practice (regular)	1	9	17	25	35	43	51	59	67			
Practice (adapted)	3	11	19	27	37	45	53	61	69			
Reteaching	5	13	21	29	39	47	55	63	71			
Guided Problem Solving	2	10	18	26	36	44	52	60	68			
Enrichment	6	14	22	30	40	48	56	64	72			
Activity Lab	4	12	20	28	38	46	54	62	70			
Daily Puzzle	8	16	23	33	42	50	57	65	74			
For Each Chapter												
Vocabulary and Study Skills												
Graphic Organizer	7											
Reading Comprehension		15										
Math Symbols					41							
Visual Vocabulary Practice						49						
Vocabulary Check				31								
Vocabulary Review/Puzzle											73	
Chapter Project											75	
Checkpoint Quizzes												79
Chapter Test (regular)												81
Chapter Test (below level)												83
Alternative Assessment												85
Cumulative Review											87	

Resource Types

Page References

Contents Chart

Chapter 1: Decimals and Integers

Lesson	1-1	1-2	1-3	1-4	1-5	1-6	1-7	1-8	1-9	1-10	Review	Assess
For Each Lesson												
Practice (regular)	1	9	17	25	33	41	49	59	67	75		
Practice (adapted)	3	11	19	27	35	43	51	61	69	77		
Reteaching	5	13	21	29	37	45	53	63	71	79		
Guided Problem Solving	2	10	18	26	34	42	50	60	68	76		
Enrichment	6	14	22	30	38	46	54	64	72	80		
Activity Lab	4	12	20	28	36	44	52	62	70	78		
Daily Puzzle	8	15	23	31	40	48	57	65	73	83		
For Each Chapter												
Vocabulary and Study Skills												
Graphic Organizer	7											
Reading Comprehension					39							
Math Symbols						47						
Visual Vocabulary Practice										81		
Vocabulary Check							55					
Vocabulary Review/Puzzle											82	
Chapter Project											84	
Checkpoint Quizzes												88
Chapter Test (regular)												89
Chapter Test (below level)												91
Alternative Assessment												93
Cumulative Review											95	

Chapter 2: Exponents, Factors, and Fractions

Lesson	2-1	2-2	2-3	2-4	2-5	2-6	2-7	2-8			Review	Assess
For Each Lesson												
Practice (regular)	97	105	113	121	129	137	147	155				
Practice (adapted)	99	107	115	123	131	139	149	157				
Reteaching	101	109	117	125	133	141	151	159				
Guided Problem Solving	98	106	114	122	130	138	148	156				
Enrichment	102	110	118	126	134	142	152	160				
Activity Lab	100	108	116	124	132	140	150	158				
Daily Puzzle	104	111	119	127	136	145	154	163				
For Each Chapter												
Vocabulary and Study Skills												
Graphic Organizer	103											
Reading Comprehension					135							
Math Symbols						153						
Visual Vocabulary Practice							161					
Vocabulary Check						143						
Vocabulary Review/Puzzle											162	
Chapter Project											164	
Checkpoint Quizzes												168
Chapter Test (regular)												169
Chapter Test (below level)												171
Alternative Assessment												173
Cumulative Review											175	

Contents Chart (continued)

Chapter 3: Operations with Fractions

Lesson	3-1	3-2	3-3	3-4	3-5	3-6	3-7				Review	Assess
For Each Lesson												
Practice (regular)	177	185	193	201	209	217	227					
Practice (adapted)	179	187	195	203	211	219	229					
Reteaching	181	189	197	205	213	221	231					
Guided Problem Solving	178	186	194	202	210	218	228					
Enrichment	182	190	198	206	214	222	232					
Activity Lab	180	188	196	204	212	220	230					
Daily Puzzle	184	191	199	207	216	225	236					
For Each Chapter												
Vocabulary and Study Skills												
Graphic Organizer	183											
Reading Comprehension						223						
Math Symbols						224						
Visual Vocabulary Practice					215							
Vocabulary Check						233						
Vocabulary Review/Puzzle											235	
Chapter Project											237	
Checkpoint Quizzes												241
Chapter Test (regular)												243
Chapter Test (below level)												245
Alternative Assessment												247
Cumulative Review											249	

Chapter 4: Algebra: Equations and Inequalities

Lesson	4-1	4-2	4-3	4-4	4-5	4-6	4-7	4-8	4-9	Review	Assess
For Each Lesson											
Practice (regular)	251	259	267	275	283	291	299	307	315		
Practice (adapted)	253	261	269	277	285	293	301	309	317		
Reteaching	255	263	271	279	287	295	303	311	319		
Guided Problem Solving	252	260	268	276	284	292	300	308	316		
Enrichment	256	264	272	280	288	296	304	312	320		
Activity Lab	254	262	270	278	286	294	302	310	318		
Daily Puzzle	258	266	274	281	289	297	305	314	324		
For Each Chapter											
Vocabulary and Study Skills											
Graphic Organizer	257										
Reading Comprehension		265									
Math Symbols			273								
Visual Vocabulary Practice							313				
Vocabulary Check								321			
Vocabulary Review/Puzzle										323	
Chapter Project										325	
Checkpoint Quizzes											329
Chapter Test (regular)											331
Chapter Test (below level)											333
Alternative Assessment											335
Cumulative Review										337	

Practice 1-1

Using Estimation Strategies

Use rounding to estimate the nearest half-dollar.

1. $4.85
    + 1.47
    _____

2. $6.79
    − 3.95
    _____

3. $14.19
    + 5.59
    _____

4. $25.43
    − 21.20
    _____

Use front-end estimation to estimate each sum.

5. 4.76 + 6.15

6. 1.409 + 3.512

7. 2.479 + 6.518

8. 3.17 + 2.72

9. 9.87 + 2.16

10. 5.89 + 7.21

Use compatible numbers to estimate each quotient.

11. 76.32 ÷ 24.98

12. 42.693 ÷ 4.7

13. 54.36 ÷ 11.001

Use any estimation strategy to calculate. Tell which strategy you used.

14. $66.93 + $72.18 + $69.18 + $71.94 + $65.75

15. 93.26 − 69.78

16. 51.12 × 87.906

17. 457.03 + 592.8

18. 702 ÷ 61

19. 12.87 + 14.31 + 15.09

20. 536 ÷ 41

Find each estimate.

21. A rare truffle once sold for $13.20 for a 0.44 oz can.
    Approximately how much would 1 lb of this truffle cost?

22. The length of the longest loaf of bread measured 1,405 ft $1\frac{3}{4}$ in. It
    was cut into slices $\frac{1}{2}$ in. thick. How many slices were there?

1-1 • Guided Problem Solving

GPS Student Page 7, Exercise 32:

Travel On vacation, you wish to send eight postcards to friends at home. You find cards costing $.59 each. Eight postcard stamps cost about $2 total. About how much will it cost to buy and mail the cards?

Understand

1. Circle the information you will need to solve the problem.

2. What are you being asked to do?

   _____

   _____

3. Before you estimate the total cost, what do you have to estimate first?

   _____

Plan and Carry Out

4. Round $.59 to the nearest tenth. _____

5. Use the answer to Step 4 to estimate the product 8×0.59.

   _____

6. About how much are eight postcard stamps?

   _____

7. About how much will it cost to buy and mail the cards?

   _____

Check

8. Is your estimate reasonable? Multiply 8 by 0.59 and then add 2.

   _____

   _____

Solve Another Problem

9. Paul stops by the market to buy his lunch. The market is selling bananas for $.22 each and sandwiches for $3.95. About how much does Paul spend if he buys a sandwich and 4 bananas?

   _____

   _____

Practice 1-1

Using Estimation Strategies

Use rounding to estimate the nearest half-dollar.

1. $4.85
+ 1.47
_____

2. $6.79
− 3.95
_____

3. $14.19
+ 5.59
_____

Use front-end estimation to estimate each sum.

4. 4.76 + 6.15

_____

5. 1.409 + 3.512

_____

6. 3.17 + 2.72

_____

7. 9.87 + 2.16

_____

Use compatible numbers to estimate each quotient.

8. 76.32 ÷ 24.98

_____

9. 42.693 ÷ 4.7

_____

Use any estimation strategy to calculate. Tell which strategy you used.

10. 93.26 − 69.78

_____

11. 51.12 × 87.906

_____

12. 457.03 + 592.8

_____

13. 702 ÷ 61

_____

14. 12.87 + 14.31 + 15.09

_____

15. 536 ÷ 41

_____

Find each estimate.

16. A rare truffle once sold for $13.20 for a 0.44 oz can.
Approximately how much would 1 lb of this truffle cost?

_____

17. The length of the longest loaf of bread measured 1,405 ft $1\frac{3}{4}$ in. It
was cut into slices $\frac{1}{2}$ in. thick. How many slices were there?

_____

Activity Lab 1-1

Using Estimation Strategies

You and your friends are going out to eat at a local diner. You each have $8.75 to spend on food. The prices of the various dishes are listed on the menu below.

Entrees		**Side Dishes**	
Sirloin Steak	$4.99	Mashed Potatoes	$0.99
Baked Chicken	$3.79	Macaroni and Cheese	$1.09
Fried Chicken	$3.59	Dinner Roll	$0.59
Meatloaf	$3.19	Creamed Corn	$1.19
Fish Sticks	$3.49	Green Beans	$0.79
Baked Fish	$5.39	Okra	$0.79
Veggie Burger	$4.19	French Fries	$1.29
Large Salad	$4.89	Glazed Carrots	$0.89
Desserts		**Drinks**	
Tapioca Pudding	$1.49	Tea	$0.99
Chocolate Pie	$1.79	Juice	$1.29
Sorbet	$0.79	Bottled Water	$1.09
Fruit Cup	$1.39		

1. Select one item from each list. Use front-end estimation and rounding to create estimates of how much your dinner will cost.

   _____

   _____

2. What was the difference in your estimates? Which estimate was higher? Do you estimate that you can afford this dinner?

   _____

   _____

3. You decide that you are hungrier than you thought, so you want to get two side dishes instead of one. Choose another side dish and make two new estimates for the cost of your meal. If your estimates suggest that you can't afford the meal, revise your choices.

   _____

   _____

4. Compute the actual price of your meal. Which estimate came closest to the actual cost?

   _____

Reteaching 1-1

One way to estimate a sum, difference, or product is to round numbers to the nearest whole number. Then add, subtract, multiply or divide.

Round to the nearest whole number

$$1.6 \rightarrow 2$$
$$+ 4.4 \rightarrow + 4$$
$$\overline{\qquad 6 \text{ Estimate}}$$

Round to the nearest whole number

$$17.2 \rightarrow 20$$
$$\times 7.3 \rightarrow \times 7$$
$$\overline{\qquad 140 \text{ Estimate}}$$

You can get a quick estimate if you use *compatible numbers* to compute mentally.

$$\begin{array}{c} \$24.27 \\ - \quad 8.79 \end{array} \longrightarrow \begin{array}{c} \$24.00 \\ - \quad 9.00 \\ \hline \$15.00 \text{ Estimate} \end{array}$$

Estimate each sum, difference, product or quotient.

Estimate   **Estimate**

1. $9.265 \rightarrow$ _____   2. $12.91 \rightarrow$ _____
    $+6.840 \rightarrow +$_____ $- 7.80 \rightarrow -$_____
    _____   _____

3. $\$16.49 \rightarrow$ _____   4. $2.362 \rightarrow$ _____
    $- 5.25 \rightarrow -$_____ $+ 0.815 \rightarrow +$_____
    _____   _____

5. $2.4 \rightarrow$ _____   6. $6.5 \rightarrow$ _____
    $\times 5.2 \rightarrow \times$_____ $\times 0.9 \rightarrow \times$_____
    _____   _____

7. $\$12.09 \rightarrow$ _____   8. $6.147 \rightarrow$ _____
    $- 10.55 \rightarrow -$_____ $+ 0.715 \rightarrow +$_____
    _____   _____

9. $65.4 \rightarrow$ _____   10. $27.14 \rightarrow$ _____
    $- 22.2 \rightarrow -$_____ $\times 3.1 \rightarrow \times$_____
    _____   _____

11. $9.21 \rightarrow$ _____   12. $110.2 \rightarrow$ _____
    $\div 3.95 \rightarrow \div$_____ $\div 10.8 \rightarrow \div$_____
    _____   _____

Enrichment 1-1

Decision Making

The Johnston Community Center is having a fundraising chili supper
and has already sold 953 tickets. This is the recipe they used.

JOHNSTON'S CHILI
9 lb hamburger   3 large cans tomato juice
6 cans chili beans   1 T salt
3 packages of macaroni   3 T chili powder
3 large onions
Serves 18

1. Estimate how many batches of chili are needed to serve
   953 people. Make estimates using front-end estimation, using
   rounding to estimate, and using compatible numbers to estimate.
   Show your work.

   _____

   _____

2. Look at your three estimates. Would all of the estimates be good
   guides for planning the amount of chili needed? Explain.

   _____

   _____

3. Suppose they predict that about 200 tickets will be sold at the
   door. How will this change the estimates?

   _____

   _____

4. Would it be more desirable to end up with too much chili or with
   not enough chili to serve the customers? How can they plan to
   handle each problem?

   _____

   _____

1A: Graphic Organizer

For use before Lesson 1-1

Study Skill As you begin a new textbook, look through the table of contents to see what kind of information you will be learning during the year. Notice that some of the topics were introduced last year. Get a head start by reviewing your old notes and problems.

Write your answers.

1. What is the chapter title? _____

2. How many lessons are there in this chapter? _____

3. What is the topic of the Test-Taking Strategies page? _____

4. Complete the graphic organizer below as you work through the chapter.
   - In the center, write the title of the chapter.
   - When you begin a lesson, write the lesson name in a rectangle.
   - When you complete a lesson, write a skill or key concept in a circle linked to that lesson block.
   - When you complete the chapter, use this graphic organizer to help you review.

Puzzle 1-1

Using Estimation Strategies

Create a path through the chart. Start where indicated, and build the path by following the steps below.

- Complete each exercise.

- Find and circle the answer in the chart that continues your path.

- Continue until your path reaches the right side of the chart.

Estimate. First round to the nearest whole number.

1. $1.82 + 4.16$

2. $7.75 - 3.02$

3. 6.19×1.76

4. $9.89 \div 5.42$

5. 2.25×3.69

6. $12.36 - 9.38$

7. $2.06 + 7.72$

8. $6.65 + 5.44$

9. $4.68 \div 5.41$

10. 3.32×3.65

11. $0.74 + 8.02$

12. $4.65 - 3.39$

5	4	2	3	8	10	12	6	F
2	15	9	2	6	9	10	1	I
4	12	2	8	4	8	1	3	N
6	5	6	3	9	12	9	2	I
6	6	9	10	12	1	9	4	S
1	5	3	11	0	2	8	5	H

(Left side labeled: S T A R T)

Name _____ Class _____ Date _____

Practice 1-2

Identify each property shown.

1. $(8.7 + 6.3) + 3.7 = 8.7 + (6.3 + 3.7)$

2. $9.06 + 0 = 9.06$

3. $4.06 + 8.92 = 8.92 + 4.06$

4. $0 + 7.13 = 7.13 + 0$

Find each sum.

5. $4.6 + 8.79$

6. $14.8 + 29.07$

7. $20.16 + 15.703$

8. $36.12 + 5.793$

9. $8.9 + 2.14 + 7.1$

10. $3.6 + 5.27 + 8.93$

11. $107.5 + 6$

12. $15.26 + 13.29 + 38.96$

13. $46.21 + 53.942$

Find each difference.

14. $8.7 - 2.03$

15. $53.86 - 4.02$

16. $14.59 - 8.3$

17. $42.75 - 26.36$

18. $53.86 - 16.47$

19. $56.89 - 48.91$

20. $5.06 - 3.297$

21. $3.4 - 2.768$

22. $5.002 - 4.3$

Use the advertisement at the right. Find each cost.

23. 1 egg _____

24. toast _____

25. bacon _____

26. milk _____

27. 1 egg and milk _____

28. 1 egg and bacon _____

2 eggs, toast, bacon, milk	$2.75
1 egg, toast, bacon, milk	$2.20
toast, milk	$0.90
toast, bacon, milk	$1.65
1 egg, toast	$0.95

1-2 • Guided Problem Solving

GPS **Student Page 11, Exercise 39:**

Weather During a 3-day storm, 8.91 in. of rain fell in Tallahassee and 4.24 in. fell in St. Augustine. How much more rain fell in Tallahassee than in St. Augustine?

Understand

1. Circle the information you will need to solve the problem.

2. What are you being asked to do?

   _____

   _____

3. Which word group tells you what operation to perform?

   _____

   _____

Plan and Carry Out

4. How do you align the addends in 8.91 and 4.24? Show your work.

   _____

5. What do you need to do in order to subtract these two numbers?

   _____

6. How much more rain was there in Tallahassee than in St. Augustine?

   _____

Check

7. How would you check the result in Step 6?

   _____

Solve Another Problem

8. Laurie has $10.59 left after buying a refreshment. If the refreshment cost $3.91 after tax, how much did Laurie have before she bought it?

   _____

Practice 1-2

Identify each property shown.

1. $(8.7 + 6.3) + 3.7 = 8.7 + (6.3 + 3.7)$

2. $9.06 + 0 = 9.06$

3. $4.06 + 8.92 = 8.92 + 4.06$

4. $0 + 7.13 = 7.13 + 0$

Find each sum.

5. $4.6 + 8.79$

6. $14.8 + 29.07$

7. $36.12 + 5.793$

8. $8.9 + 2.14 + 7.1$

9. $107.5 + 6$

10. $15.26 + 13.29 + 38.96$

Find each difference.

11. $8.7 - 2.03$

12. $53.86 - 4.02$

13. $42.75 - 26.36$

14. $53.86 - 16.47$

15. $5.06 - 3.297$

16. $3.4 - 2.768$

Use the advertisement at the right. Find each cost.

17. 1 egg _____

18. toast _____

19. bacon _____

20. milk _____

21. 1 egg and milk _____

22. 1 egg and bacon _____

2 eggs	$1.10
1 egg, toast, bacon, milk	$2.20
toast, milk	$0.90
toast, bacon, milk	$1.65
1 egg, toast	$0.95

Activity Lab 1-2

Adding and Subtracting Decimals

Use the map to make your decisions on which routes to take.
Sometimes you can choose different types of routes between two
cities. The route may be mostly toll roads, mostly divided highways, or
mostly scenic routes.

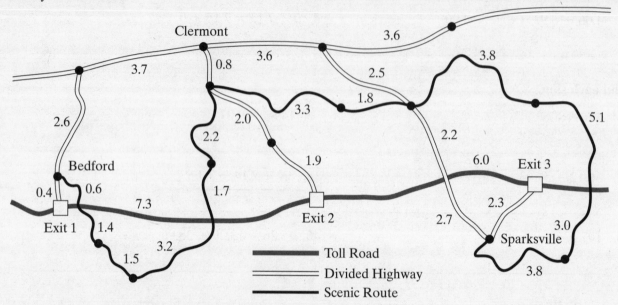

1. Find the total distance in miles between the two given cities for
   each type of route. Include not only the miles traveled mostly on
   a specific type of road but also the miles traveled to reach the
   road. Circle the miles in the route you would rather take.

Distance in miles when driving mostly:

	Toll roads	Divided highways	Scenic routes
Bedford to Clermont			
Clermont to Sparksville			
Bedford to Sparksville			

2. Explain why you chose each route.

   _____

   _____

   _____

3. Other than looking at different routes on a map, what
   other factors do you need to know in order to make an
   informed choice?

   _____

   _____

Reteaching 1-2

Add 3.19 + 6.098 + 26.7.

① Round to estimate.

$$3.19 \rightarrow 3$$
$$6.098 \rightarrow 6$$
$$+ \ 26.7 \rightarrow + 27$$
$$\overline{\hphantom{+ \ 26.7 \rightarrow} 36}$$

② Line up the decimal points.

$$3.19$$
$$6.098$$
$$+ \ 26.700$$

③ Write zeros. Then add.

$$3.190$$
$$6.098$$
$$+ \ 26.700$$
$$\overline{35.988}$$

Compare to make sure your answer is reasonable: 35.988 is close to 36.

Subtract 8.7 − 4.97.

① Round to estimate.

$$8.7 \rightarrow 9$$
$$- \ 4.97 \rightarrow - 5$$
$$\overline{\hphantom{- \ 4.97 \rightarrow} 4}$$

② Line up the decimal points.

$$8.7$$
$$- \ 4.97$$

③ Write zeros. Then subtract.

$$8.70$$
$$- \ 4.97$$
$$\overline{3.73}$$

Compare to make sure your answer is reasonable: 3.73 is close to 4.

Find each sum or difference.

1.
$$46.2$$
$$- \ 34.09$$

2.
$$3.31$$
$$+ \ 9.075$$

3.
$$9.06$$
$$- \ 7.2$$

4.
$$84.32$$
$$+ \ 6.94$$

5.
$$8.037$$
$$+ \ 1.9$$

6.
$$10.6$$
$$- \ 4.59$$

7. 4.102 + 7.7

8. 5.4 − 1.6

9. 7.09 + 4.3 + 20.1

10. 0.392 − 0.26

11. 15.64 − 8.5

12. 8.709 + 3.2

Enrichment 1-2

Adding and Subtracting Decimals

Critical Thinking

Ramona's dog walked across her math homework with his muddy paws.

She reconstructed the problem like this:

- There is a 0 in the hundredths place in the second number, so the missing digit must be **7**.

- In the tenths place, 6 added to 2 is 8. The missing digit must be **6**.

- The sum shows a 1 as the sum in the ones place. So the actual sum must have been 11. Add **2** to 9 to get 11.

- In the tens place, the sum of the 1 ten from the ones column, 3 tens and 1 ten is **5** tens.

- There is no digit in the hundreds place in the first number. So the missing digit must be **4**.

```
    3 □ . 2 □
  + □ 1 9 . □ 0
  ─────────────
    4 □ 1 . 8 7
         ↓
    3 [2] . 2 [7]
  + [4] 1 9 . [6] 0
  ─────────────
    4 [5] 1 . 8 7
```

Ramona's reconstructed problem is 32.27 + 419.6 = 451.87.

Help Ramona reconstruct the rest of her problems.

1.
```
    9 9 . 9 9 9
  + □ □ . □ □ □
  ─────────────
  1 8 7 . 6 5 4
```

2.
```
    2 3 . 0 □ 9
  +   □ 7 . □ 9 □
  ─────────────
    □ 3 2 . 9 0 1
```

3.
```
    7 □ 8 . 6 □ 9
  + □ 3 0 . □ 8 □
  ─────────────
  1 1 3 □ . 6 1 5
```

4.
```
    □ 2 7 . 3 □ 0
  - 6 □ □ . 0 5 □
  ─────────────
    1 9 1 . □ 8 1
```

Name _____ Class _____ Date _____

Puzzle 1-2
Adding and Subtracting Decimals

Fill in the boxes below to make each sum or difference true.

1.
```
    9  9  .  9  9  9
 +  □  □  .  □  □  □
 ─────────────────────
 1  8  7  .  6  5  4
```

2.
```
    2  3  □  .  0  □  9
 +     □  7  .  □  9  □
 ──────────────────────
    □  3  2  .  9  0  1
```

3.
```
    7  □  8  .  6  □  9
 +  □  3  0  .  □  8  □
 ─────────────────────
 1  1  3  □  .  6  1  7
```

4.
```
    □  2  7  .  3  □  0
 −  6  □  □  .  0  5  □
 ─────────────────────
    1  9  1  .  □  8  1
```

5.
```
    □  2  .  6  □  1
 −  7  □  .  5  7  □
 ────────────────────
       7  .  □  8  2
```

Find the sum of the numbers in the boxes to fill in the blank:

As of 2006, the Amercian Kennel Club recognizes _____ different breeds of dogs.

Practice 1-3

Multiplying Decimals

Find each product.

1. 28×6

2. $7.3 \cdot 0.9$

3. $58 \cdot 2.1$

_____

4. $15(187)$

5. 6.6×25

6. $(1.8)(0.7)$

_____

7. $0.91 \cdot 2.7$

8. $4.6(3.9)$

9. 17.3×15.23

_____

10. $2.33(3.56)$

11. 12.15×19

12. 481.51×623.42

_____

Rewrite each equation with the decimal point in the correct place in the product.

13. $5.6 \times 1.2 = 672$

14. $3.7 \times 2.4 = 888$

15. $6.5 \times 2.5 = 1625$

_____

16. $1.02 \times 6.9 = 7038$

17. $4.4 \times 6.51 = 28644$

18. $0.6 \times 9.312 = 55872$

_____

Name the property of multiplication shown.

19. $3 \times 4 = 4 \times 3$

20. $9 \times (6 \times 3) = (9 \times 6) \times 3$

_____

21. $2 \times 0 = 0$

22. $10 \times 1 = 10$

_____

Solve.

23. Each trip on a ride at the carnival costs $1.25. If Tara goes on 4 rides, how much will it cost her?

24. Postage stamps cost $0.37 each. How much does a book of 50 stamps cost?

_____

1-3 • Guided Problem Solving

GPS Student Page 17, Exercise 39:

One year, Texas had about 2.6 times as many head of cattle as Oklahoma. Oklahoma had 5.2 million. How many head of cattle did Texas have?

Understand

1. Circle the information you will need to solve the problem.

2. What are you being asked to do? _____

_____

Plan and Carry Out

3. How many million head of cattle were in Oklahoma?

_____

4. How many times more cattle did Texas have than Oklahoma?

_____

5. Write an expression for the number of cattle in Texas (in millions).

_____

6. How many decimal places are in both factors?

_____

7. Multiply as if the numbers are whole numbers.

_____

8. Place the decimal in the product using the total number of decimal places from Step 6.

_____

Check

9. Estimate the product of 2.6 × 5.2, and compare it to your answer. Is your answer reasonable?

_____

Solve Another Problem

10. You buy 6.5 yards of fabric that costs $7.95 per yard. How much money does it cost?

_____

Practice 1-3

Find each product.

1. 28×6

2. $7.3 \cdot 0.9$

3. $58 \cdot 2.1$

4. $15(187)$

5. 6.6×25

6. $(1.8)(0.7)$

7. $0.91 \cdot 2.7$

8. $4.6(3.9)$

9. 17.3×15.23

Rewrite each equation with the decimal point in the correct place in the product.

10. $5.6 \times 1.2 = 672$

11. $3.7 \times 2.4 = 888$

12. $1.02 \times 6.9 = 7038$

13. $4.4 \times 6.51 = 28644$

Name the property of multiplication shown.

14. $3 \times 4 = 4 \times 3$

15. $9 \times (6 \times 3) = (9 \times 6) \times 3$

16. $2 \times 0 = 0$

17. $10 \times 1 = 10$

Solve.

18. Each trip on a ride at the carnival costs $1.25.
If Tara goes on 4 rides, how much will it cost her?

19. Postage stamps cost $0.37 each. How much does
a book of 50 stamps cost?

Activity Lab 1-3

Multiplying Decimals

Taxing Problems

A city requires an 8.25% sales tax to be added to all merchandise sold at shops or restaurants. You can use decimal multiplication to determine the total cost of an item as follows:

Original Cost $\times$ 1.0825 = Cost Including Sales Tax.

For example, if a CD is priced at $11.99, the total cost rounded to the nearest cent is:

$11.99 \times 1.0825 = 12.98

Randy is opening a new coffee shop. He created the menu listed in the table below, and now wants to figure out how much each item will cost including sales tax. Complete the table. Round each answer to the nearest cent.

Item	Original Price	Price Including Sales Tax
Bagel	$1.20	$1.20 $\times$ 1.0825 = $1.30
Muffin	$1.75	
Cinnamon Roll	$2.00	
Scone	$1.35	
Hot Chocolate	$2.15	
Hot Tea	$1.60	
Iced Tea	$1.80	
Small Coffee	$0.98	
Medium Coffee	$1.15	
Large Coffee	$1.70	

Reteaching 1-3

Multiplying Decimals

Multiply 5.43 × 1.8.

① Multiply as if the numbers
were whole numbers.

② Count the total number of
decimal places in the
factors.

$$
\begin{array}{r}
5.43 \\
\times\ \ 1.8 \\
\hline
4344 \\
+\ 543\ \ \\
\hline
9.774
\end{array}
$$

⎱ 3 decimal places

← 3 decimal places

③ Place the decimal
point in the product.

Find each product.

1. $\begin{array}{r} 1.42 \\ \times\ 7.2 \\ \hline \end{array}$

2. $\begin{array}{r} 2.2 \\ \times\ 4.1 \\ \hline \end{array}$

3. $\begin{array}{r} 5.11 \\ \times\ 0.3 \\ \hline \end{array}$

4. $\begin{array}{r} 3.68 \\ \times\ 5.8 \\ \hline \end{array}$

5. 2.8 × 0.05

6. 1.45 · 0.7

7. (2.07)(4.9)

_____

_____

_____

8. 9.3(0.56)

9. 0.006(3.75)

10. 3.8 × 912

_____

_____

_____

Rewrite each equation with the decimal point in the correct place in the product.

11. 19.2 × 12.3 = 23616

12. 4.35(2.44) = 106140

13. 14 × 8.66 = 12124

_____

_____

_____

14. 10.821 × 62.4 = 6752304

15. 1.321 × 2.23 = 294583

16. 0.233 × 19.22 = 447826

_____

_____

_____

Enrichment 1-3

Patterns in Numbers

Find each product.

1. 26×3 _____

26×0.3 _____

26×0.03 _____

26×0.003 _____

2. 26×3 _____

2.6×3 _____

0.26×3 _____

0.026×3 _____

3. What pattern do you notice in the products?

_____

_____

_____

4. Use the digits 3 and 26 as factors. Find three different pairs of numbers using any combination of decimal places whose product is 0.0000078.

_____

_____

Rewrite each equation, adding one or more decimal points to make the equation true. You may also need to add zeros. Each exercise may have more than one correct answer.

5. $16 \times 1{,}175 = 188$

_____

6. $16 \times 1{,}175 = 18.8$

_____

7. $16 \times 1{,}175 = 1.88$

_____

8. $16 \times 1{,}175 = 0.188$

_____

9. $16 \times 1{,}175 = 0.0188$

_____

10. $16 \times 1{,}175 = 0.00188$

_____

11. $16 \times 1{,}175 = 0.000188$

_____

12. $16 \times 1{,}175 = 0.0000188$

_____

13. $16 \times 1{,}175 = 0.0000188$

_____

Puzzle 1-3

Find the answer to each question. Then fill in the puzzle so that all of the digits match correctly.

1. Charlotte has seven pennies, two dimes, and five nickels. How much money does she have in total?

   $0.52
   _____

2. Jim has three boxes of nickels. Each box contains 17 nickels. How much money does Jim have in total?

   _____

3. Three friends are having lunch at a restaurant. When the bill arrives, they decide to split the cost evenly. If each person contributes $8.12, what is the total bill?

   _____

4. Jack earns $7.16 per hour. His older brother earns 3.5 times as much per hour as Jack earns. How much does Jack's brother earn?

   _____

5. A garage door is twice as long as it is tall. If the door is 25.1 feet tall, how long is it?

   _____

6. The depth of East Mountain Creek is 0.3 times its width. At one point, the creek is 14.1 feet wide. How deep is the creek at this point?

   _____

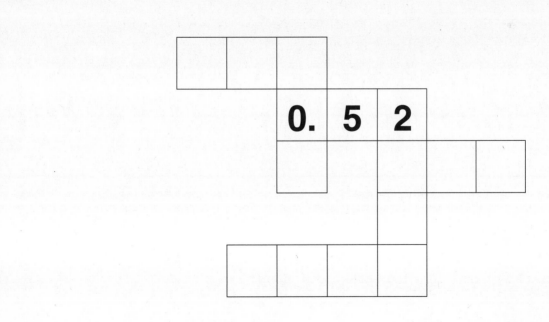

Practice 1-4

Find each quotient.

1. $0.7 \div 100$

2. $4.85 \div 0.1$

3. $7.08 \div 10$

4. $3.5 \div 0.1$

5. $847 \div 0.01$

6. $0.3 \div 0.1$

7. $32.6 \div 0.01$

8. $5.02 \div 0.1$

9. $2.1\overline{)12.6}$

10. $29.75 \div 0.7$

11. $37 \div 0.2$

12. $4.74 \div 0.06$

13. $1.414 \div 1.4$

14. $0.78\overline{)0.16614}$

15. $0.154 \div 5.5$

16. $0.85\overline{)0.0527}$

Annex zeros to find each quotient.

17. $1.3 \div 0.8$

18. $2.4\overline{)5.4}$

19. $79.04 \div 9.5$

20. $36.78 \div 2.4$

21. $\frac{58.5}{10.4}$

22. $1.2\overline{)38.7}$

Solve.

23. Alicia paid $1.32 for a bag of pinto beans. The beans cost $.55 per lb. How much did the bag of pinto beans weigh?

24. Nina and 3 friends ate lunch at a cafe. They decided to split the bill evenly. The total bill was $17.84. How much was each person's share?

1-4 • Guided Problem Solving

GPS **Student Page 23, Exercise 33:**

Landscaping After digging up lilac bushes in the garden, a landscape architect uses sod to cover the dirt. The sod costs $2.25/yd. He pays $31.50. How much sod does he buy?

Understand

1. Circle the information you will need to solve the problem.

2. What are you being asked to do?

   _____

   _____

3. Which operation must you perform to determine the answer?

   _____

Plan and Carry Out

4. How much money does the landscape architect spend?

   _____

5. How much is each yard of sod?

   _____

6. What is $31.50 ÷ $2.25/yd?

   _____

Check

7. Calculate $2.25/yd × 14 yd. Does your answer equal the total amount of money spent?

   _____

Solve Another Problem

8. Marissa created a platform for the set of the school play. She used boards that are each 3.15 in. wide. If the platform is 37.8 inches wide, how many boards did Marissa use?

   _____

Practice 1-4

Find each quotient.

1. $0.7 \div 100$

2. $4.85 \div 0.1$

3. $7.08 \div 10$

4. $3.5 \div 0.1$

_____

5. $847 \div 0.01$

6. $0.3 \div 0.1$

7. $32.6 \div 0.01$

8. $5.02 \div 0.1$

_____

9. $2.1\overline{)12.6}$

10. $29.75 \div 0.7$

11. $37 \div 0.2$

12. $4.74 \div 0.06$

_____

Annex zeros to find each quotient.

13. $1.3 \div 0.8$

14. $2.4\overline{)5.4}$

_____

15. $36.78 \div 2.4$

16. $\frac{58.5}{10.4}$

_____

Solve.

17. Alicia paid $1.32 for a bag of pinto beans. The beans cost $.55 per lb. How much did the bag of pinto beans weigh?

_____

18. Nina and 3 friends ate lunch at a cafe. They decided to split the bill evenly. The total bill was $17.84. How much was each person's share?

_____

Activity Lab 1-4

Dividing Decimals

Find each product.

1. 26 × 3 _____

26 × 0.3 _____

26 × 0.03 _____

2. 26 × 3 _____

2.6 × 3 _____

0.26 × 3 _____

3. What pattern do you notice in the products?

_____

_____

4. Use the digits 3 and 26 as factors. Find three different pairs of numbers whose product is 0.0000078, using any combination of decimal places.

_____

Find each quotient.

5. 408 ÷ 12 _____

408 ÷ 1.2 _____

408 ÷ 0.12 _____

408 ÷ 0.012 _____

6. 408 ÷ 12 _____

40.8 ÷ 12 _____

4.08 ÷ 12 _____

0.408 ÷ 12 _____

7. What pattern do you notice in the quotients?

_____

_____

_____

8. Use the digits 12 as the divisor and 408 as the dividend. Find three different pairs of numbers whose quotient is 0.000034, using any combination of decimal places.

_____

Name _____ Class _____ Date _____

Reteaching 1-4

Dividing Decimals

Divide $38.25 \div 1.5$.

① Rewrite the problem with a whole number divisor. $1.5\overline{)38.25}$
                                                              ↓

② Place the decimal point in the quotient. $1.5.\overline{)38.2.5}$
                                                    ↑   ↑
                                              Move 1 place each.

③ Divide. Then check.

$$
\begin{array}{r}
25.5 \\
15\overline{)382.5} \\
-30 \\
\hline
82 \\
-75 \\
\hline
7\,5 \\
-7\,5 \\
\hline
0
\end{array}
$$

$25.5 \times 15 = 382.5$ ✔
Multiply to check.

Rewrite each problem so the divisor is a whole number.

1. $5.1\overline{)351.9}$ _____

2. $1.8\overline{)14.9}$ _____

3. $0.32\overline{)3968}$ _____

4. $0.06\overline{)0.948}$ _____

5. $0.8\overline{)2112}$ _____

6. $0.49\overline{)9.457}$ _____

Find each quotient.

7. $2\overline{)15.8}$

8. $0.4\overline{)22}$

9. $0.09\overline{)99}$

10. $2.7\overline{)12.15}$

11. $0.14\overline{)2814}$

12. $0.08\overline{)0.64}$

Rewrite each equation with the decimal point in the correct place in the quotient.

13. $18.6 \div 2.4 = 775$

14. $44.66 \div 11.2 = 39875$

15. $48.15 \div 16.05 = 30$

_____

_____

_____

16. $10.8 \div 0.9 = 120$

17. $111.6018 \div 16.2 = 6889$

18. $41.35456 \div 3.2 = 129233$

_____

_____

_____

Enrichment 1-4

Patterns in Numbers

Find each quotient.

1. $408 \div 12$ _____

$408 \div 1.2$ _____

$408 \div 0.12$ _____

$408 \div 0.012$ _____

2. $408 \div 12$ _____

$40.8 \div 12$ _____

$4.08 \div 12$ _____

$0.408 \div 12$ _____

3. What pattern do you notice in the quotients?

_____

_____

_____

_____

4. Use the digits 12 as the divisor and 408 as the dividend. Find three different pairs of numbers using any combination of decimal places whose quotient is 0.000034.

_____

_____

5. Fill in the empty boxes in the table below.

34.83	÷	0.0000215	=	
34.83	÷		=	162,000
34.83	÷	0.00215	=	
34.83	÷	0.0215	=	
34.83	÷		=	162
34.83	÷		=	16.2
34.83	÷	21.5	=	
34.83	÷		=	0.162

Puzzle 1-4

Dividing Decimals

Frank's suitcase has a lock with a five-digit code. He created the chart
below so that if he ever forgot the code, he could re-create it. Use the
flowchart with the given operations to determine the code.

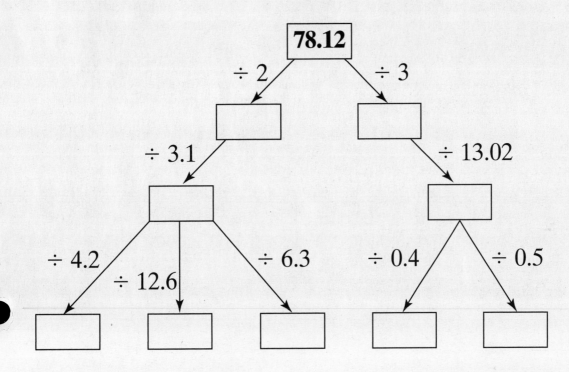

What is the code to Frank's suitcase?

___ ___ ___ ___ ___

Name _____ Class _____ Date _____

Practice 1-5

Measuring in Metric Units

Choose a reasonable estimate.

1. Length of a calculator   18 m   18 cm   18 mm

2. Length of a football field   100 km   100 m   100 cm

3. Thickness of a paperback book   25 km   25 m   25 mm

4. Capacity of a bottle of shampoo   250 mL   250 L   250 kL

Complete each statement. If necessary, use a number line.

5. 0.7 km = _____ m   6. _____ L = 40 mL   7. 83 m = _____ mm

8. 9,500 m = _____ km   9. 8 g = _____ kg   10. _____ m = 800 km

Change each measurement to the given unit.

11. 43 km 14 m to kilometers _____

12. 84 m 15 cm to centimeters _____

13. 9 kg 421 g to kilograms _____

14. 14 L 7 mL to liters _____

Write the metric unit that makes each statement true.

15. 9.85 kg = 9,850 _____   16. 87.43 m = 8,743 _____

17. 10,542 mL = 10.542 _____   18. 8.42 mm = 0.842 _____

19. 2,347 m = 2.347 _____   20. 0.356 m = 356 _____

Solve.

21. The capacity of a beaker is 150 mL. How many beakers can be filled from a 4 L container?

    _____

22. Vitamin C comes in pills with a strength of 500 mg. How many pills would you need to take if you want a dosage of one gram?

    _____

23. Your science teacher mixes the contents of two beakers containing 2.5 L and 800 mL of a liquid. What is the combined amount?

    _____

24. A teaspoon of common table salt contains about 2,000 mg of sodium. How many grams of sodium is this?

    _____

1-5 • Guided Problem Solving

GPS Student Page 30, Exercise 35:

Food The capacity of a coffee mug is 350 mL. How many coffee mugs can you fill from a 2 L container?

Understand

1. Circle the information you will need to solve the problem.

2. What are you being asked to do?

   _____

   _____

3. How many milliliters are there in one liter?

   _____

Plan and Carry Out

4. How many liters does the container hold?

   _____

5. Do you multiply or divide to change liters into milliliters?

   _____

6. How many milliliters are there in 2 L?

   _____

7. Do you multiply or divide to find how many coffee mugs can be filled?

   _____

8. How many coffee mugs can be filled from a 2 L container?

   _____

Check

9. Is the total capacity of the coffee mugs filled less than or equal to 2,000 mL? Does your answer make sense?

   _____

Solve Another Problem

10. Lily drinks 0.5 L of water during her exercise routine. If her aerobics instructor tells her that she should be drinking at least 300 mL of water, is Lily drinking enough? Explain.

   _____

Practice 1-5

Choose a reasonable estimate.

1. Length of a calculator   18 m   18 cm   18 mm

2. Length of a football field   100 km   100 m   100 cm

3. Thickness of a paperback book   25 km   25 m   25 mm

4. Capacity of a bottle of shampoo   250 mL   250 L   250 kL

Complete each statement. If necessary, use a number line.

5. 0.7 km = _____ m

6. _____ L = 40 mL

7. 9,500 m = _____ km

8. 8 g = _____ kg

Change each measurement to the given unit.

9. 43 km 14 m to kilometers _____

10. 84 m 15 cm to centimeters _____

11. 9 kg 421 g to kilograms _____

Write the metric unit that makes each statement true.

12. 9.85 kg = 9,850 _____

13. 87.43 m = 8,743 _____

14. 10,542 mL = 10.542 _____

15. 8.42 mm = 0.842 _____

Solve.

16. The capacity of a beaker is 150 mL. How many beakers can be filled from a 4 L container?

   _____

17. Vitamin C comes in pills with a strength of 500 mg. How many pills would you need to take if you want a dosage of one gram?

   _____

18. A teaspoon of common table salt contains about 2,000 mg of sodium. How many grams of sodium is this?

   _____

Activity Lab 1-5

Measuring in Metric Units

Materials needed: metric ruler marked in mm and cm, calculator

Work with a partner.

On a separate sheet of paper, list the objects in 2 columns as shown below. Measure the objects in each row. Then draw lines on your paper to match equivalent measurements between the two columns.

Measure each object in centimeters.

Measure each object in millimeters.

1. kidney bean

a. kernel of corn

2. string bean

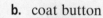

b. coat button

3. grain of rice

c. penny

4. grape

d. paper clip

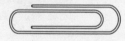

5. spiral noodle (uncooked)

e. eraser

Reteaching 1-5

The **metric system** of measurements uses *prefixes* to describe amounts that are much larger or smaller than the base unit. The base units for measuring length, mass, and volume are shown in the table below.

÷ 1000	÷ 100	÷ 10	base unit	× 10	× 100	× 1000
kilo-	hecto-	deca-	meter gram liter	deci-	centi-	milli-
× 1000	× 100	× 10	base unit	÷ 10	÷ 100	÷ 1000

To change a unit in the metric system, you multiply or divide by a power of 10.

① Change 34,000 mL to L.   34,000 mL = ? L

② Look at the table. To convert mL to L, divide by 1,000.   34,000 ÷ 1,000 = 34

③ Answer: 34,000 mL = 34 L

Write the number that makes each statement true.

1. 16 grams = __?__ milligrams

Are you converting from a smaller unit to a larger unit or a larger unit to a smaller unit?

_____

Will you multiply or divide?

_____

What number will you multiply or divide by?

_____

16 grams = _____ milligrams

2. 1,600 meters = __?__ kilometers

Are you converting from a smaller unit to a larger unit or a larger unit to a smaller unit?

_____

Will you multiply or divide?

_____

What number will you multiply or divide by?

_____

1,600 meters = _____ kilometers

3. 6 meters = _____ centimeters

4. 162 kilograms = _____ grams

Choose a reasonable estimate.

5. width of a dime:
1 m, 1 cm, 1 mm

_____

6. height of a building
50 m, 50 cm, 50 mm

_____

Enrichment 1-5

Measurement Conversions

In 1960 an international conference formulated a system of metric units that is widely accepted. It is known as the Système Internationale d'Unités, or the SI system for short. The measurement system in the United States uses customary units of measure. *Conversion factors* are used to change from one system of units to another.

Use these conversion factors to do the following exercises. Round to the nearest hundredth, when necessary.

1 m = 100 cm = 1,000 mm = 39.37 in. = 3.2808 ft = 1.0936 yd = 0.0006214 mile

1. Use a conversion factor to convert 12 m to inches.

_____

2. Use a conversion factor to convert 108 mm to feet.

_____

3. Which unit is smaller, one centimeter or one inch?

_____

4. Which unit is larger, one meter or one foot?

_____

5. What pattern do you notice about the quantity of units as you convert from a smaller unit to a larger unit?

_____

6. What pattern do you notice about the quantity of units as you convert from a larger unit to a smaller unit?

_____

7. Use a conversion factor to convert 48 yards to centimeters.

_____

8. What general statement can you make about the quantity of units relative to their size?

_____

_____

Name _____ Class _____ Date _____

1B: Reading Comprehension

For use after Lesson 1-5

Study Skill Practice reading charts and tables in books, magazines, or newspapers since information is often organized this way.

The table below contains information about four of the highest-ranked centers in the history of the National Basketball Association (NBA).

Use the table below to answer the questions.

Player	Height, Weight Playoffs	Number of Seasons to Regular Season	Points Per Game (PPG) During Playoffs	PPG During	NBA Titles	Age at Retirement
Kareem Abdul-Jabbar	7 ft 2 in. 267 lb	20 to 18	24.6	24.3	6	42
Wilt Chamberlain	7 ft 1 in. 275 lb	14 to 13	30.1	22.5	2	37
Shaquille O'Neal	7 ft 1 in. 325 lb	13 to 12	27.6	26.7	2	*
Bill Russell	6 ft 10 in. 220 lb	13 to 13	15.1	16.2	11	35

* still playing

1. Which of these centers is the tallest? _____

2. Which center is the shortest? _____

3. Which center won the most NBA titles? _____

4. Which center weighed the greatest amount? _____

5. Which center played the most regular seasons? _____

6. Which center(s) played in the playoffs 13 times?

   _____

7. What does PPG stand for? _____

8. Which center had the highest PPG during the regular season?

   _____

9. **High-Use Academic Words** In the directions, you are told that the NBA centers in the table are *ranked* the highest. What does it mean to *rank*?

   a. to show clearly　　　　　　　　　　b. to determine the relative position of

Puzzle 1-5

Measuring in Metric Units

During a trip to the zoo, you are asked to take a series of measurements for a scientific study. Match each measurement with the appropriate metric unit.

1. The mass of an elephant   **A.** millimeter

2. The capacity of the shark tank

       B. gram

3. The mass of a beetle

       C. kilogram

4. The length of a tiger's tail

       D. liter

5. The perimeter of the entire zoo

       E. centimeter

6. The diameter of a camel's eye

       F. kilometer

7. The amount of water per day consumed by a guinea pig.

       G. milliliter

8. The length of a giraffe's neck

       H. meter

Practice 1-6

Comparing and Ordering Integers

Name the integer represented by each point on the number line.

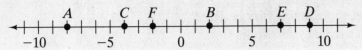

1. A _____   2. B _____   3. C _____   4. D _____   5. E _____   6. F _____

Compare. Use <, >, or =.

7. -8 ☐ 8 8. 4 ☐ -4 9. $|5|$ ☐ $|-5|$ 10. -8 ☐ 0

11. -6 ☐ -2 12. -1 ☐ -3 13. $|-4|$ ☐ 0 14. $|-3|$ ☐ 2

Graph each integer and its opposite on the number line.

15. -9

16. 5

17. 8

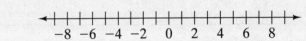

18. -2

Find each absolute value.

19. $|2|$ 20. $|-3|$ 21. $|-38|$ 22. $|-2 + 5|$

_____   _____   _____   _____

23. $|-44|$ 24. $|5 + 2|$ 25. $|-16|$ 26. $|3 - 7|$

_____   _____   _____   _____

Write an integer to represent each situation.

27. a gain of 5 yards

_____

28. a debt of $5

_____

29. a temperature of 100°F

_____

30. 135 feet below sea level

_____

1-6 • Guided Problem Solving

GPS Student Page 34, Exercise 48:

Sports In golf, the person with the lowest score is the winner. Rank the players below by ordering their scores from lowest to highest.

Player	Score
T. Woods	−12
V. Singh	−4
E. Els	+10
P. Mickelson	−3
R. Goosen	−5

Understand

1. Who wins in a golf game?

_____

2. How will you determine the lowest number?

_____

Plan and Carry Out

3. Draw a number line. Plot each score. Which number is the farthest to the left of zero on the number line?

_____

4. What is the order of all five numbers? _____

5. Rank the players from lowest score to highest score.

_____

Check

6. Is the person with the highest score last? Is the person with the lowest score first?

_____

Solve Another Problem

7. Anne had the following golf scores this week: −6, +5, −4, +13, −2, +4, +6, −11. Which was her best score? Which was her worst score?

_____

Name _____ Class _____ Date _____

Practice 1-6

Name the integer represented by each point on the number line.

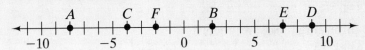

1. A _____   2. B _____

3. C _____   4. D _____

5. E _____   6. F _____

Compare. Use <, >, or =.

7. -8 ☐ 8 8. 4 ☐ -4 9. $|5|$ ☐ $|-5|$

10. -6 ☐ -2 11. -1 ☐ -3 12. $|-4|$ ☐ 0

Graph each integer and its opposite on the number line.

13. -9 14. 5

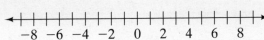   

15. 8 16. -2

   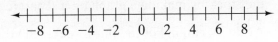

Find each absolute value.

17. $|2|$ 18. $|-3|$ 19. $|-38|$

_____   _____   _____

20. $|-44|$ 21. $|5 + 2|$ 22. $|-16|$

_____   _____   _____

Write an integer to represent each situation.

23. a gain of 5 yards   24. a debt of $5

_____   _____

25. a temperature of 100°F   26. 135 feet below sea level

_____   _____

Activity Lab 1-6

Comparing and Ordering Integers

| **Materials needed:** 3 weeks of issues of a daily newspaper |

1. During the first week, choose three different stocks and record the gains and losses each day for a week.

Stock Name	Mon	Tues	Wed	Thurs	Fri

2. Suppose you have $3,000. At the beginning of the second week, choose one of the stocks you have followed and purchase as many shares as you can.

   a. Which stock did you buy? Why did you choose that stock?

   _____

   _____

   b. How many shares did you purchase? _____

   c. What was the price per share? _____

3. Each day during the second week, record the closing price for the stock by making a graph on a separate sheet of paper.

4. At the beginning of the third week, sell your shares at the previous Friday's closing price.

   a. What was the total amount of this sale? _____

   b. Did you make a profit or a loss from the sale? _____

5. Keep watching your stock for another week. Suppose you sold your shares at that Friday's closing price. What would have been the total amount of that sale?

   _____

6. Would you have been better or worse off waiting and selling the stock one week later? Explain.

   _____

   _____

Reteaching 1-6

Comparing and Ordering Integers

The numbers 2 and −2 are opposites. The numbers 7 and −7 are opposites.
Integers are the set of positive whole numbers, their opposites, and zero.

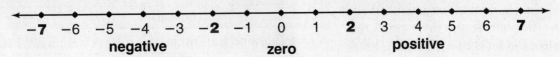

−7 −6 −5 −4 −3 **−2** −1 0 1 **2** 3 4 5 6 **7**

negative   zero   positive

You can use the number line to compare integers.

−2 is less than 0.   7 is greater than 2.
$-2 < 0$ $7 > 2$

Numbers to the left are less.	Numbers to the right are greater.
−2 is farther left than 0.	7 is farther to the right than 2.

The **absolute value** of an integer is its distance from zero on the
number line. Distance is always positive.

The absolute value of −5 is 5.   The absolute value of 3 is 3.
$|-5| = 5$ $|3| = 3$

Compare using <, >, or =.

1. 4 ☐ 2

2. −3 ☐ −2

3. 3 ☐ −4

4. −1 ☐ −2

5. 0 ☐ 5

6. 0 ☐ −4

7. −6 ☐ 4

8. −8 ☐ −2

9. 3 ☐ 0

10. −7 ☐ −10

11. −10 ☐ 10

12. 1 ☐ −1

Find each absolute value.

13. $|-6| = $ _____

14. $|3| = $ _____

15. $|-8| = $ _____

16. $|9| = $ _____

17. $|-5| = $ _____

18. $|0| = $ _____

19. $|6| = $ _____

20. $|-10| = $ _____

21. $|-20| = $ _____

Order the numbers from least to greatest.

22. −4, 5, −2, 0, 1

_____

23. 6, −3, −5, 4, −6

_____

24. 3, −5, 4, −4, −7, 0

_____

25. 1, 3, −7, −6, 5, −2

_____

Enrichment 1-6

Comparing and Ordering Integers

Critical Thinking

A *borehole* is a hole that has been drilled in the earth. The chart to the right shows the depth below sea level of several boreholes.

Location	Depth
Belridge, California	11,357 ft
Kola Peninsula, Russia	31,911 ft
Northwest Province, South Africa	15,005 ft
Szechwan, China	2,000 ft

1. Which depths can be represented by a negative integer? Explain.

_____

2. Write the integers to represent each depth.

_____

_____

3. Mark each integer on the number line.

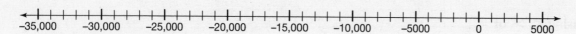

-35,000   -30,000   -25,000   -20,000   -15,000   -10,000   -5000   0   5000

4. How can you tell which of two negative integers is less?

_____

5. Write the integers in order from least to greatest.

_____

6. How could you order the negative integers without using a number line?

_____

7. The chart to the right shows the depth below sea level of several locations. Order the integers from least to greatest.

Location	Depth
Dead Sea	1,312 ft
Valdes Peninsula	131 ft
Death Valley	282 ft
Lake Assal	512 ft

_____

8. Which location is closest to sea level?

_____

1C: Reading/Writing Math Symbols   For use after Lesson 1-6

Study Skill Finish one homework assignment before beginning another.
Sometimes it helps to start with the most difficult assignment first.

Match the symbol in Column A with its meaning in Column B.

Column A	Column B
1. ·	**A.** division
2. ≈	**B.** degrees
3. ÷	**C.** is approximately equal to
4. ||	**D.** the opposite of
5. °	**E.** multiplication
6. ≤	**F.** is less than or equal to
7. −	**G.** absolute value

Match the metric abbreviation in Column A with the appropriate word in Column B.

Column A	Column B
8. mL	**A.** kilometers
9. L	**B.** decimeters
10. dm	**C.** milliliters
11. cL	**D.** centiliters
12. mg	**E.** grams
13. km	**F.** liters
14. g	**G.** milligrams

Puzzle 1-6

Comparing and Ordering Integers

You travel to a strange new city where the mayor has developed a very unusual system for determining house addresses. The address of City Hall is 0 Main St. As you walk east of City Hall, you notice the addresses are increasing positive integers. As you walk west of City Hall, you realize that the addresses are decreasing negative integers. Use the clues below to complete the map of Main Street by drawing each house in the proper place and writing its address.

Hint: think of the map as a number line.

Clues:

1. Francis's address is the opposite of Jim's.

2. Eduardo's address is 103 greater than Jim's.

3. Henrietta's house is the same distance from City Hall as Juan's house, but in the opposite direction.

4. Thuy's address is 500 greater than Juan's.

5. Vanita's address is 52 greater than Francis's.

Map:

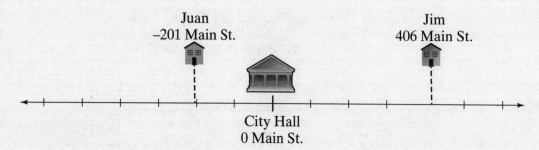

Juan
−201 Main St.

Jim
406 Main St.

City Hall
0 Main St.

Address List:

Francis: _____ Main St.

Eduardo: _____ Main St.

Henrietta: _____ Main St.

Thuy: _____ Main St.

Vanita: _____ Main St.

Practice 1-7

Adding and Subtracting Integers

Find each sum.

1. $-2 + (-3)$ **2.** $8 - 7 + 4$ **3.** $8 + (-5)$ **4.** $15 + (-3)$

_____   _____   _____   _____

5. $-16 + 8$ **6.** $7 + (-10)$ **7.** $-9 + (-5)$ **8.** $-12 + 14$

_____   _____   _____   _____

Find each difference.

9. $9 - 26$ **10.** $-4 - 15$ **11.** $21 - (-7)$ **12.** $27 - (-16)$

_____   _____   _____   _____

13. $-16 - (-43)$ **14.** $47 - 19$ **15.** $-156 - 98$ **16.** $-192 - 47$

_____   _____   _____   _____

17. $0 - (-51)$ **18.** $-63 - 89$ **19.** $-12 - (-21)$ **20.** $92 - (-16)$

_____   _____   _____   _____

Find the value of each expression.

21. $3 + 8 + (-4)$ **22.** $2 + |-3| + (-3)$ **23.** $9 + 7 - 6$

_____   _____   _____

24. $56 + (-4) + (-58)$ **25.** $-4 - 3 + (-2)$ **26.** $|-8| - 15 + (-8)$

_____   _____   _____

Use >, <, or = to complete each statement.

27. $-9 - (-11)$ ☐ 0 **28.** $-17 + 20$ ☐ 0 **29.** $11 - (-4)$ ☐ 0

30. $28 - 19$ ☐ 0 **31.** $52 + (-65)$ ☐ 0 **32.** $-28 - (-28)$ ☐ 0

Solve.

33. The highest and lowest temperatures ever recorded in Africa are 136°F and −11°F. The highest temperature was recorded in Libya, and the lowest temperature was recorded in Morocco. What is the difference in these temperature extremes?

_____

34. The highest and lowest temperatures ever recorded in South America are 120°F and −27°F. Both the highest and lowest temperatures were recorded in Argentina. What is the difference in these temperature extremes?

_____

1-7 • Guided Problem Solving

GPS Student Page 41, Exercise 27:

Temperature The highest temperature ever recorded in the United States was 134°F, measured at Death Valley, California. The coldest temperature, −80°F, was recorded at Prospect Creek, Alaska. What is the difference between these temperatures?

Understand

1. Circle the information you will need to solve the problem.

2. What are you being asked to do?

   _____

3. Which word tells you what operation to perform?

   _____

Plan and Carry Out

4. Write a subtraction expression for the problem.

   _____

5. Subtracting a negative number is the same as adding what type of number?

   _____

6. Write an addition expression that is the same as the expression you wrote in Step 4.

   _____

7. What is the difference between these temperatures?

   _____

Check

8. What is 134°F − 214°F?

   _____

Solve Another Problem

9. At 6:00 A.M. the temperature was 25°F. At 9:00 P.M. the temperature was −13°F. What was the difference in the temperature?

   _____

Practice 1-7

Adding and Subtracting Integers

Find each sum.

1. $-2 + (-3)$

2. $8 - 7 + 4$

3. $8 + (-5)$

4. $-16 + 8$

5. $7 + (-10)$

6. $-9 + (-5)$

Find each difference.

7. $9 - 26$

8. $-4 - 15$

9. $21 - (-7)$

10. $-16 - (-43)$

11. $47 - 19$

12. $-156 - 98$

13. $0 - (-51)$

14. $-63 - 89$

15. $-12 - (-21)$

Find the value of each expression.

16. $3 + 8 + (-4)$

17. $2 + |-3| + (-3)$

18. $56 + (-4) + (-58)$

19. $-4 - 3 + (-2)$

Use >, <, or = to complete each statement.

20. $-9 - (-11)$ ☐ 0

21. $-17 + 20$ ☐ 0

22. $28 - 19$ ☐ 0

23. $52 + (-65)$ ☐ 0

Solve.

24. The highest and lowest temperatures ever recorded in Africa are 136°F and −11°F. The highest temperature was recorded in Libya, and the lowest temperature was recorded in Morocco. What is the difference in these temperature extremes?

Activity Lab 1-7

Adding and Subtracting Integers

> **Materials needed:** sheets of $8\frac{1}{2}"\times 11"$ paper with all the integers from -6 to 6 written on them, one integer per paper (13 sheets), a box to hold slips of paper

1. Your class will be divided into two teams, Team 1 and Team 2. If your teacher calls your name to be a member of Team 1, draw a slip of paper from the box.

2. When all of the members of Team 1 have drawn a piece of paper, arrange yourselves in a human number line. Your position on the number line should be based on the number you drew, with the person who drew the smallest number standing farthest to the left and the one who drew the largest number standing farthest to the right. Hold your paper so the members of the class can see your number.

3. Your teacher will call out two integers whose sum is on the number line. If either of the numbers is the one you drew, step forward.

4. If you are a member of Team 2 and your teacher calls your name, add the two integers that were called and instruct your classmate who represents that integer on the number line to step forward.

5. Your classmates will determine if you are correct. If so, your team receives one point. If you are incorrect, the other team receives one point if they can correctly identify the student who should have stepped forward.

6. Complete five rounds of adding integers and five rounds of subtracting integers. Keep a tally of each team's points. Then, Team 1 and Team 2 will trade places.

7. Begin the next round by putting the numbers back into the box. Each member of Team 2 draws a slip of paper from the box. (Add or remove integers from the number line depending on the number of students.) Repeat Steps 2–6.

8. The team with the most points at the end of the game wins.

Name _____ Class _____ Date _____

Reteaching 1-7

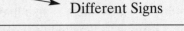

Use these rules to add and subtract integers.

Adding Integers

Same Sign   Different Signs

• The sum of two positive integers is positive. Example: $6 + 16 = 22$ • The sum of two negative integers is negative Example: $-9 + (-3) = -12$
• First find the absolute values of each number.   • Then subtract the lesser absolute value from the greater.   • The sum has the sign of the integer with the greater absolute value. Example: $-10 + 9 = -1$

Subtracting Integers

• To subtract integers, add the opposite.   • Then following the rules for adding integers. Example: $6 - (-3) = 6 + 3 = 9$

Find each sum.

1. $8 + (-2)$ _____

2. $-9 + 4$ _____

3. $3 + (-2)$ _____

4. $-1 + 11$ _____

5. $12 + 13$ _____

6. $-9 + 5$ _____

7. $7 + 2$ _____

8. $-1 + (-7)$ _____

9. $-3 + 0$ _____

10. $-1 + (-1)$ _____

11. $6 + 5$ _____

12. $3 - (-2)$ _____

Complete.

13. $-3 - 4$ Change to addition: $-3 +$ _____ $=$ _____

14. $5 - 2$ Change to addition: $5 +$ _____ $=$ _____

15. $-6 - (-10)$ Change to addition: $-6 +$ _____ $=$ _____

Find each difference.

16. $4 - 5$ _____

17. $-5 - 4$ _____

18. $-8 - (-7)$ _____

19. $19 - (-6)$ _____

20. $-10 - 12$ _____

21. $-12 - 10$ _____

22. $-4 - (-5)$ _____

23. $-2 - (-3)$ _____

24. $9 - (-7)$ _____

25. $0 - 3$ _____

26. $6 - 8$ _____

27. $0 - (-10)$ _____

Enrichment 1-7

Adding and Subtracting Integers

Critical Thinking

Alice has started a business baking cookies. Although she makes money by selling cookies, she has also had to spend money for equipment and supplies. Alice made the cash flow table below to help her keep track of her finances for her first month in business.

Item	Money
Cookie sheets	–$7
Storage tins	–$12
Ingredients for sale #1	–$14
Money earned from sale #1	$28
Ingredients for sale #2	–$20
Money earned from sale #2	$40
Allowance	$5

1. How much money has Alice spent on her business?

   _____

2. What is the total amount of money that Alice has earned this month? Do not account for money that she has spent. This amount is the *gross income*.

   _____

3. What is the total amount of money Alice has left over after her expenses are subtracted from her earnings? This amount is the *net income*.

   _____

4. Alice projects that in Month 2 she will earn and spend the same amounts as in Month 1, but that she will not have to pay for cookie sheets or storage tins. If this happens, what will Alice's net income be in Month 2?

   _____

1E: Vocabulary Check

Study Skill Strengthen your vocabulary. Use these pages and add cues and summaries by applying the Cornell Notetaking style.

Write the definition for each word or term at the right. To check your work, fold the paper back along the dotted line to see the correct answers.

_____

_____

_____

absolute value

_____

_____

_____

integers

_____

_____

_____

compatible numbers

_____

_____

_____

Zero Property

_____

_____

_____

additive inverses

_____

_____

1E: Vocabulary Check (continued)

For use after Lesson 1-7

Write the vocabulary word or term for each definition. To check your work, fold the paper forward along the dotted line to see the correct answers.

the distance of a number from
0 on the number line

_____

the set of positive whole numbers,
their opposites, and 0

_____

numbers that are easy to
compute mentally

_____

The product of 0 and any
number is 0.

_____

any two numbers whose
sum is 0

_____

Puzzle 1-7 .... **Adding and Subtracting Integers**

Complete the square at the right using counting chips and the following steps:

- Add across.
- Add down.
- Add your sums across and down.
- Write your sums in the triangles.

What did you find about the numbers in the triangles?

_____

1.

+4	−3	= ___
−5	+6	= ___
=	=	

___ ___

Complete the squares below. Use the counting chips if necessary.

2.

−8	+4	= ___
+10	−5	= ___
=	=	

___ ___

3.

+7	−7	= ___
−5	+5	= ___
=	=	

___ ___

4.

+2	−8	= ___
+3	+6	= ___
=	=	

___ ___

5.

−1	−2	= ___
−3	−4	= ___
=	=	

___ ___

Find the sum of all the positive integers in the triangles to determine the mystery number.

This number is:

- the number of pairs of ribs in the human body
- part of the title of six movies
- the minimum wind speed of a hurricane on the Beaufort wind force scale

The mystery number is _____!

Practice 1-8

Multiplying and Dividing Integers

Complete each statement. Then write two examples to illustrate each relationship.

1. positive ÷ positive = ?

_____

2. negative · positive = ?

_____

3. positive · positive = ?

_____

4. negative ÷ negative = ?

_____

5. negative ÷ positive = ?

_____

6. positive · positive = ?

_____

7. positive ÷ negative = ?

_____

8. negative · negative = ?

_____

Estimate each product or quotient.

9. $-72 \cdot 57$

_____

10. $-92 \cdot (-41)$

_____

11. $-476 \div 90$

_____

12. $-83 \cdot 52$

_____

13. $538 \div (-63)$

_____

14. $-803 \cdot (-106)$

_____

15. $49 \cdot 61$

_____

16. $479 \div (-61)$

_____

Find each product or quotient.

17. $\dfrac{-36}{9}$

_____

18. $\dfrac{-52}{-4}$

_____

19. $(-5) \cdot (-20)$

_____

20. $\dfrac{-63}{-9}$

_____

21. $(-15) \cdot (2)$

_____

22. $\dfrac{22}{-2}$

_____

23. $(13) \cdot (-6)$

_____

24. $\dfrac{-100}{-5}$

_____

25. $(-60) \cdot (-3)$

_____

26. $\dfrac{-240}{30}$

_____

27. $(43) \cdot (-8)$

_____

28. $\dfrac{-169}{-13}$

_____

1-8 • Guided Problem Solving

GPS **Student Page 47, Exercise 35:**

Hobbies A scuba diver is 180 ft below sea level and rises to the surface at a rate of 30 ft/min. How long will the diver take to reach the surface?

Understand

1. Circle the information you will need to solve the problem.

2. What are you being asked to do?

   _____

   _____

Plan and Carry Out

3. Will you multiply or divide to solve this problem?

   _____

4. How far below sea level is the diver?

   _____

5. How fast is the diver rising?

   _____

6. How long will the diver take to reach the surface?

   _____

Check

7. What is 30 ft/min × 6 min? Does your answer equal the original distance below sea level?

   _____

Solve Another Problem

8. A rock climber climbs down into the Grand Canyon at a rate of 2 ft/min. How long will it take him to climb down 50 ft?

   _____

Name _____ Class _____ Date _____

Practice 1-8

Complete each statement. Then write two examples to illustrate each relationship.

1. positive ÷ positive = ?

2. negative · positive = ?

3. positive · positive = ?

4. negative ÷ negative = ?

5. negative ÷ positive = ?

6. positive · positive = ?

7. positive ÷ negative = ?

8. negative · negative = ?

Estimate each product or quotient.

9. $-72 \cdot 57$

10. $-92 \cdot (-41)$

11. $-476 \div 90$

12. $538 \div (-63)$

13. $-803 \cdot (-106)$

14. $49 \cdot 61$

Find each product or quotient.

15. $\dfrac{-36}{9}$

16. $\dfrac{-52}{-4}$

17. $(-5) \cdot (-20)$

18. $\dfrac{-63}{-9}$

19. $(-15) \cdot (2)$

20. $\dfrac{22}{-2}$

21. $(13) \cdot (-6)$

22. $\dfrac{-100}{-5}$

23. $(-60) \cdot (-3)$

Activity Lab 1-8

Multiplying and Dividing Integers

Multiplication Madness

Look at patterns of integer multiplication:

1. $6 \times -18 =$ _____

2. $(-2 \times 5) \times 3 =$ _____

3. $(4 \times -6) \times 7 =$ _____

4. $(8 \times 9)(2 \times -1) =$ _____

5. Each problem above has _____ negative factor(s).

6. Each product is _____ .

7. $-17 \times -3 =$ _____

8. $(-6 \times 5) \times -8 =$ _____

9. $(9 \times -2)(-3 \times 1) =$ _____

10. $(-4 \times -7)(2 \times 2) =$ _____

11. Each problem above has _____ negative factor(s).

12. Each product is _____ .

13. $(-5 \times -4) \times -7 =$ _____

14. $-3 \times (-8 \times -2) =$ _____

15. $(-3 \times -4)(-2 \times 8) =$ _____

16. $(-10 \times 1)(-7 \times -1) =$ _____

17. Each problem above has _____ negative factor(s).

18. Each product is _____ .

19. $(-3 \times -5)(-2 \times -2) =$ _____

20. $(-9 \times -1)(-4 \times -3) =$ _____

21. $(-6 \times -1)(-4 \times -11) =$ _____

22. $(-20 \times -5)(-3 \times -6) =$ _____

23. Each problem above has _____ negative factor(s).

24. Each product is _____ .

25. Draw a conclusion about the product of postive and negative integers.

_____

Reteaching 1-8

Multiplying and Dividing Integers

To multiply integers:

- If the signs are alike, the product is positive.

$$2 \cdot 3 = 6$$
$$-2 \cdot -3 = 6$$

- If the signs are different, the product is negative.

$$2 \cdot -3 = -6$$
$$-2 \cdot 3 = -6$$

To divide integers:

- If the signs are alike, the quotient is positive.

$$6 \div 3 = 2$$
$$-6 \div -3 = 2$$

- If the signs are different, the quotient is negative.

$$6 \div -3 = -2$$
$$-6 \div 3 = -2$$

Study these four examples. Write positive or negative to complete each statement.

$$7 \cdot 3 = 21 \qquad\qquad\qquad 7 \cdot -3 = -21$$
$$-7 \cdot -3 = 21 \qquad\qquad\qquad -7 \cdot 3 = -21$$

1. When both integers are positive, the product is _____.

2. When one integer is positive and one is negative, the product is _____.

3. When both integers are negative, the product is _____.

$$21 \div 3 = 7 \qquad\qquad\qquad -21 \div -3 = 7$$
$$21 \div -3 = -7 \qquad\qquad\qquad -21 \div 3 = -7$$

4. When both integers are positive, the quotient is _____.

5. When both integers are negative, the quotient is _____.

6. When one integer is positive and one is negative, the quotient is _____.

Tell whether each product or quotient will be *positive* or *negative*.

7. $4 \cdot 7$

8. $-4 \cdot 7$

9. $-4 \cdot -7$

10. $4 \cdot -7$

_____ _____ _____ _____

11. $10 \cdot -4$

12. $-25 \div 5$

13. $-2 \cdot -2$

14. $100 \div 10$

_____ _____ _____ _____

Enrichment 1-8

Multiplying and Dividing Integers

Patterns in Numbers

The multiplication table below is separated into four sections.

Column −3										Column 3		
					5				15			
					4				12			
					3	0	3	6	9	12	15	Row 3
					2				6			
					1				3			
					0				0			
−5	−4	−3	−2	−1	×	0	1	2	3	4	5	
					−1							
					−2							
					−3							Row −3
					−4							
					−5							

1. What pattern do you see as you read the numbers from top to bottom in column 3? As you read from right to left in row 3?

   _____

   _____

2. Complete row 3 and column 3 by applying the pattern in the table to the upper left section and to the bottom right section. Complete row −3 and column −3. Then complete the table.

3. How does the table show the rules for multiplying positive and negative numbers?

   _____

   _____

   _____

Puzzle 1-8

Multiplying and Dividing Integers

1. In the following equations, each letter represents a number from 0 to 5. Study the equations. Decide what number the letter represents and write the letter on the line above the number. If correct, you will find the hidden word. Then write each equation as a number sentence to verify your answer.

   a. $T + N = R$ _____

   b. $N + N = E$ _____

   c. $T \times I = T$ _____

   d. $N + I = T$ _____

   e. $N + W = N$ _____

   ____ ____ ____ ____ ____ ____
    0   1   2   3   4   5

2. In the following equations, each letter represents one of the numbers from 0 to 4. Decide what number the letter represents and write the letter on the line above the number. If correct, you will find the hidden word. Then write each equation as a number sentence to verify your answer.

   a. $E + R = A$ _____

   b. $A \times R = A$ _____

   c. $A + B = A$ _____

   d. $E + E = K$ _____

   ____ ____ ____ ____ ____
    0   1   2   3   4

3. Make up your own puzzle. Trade with a classmate and solve.

Name _____ Class _____ Date _____

Practice 1-9

Order of Operations and the Distributive Property

Find the value of each expression.

1. $(8 + 2) \times 9$

   _____

2. $5 - 1 \div 4$

   _____

3. $(6 + 3) \div 18$

   _____

4. $80 - 6 \times 7$

   _____

5. $4 \times 6 + 3$

   _____

6. $4 \times (6 + 3)$

   _____

7. $35 - 6 \times 5$

   _____

8. $9 \div 3 + 6$

   _____

Find the missing numbers. Then simplify.

9. $5(9 + 6) = 5\,(\underline{\ ?\ }) + 5\,(\underline{\ ?\ })$

   _____

10. $4(9.7 - 8.1) = \underline{\ ?\ }(9.7) - \underline{\ ?\ }(8.1)$

    _____

11. $\underline{\ ?\ }(3.8) = 9(4) - 9(\underline{\ ?\ })$

    _____

12. $\underline{\ ?\ }(17.1 + 12.6) = 6(17.1) + 6(12.6)$

    _____

Use the Distributive Property and mental math to find each product.

13. $3(6.4)$

    _____

14. $5(7.1)$

    _____

15. $5(8.9)$

    _____

16. $4(9.2)$

    _____

17. $9(11.1)$

    _____

18. $7(8.9)$

    _____

Copy each statement and add parentheses to make it true.

19. $6 + 6 \div 6 \times 6 + 6 = 24$

    _____

20. $6 \times 6 + 6 \times 6 - 6 = 426$

    _____

21. $6 + 6 \div 6 \times 6 - 6 = 0$

    _____

22. $6 - 6 \times 6 + 6 \div 6 = 1$

    _____

23. A backyard measures 80 ft $\times$ 125 ft. A garden is planted in one corner of it. The garden measures 15 ft $\times$ 22 ft. How much of the backyard is *not* part of the garden?

    _____

1-9 • Guided Problem Solving

GPS Student Page 51, Exercise 30:

Business A florist is buying flowers to use in centerpieces. Each centerpiece has 3 lilies. There are a total of 10 tables. Each lily costs $.98. Use mental math to find the cost of the lilies.

Understand

1. What are you being asked to do?

   _____

2. Which method are you to use to determine the cost?

   _____

Plan and Carry Out

3. How many lilies do you need in all?

   _____

4. Write an expression to find the total cost of the lilies.

   _____

5. The amount $.98 can also be written as $1.00 – $.02. Rewrite your expression from Step 4 using $1.00 – $.02.

   _____

6. Simplify the expression using mental math.

   _____

7. How much do the lilies cost?

   _____

Check

8. Use a calculator to determine the cost of the lilies. Is your answer from step 7 correct?

   _____

Solve Another Problem

9. Your horticulture club is planting a garden at school as a beautification project. The principal is allowing you to use an area that is 5 yd^2. If it costs $8.93 to buy enough rose bulbs to plant 1 yd^2, how much will it cost to buy bulbs to fill 5 yd^2?

   _____

Practice 1-9

Order of Operations and the Distributive Property

Find the value of each expression.

1. $(8 + 2) \times 9$

2. $5 - 1 \div 4$

3. $(6 + 3) \div 18$

_____

_____

_____

4. $80 - 6 \times 7$

5. $4 \times 6 + 3$

6. $4 \times (6 + 3)$

_____

_____

_____

7. $35 - 6 \times 5$

8. $9 \div 3 + 6$

9. $(8 + 1) \div 3$

_____

_____

_____

Find the missing numbers. Then simplify.

10. $5(9 + 6) = 5 \,(\underline{\ ?\ }) + 5 \,(\underline{\ ?\ })$

11. $4(9.7 - 8.1) = \underline{\ ?\ }(9.7) - \underline{\ ?\ }(8.1)$

_____

_____

Use the Distributive Property and mental math to find each product.

12. $5(7.1)$

13. $5(8.9)$

_____

_____

14. $9(11.1)$

15. $7(8.9)$

_____

_____

Copy each statement and add parentheses to make it true.

16. $6 + 6 \div 6 \times 6 + 6 = 24$

17. $6 \times 6 + 6 \times 6 - 6 = 426$

_____

_____

18. A backyard measures 80 ft $\times$ 125 ft. A garden is planted in one corner of it. The garden measures 15 ft $\times$ 22 ft. How much of the backyard is *not* part of the garden?

_____

Activity Lab 1-9   Order of Operations and the Distributive Property

Materials needed: scientific calculator

Scientific calculators follow the order of operations. You will use your scientific calculator to solve number puzzles. Unless you are told otherwise, for each puzzle:

- You may use any of these operations: $+, -, \times, \div$

- You may use as many pairs of parentheses as you wish.

1. You can use four 4s and the following key sequence to get a result of 2:

4 ÷ (4 + 4) × 4 =

Find two more key sequences, one with parentheses and one without parentheses, that use four 4s to get a result of 2.

_____

_____

2. What is the largest possible result using four 4s? _____

What key sequence gives that result? _____

3. Find a key sequence that uses five 5s to get a result of 1.

_____

_____

4. What result do you get for the following key sequence?

3 + 5 × 6 + 12 ÷ 6 = _____

Insert parentheses in the key sequence so the result is 50.

_____

Insert parentheses in the key sequence so the result is 24.

_____

Insert parentheses in the key sequence so the result is 35.

_____

5. Make up your own key sequencing. Tell a partner the result and the numbers you used and challenge him or her to find a key sequence that produces the result.

_____

Name _____ Class _____ Date _____

Reteaching 1-9

Order of Operations and the Distributive Property

You can remember the order of operations using this phrase:

Please, My Dear Aunt Sally

Parentheses Multiply Divide Add Subtract

(1) First, do operations within parentheses.

$7 + 8 \cdot \boxed{(5 + 3)} - 1$ $3 \div \boxed{(5 - 2)} + 36$

$7 + 8 \cdot \quad 8 \quad - 1$ $3 \div \quad 3 \quad + 36$

(2) Next, multiply and divide from left to right.

$7 + \boxed{8 \cdot 8} - 1$ $\boxed{3 \div 3} + 36$

$7 + \quad 64 \quad - 1$ $1 \quad + 36$

(3) Then, add and subtract from left to right.

$\boxed{7 + 64} - 1$ $\boxed{1 + 36}$

$71 \quad - 1$ 37

70

Complete.

1. $3 + 2 \cdot 4$

$3 + \underline{\hspace{2cm}}$

$\underline{\hspace{2cm}}$

2. $5 \cdot 4 + 3 \cdot 2$

$\underline{\hspace{1.5cm}} + \underline{\hspace{1.5cm}}$

$\underline{\hspace{2cm}}$

3. $(5 \cdot 4) + 3 - 2$

$\underline{\hspace{3cm}}$

4. $5 + 7 \cdot 2$

$5 + \underline{\hspace{2cm}}$

$\underline{\hspace{2cm}}$

5. $8 \cdot 6 + 4 \cdot 4$

$\underline{\hspace{1.5cm}} + \underline{\hspace{1.5cm}}$

$\underline{\hspace{2cm}}$

6. $(6 \cdot 2) + (12 \div 2)$

$\underline{\hspace{1.5cm}} + \underline{\hspace{1.5cm}}$

$\underline{\hspace{2cm}}$

Find the value of each expression.

7. $8 + 5 \cdot 6 + 2$

$\underline{\hspace{2cm}}$

8. $7 - 4 + 5 \cdot 3$

$\underline{\hspace{2cm}}$

9. $9 + 3 \cdot 7 - 5$

$\underline{\hspace{2cm}}$

10. $(15 + 9) \div (8 - 2)$

$\underline{\hspace{2cm}}$

11. $80 - 6 \cdot 7$

$\underline{\hspace{2cm}}$

12. $15 \div (5 - 2)$

$\underline{\hspace{2cm}}$

Find the missing numbers. Then simplify.

13. $8(5 + 2) = \boxed{}(5) + \boxed{}(2) = \boxed{}$

14. $\boxed{}(5.6) = 4(6.0) - 4(\boxed{}) = \boxed{}$

15. $\boxed{}(3.4 + 7) = 5(3.4) + 5(7) = \boxed{}$

16. $\boxed{}(10 - 5) = 14(10) - 14(5) = \boxed{}$

Enrichment 1-9

Order of Operations and the Distributive Property

Decision Making

The formula $C = p + ip$ gives the total cost (C) of an item where p is the cost of the item before tax and i is the tax rate.

    a. What is the total cost of a $62 car battery if the tax rate is 5% (0.05)?

    b. The formula $C = p(1 + i)$ will also give you the total cost. Use this formula to find the total cost of a $62.00 battery at the same tax rate.

    c. How are the two formulas related?

Use the following questions to help you solve the exercise.

1. Which numbers will you substitute for p and i to find the cost of the $62 battery?

    _____

2. Which operation will you do first in order to solve $C = p + ip$?

    _____

3. Which operation will you do first in order to solve $C = p(1 + i)$?

    _____

4. Use the formula $C = p + ip$ to find the total cost of a $62 car battery if the tax rate is 5% (0.05).

    _____

5. Use the formula $C = p(1 + i)$ to find the total cost of a $62.00 battery at the same rate.

    _____

6. The two formulas give the same answer, so $p + ip = p(1 + i)$. How do you know this is true and that the formulas are related?

    _____

    _____

    _____

7. Which formula is easier to use? Explain.

    _____

    _____

Name _____ Class _____ Date _____

Puzzle 1-9

Order of Operations and the Distributive Property

| 1 | 4 | 3 | 2 | + | − | (|) |

Use the number cards to create expressions with the given answers.
You must use every tile to build an expression, and cannot repeat the
same tile in one expression.

Example:

| 4 | (| 3 | + | 2 |) | − | 1 | = 19

A.

| ☐ | ☐ | ☐ | ☐ | ☐ | ☐ | ☐ | ☐ | = −19

B.

| ☐ | ☐ | ☐ | ☐ | ☐ | ☐ | ☐ | ☐ | = −13

C.

| ☐ | ☐ | ☐ | ☐ | ☐ | ☐ | ☐ | ☐ | = 5

D.

| ☐ | ☐ | ☐ | ☐ | ☐ | ☐ | ☐ | ☐ | = 13

E.

| ☐ | ☐ | ☐ | ☐ | ☐ | ☐ | ☐ | ☐ | = 3

F.

| ☐ | ☐ | ☐ | ☐ | ☐ | ☐ | ☐ | ☐ | = 7

G.

| ☐ | ☐ | ☐ | ☐ | ☐ | ☐ | ☐ | ☐ | = 11

Name _____ Class _____ Date _____

Practice 1-10

Mean, Median, Mode, and Range

The sum of the heights of all the students in a class is 1,472 in.

1. The mean height is 5 ft 4 in. How many students are in the class?
   (1 ft = 12 in.)

   _____

2. **a.** The median height is 5 ft 2 in. How many students are 5 ft 2 in.
   or taller?

   _____

   b. How many students are shorter than 5 ft 2 in.?

   _____

The number of pages read (to the nearest multiple of 50) by the students in history class last week are shown in the tally table at the right.

Pages	Tally
50	I
100	
150	II
200	|||| I
250	I
300					
350	III
400	IIII
450	I
500	I

3. Find the mean, median, mode, and range of the data.

   _____

4. What is the outlier in this set of data? _____

5. Does the outlier raise or lower the mean? _____

A student hopes to have a 9-point average on his math quizzes. His quiz scores are 7, 6, 10, 8, and 9. Each quiz is worth 12 points.

6. What is his average quiz score?

   _____

7. There are two more quizzes. How many more points will be
   needed to give a 9-point quiz average?

   _____

Find the mean, median, mode, and range for each situation.

8. number of miles biked in one week

   21, 17, 15, 18, 22, 16, 20 _____

9. number of strikeouts per inning

   3, 2, 0, 0, 1, 2, 3, 0, 2 _____

1-10 • Guided Problem Solving

GPS **Student Page 56, Exercise 26:**

Find the mean, median, and mode for the hours of practice before a concert:

2 1 0 1 5 3 4 2 0 3 1 2

Understand

1. What does this data set refer to?

   _____

2. What are you being asked to do?

   _____

3. How many numbers are in the data set? _____

Plan and Carry Out

4. Find the sum of the numbers in the data set. _____

5. Find the mean by dividing the sum of the numbers by the total number of numbers. _____

6. Order the numbers in the data set in increasing order.

   _____

7. What are the two middle numbers? _____

8. Find the median of the data by finding the mean of the two middle numbers. _____

9. Find the mode by finding which number is listed most often. _____

10. How many modes are there? _____

Check

11. What do you notice about the mean, median, and mode of this data?

   _____

Solve Another Problem

12. Millie has 3 siblings, Peggy has one sister, Larry has 5 brothers, Joey is an only child, and Marie has 6 siblings. What is the mean number of siblings for this group of people? _____

Name _____ Class _____ Date _____

Practice 1-10

Mean, Median, Mode, and Range

The sum of the heights of all the students in a class is 1,472 in.

1. The mean height is 5 ft 4 in. How many students are in the class? (1 ft = 12 in.)

   _____

2. The median height is 5 ft 2 in. How many students are 5 ft 2 in. or taller?

   _____

The number of pages read (to the nearest multiple of 50) by the students in history class last week are shown in the tally table at the right.

Pages	Tally
50	I
100	
150	II
200	++++ I
250	I
300	++++
350	III
400	IIII
450	I
500	I

3. Find the mean, median, mode, and range of the data.

   _____

   _____

4. What is the outlier in this set of data? _____

A student hopes to have a 9-point average on his math quizzes. His quiz scores are 7, 6, 10, 8, and 9. Each quiz is worth 12 points.

5. What is his average quiz score?

   _____

6. There are two more quizzes. How many more points will be needed to give a 9-point quiz average?

   _____

Find the mean, median, mode, and range for each situation.

7. number of miles biked in one week

   21, 17, 15, 18, 22, 16, 20

   _____

8. number of strikeouts per inning

   3, 2, 0, 0, 1, 2, 3, 0, 2

   _____

Activity Lab 1-10

Mean, Median, Mode, and Range

Dunston Data Company's ten employees made the following salaries during the past year.

$17,000, $17,000, $25,000, $25,000, $25,000, $27,000, $32,000, $32,000, $83,000, $102,000

1. For the salaries listed above, find each of the following.

   a. mean _____   **b.** median _____

   c. mode _____   **d.** range _____

2. How should the company's advertisement for new employees describe salaries? Should it use the mean, median, mode, or range?

   _____

   _____

3. Suppose a newspaper article states that $38,500 is the "average" salary of Dunston employees. Would the article be accurate? Could it be misleading? How?

   _____

   _____

   _____

4. Recently, CompuData Corporation claimed that Dunston's employees are overpaid for the work they perform. In an article defending against such claims, which number would most likely be used? Explain.

   _____

   _____

   _____

5. If you worked for the Dunston Data Company, which number would you use to describe the typical earnings of its employees? Explain.

   _____

   _____

   _____

Name _____ Class _____ Date _____

Reteaching 1-10

Mean, Median, Mode, and Range

Alexis, Rita, Ming, Mario, and Jewel are in the Library Club.
During the summer they read the following numbers of books.

11, 6, 11, 8, 3

To find the **mean,** or average, number of books read
by the Library Club members:

① Find the sum of the numbers of books read. $11 + 6 + 11 + 8 + 3 = 39$

② Divide the sum by the number of readers, 5. $39 \div 5 = 7.8$

The mean is 7.8 books.

To find the **median,** or middle value, of the data set:

① Arrange the numbers in order.   3, 6, **8**, 11, 11

② Find the middle number.   ↑

8 is the middle number.

The median is 8 books.

The **mode** is the number that occurs most often.   3, 6, 8, **11, 11**
In this data set, 11 occurs twice. The mode is 11.

The **range** is the difference between the greatest and the $11 - 3 = 8$
least values. The range is 8.

Use the table to complete Exercises 1–4.

1. Jerry plays basketball. What number would
   you divide by to find the mean number of
   points Jerry scored per game? _____

2. What is the mean number of points Jerry scored?

   _____

3. Write the data in order. Then find the median number of points
   Jerry scored.

F _____

4. What is the mode of the data? _____

5. What is the range between Jerry's highest- and lowest-scoring
   games? _____

Points Scored by Jerry per Game		
10	11	15
18	9	16
10	12	10

Find the mean, median, mode, and range for the following situation.

6. the miniature golf scores for 7 friends:

   23, 30, 39, 32, 35, 14, 23

   mean _____   median _____   mode _____   range _____

Enrichment 1-10

Mean, Median, Mode, and Range

Critical Thinking

Data Company's ten employees made the following salaries during the past year.

$17,000, $17,000, $25,000, $25,000, $25,000, $27,000, $32,000, $32,000, $83,000, $102,000

1. For the salaries listed above, find each of the following.

   a. mean _____   **b.** median _____

   c. mode _____   **d.** range _____

2. How should the company's advertisement for new employees describe salaries? Should it use the mean, median, mode, or range?

   _____

   _____

3. Suppose a newspaper article states that $38,500 is the "average" salary of Data Company's employees. Would the article be accurate? Could it be misleading? How?

   _____

   _____

4. Recently, the CompuData Corporation claimed that Data Company's employees are overpaid for the work they perform. In an article defending against such claims, which number would most likely be used? Explain.

   _____

   _____

5. If you worked for Data Company, which number would you use to describe the typical earnings of its employees? Explain.

   _____

   _____

   _____

1D: Visual Vocabulary Practice

Study Skill If a word is not in the glossary, use a dictionary to find its meaning.

Concept List

Associative Property of Addition   Associative Property of Multiplication

Commutative Property of Addition   Distributive Property

mean   order of operations

median   range

mode

Write the concept that best describes each exercise. Choose from the concept list above.

1. $(3 - (-2)^2) \times 5 + 3 =$ $(3 - 4) \times 5 + 3 =$ $-1 \times 5 + 3 = -5 + 3 = -2$	2. $(8 + x) + 2x = 8 + (x + 2x)$	3. The number 14 represents this in the data set $\{14, 30, 14, 31, 30, 18, 14, 12\}$.
4. The average temperatures in a city over seven days included 54°F, 51°F, 42°F, 47°F, 58°F, 54°F, and 53°F. What does the number $58 - 42 = 16$ represent for this set of temperatures?	5. Blanes's grades in history class are 82, 82, 92, 90, and 84. What does the number $\frac{82 + 82 + 92 + 90 + 84}{5} = 86$ represent for this set of grades?	6. $8(2^3 + 16) = 8(2^3) + 8(16)$
7. $b + c = c + b$	8. $14 \times (50 \times 21) =$ $(14 \times 50) \times 21$	9. The set $\{1, 1, 3, 5, 10\}$ represents the number of hours that five students watched TV last week. What does the number 3 represent for this set of hours?

1F: Vocabulary Review Puzzle   **For use with the Chapter Review**
....

Study Skill Vocabulary is an important part of every subject you learn. Review new words and their definitions using flashcards.

Find each of the following words in the word search. Circle the word and then cross it off the word list. Words can be displayed forwards, backwards, up, down, or diagonally.

absolute value	integers	order
median	mode	mean
opposites	outlier	range
compatible	distributive	multiplication

```
C Q E D E T A J P K A Z L H N
F K E E R E D R O N D A H U N
M Z D W I T E P I E B B I P O
R N O U R O L C C V E S E F I
A O M B A P B M E I T O V X T
N P R J N P I E P T I L A S A
G F I R L O T T E U F U T E C
E I N P M S A R T B E T K T I
Y O T H G I P A A I I E O R L
I D E O O T M N R R N V U O P
W A G R F E O V O T K A T I I
P D E F N S C O O S E L L J T
G K R N N A W S O I G U I R L
N M S D K A E V N D S E E U U
M E D I A N F M A R O M R L M
```

Puzzle 1-10

Mean, Median, Mode, and Range

Choose values from the chart to create a data set that satisfies each of the clues below.

Possible Values:

5	6	4
3	5	2
1	1	3
1	1	4

Clues:

1. I am a set that contains three numbers. My mean is 5.

2. I contain 5 numbers, my range is 5, my median is 3, and my mode is 1.

3. I'm also a set with five numbers. My mode and my range are 5, and my mean is 4.

4. There are only 2 numbers in my set. There is no mode, and a mean of 5.

5. I am a set that contains four numbers. My mode is 4, and my mean is 4.

6. I am a large set of seven numbers. My mean is 2, and my mode is 1.

7. There are four numbers in my set, my mode is 1 and my mean is 2.

8. I am a set that contains three numbers. My median is 3, my range is 4, and my mean is 3.

Chapter 1 Project: Board Walk

Create a Board Game

Beginning the Chapter Project

What makes a board game so much fun? You have challenges like road blocks or false paths that make you backtrack. Then you land on a lucky square that lets you leap forward past your opponent. Best of all, you are with your friends as you play.

For this chapter project, you will use integers to create a game. Then you will play your game with friends or family for a trial run. Finally, you will decorate your game and bring it to class to play.

Activities

Activity 1: Planning

Choose a setting for your game board. Is the game in a cave, in a castle, in a person's digestive tract? Decide whether you want players to move by selecting cards, rolling number cubes, or both. Do you want the end of the game to be determined by the number of points someone has or by moving to an end square?

Activity 2: Developing

Make a draft of your game board. Add details. Use integers to determine positive and negative points or positive and negative movement on the game board. Think of adventures and misadventures for your game like "Catch a falling star. Get +10 points" or "Fall off a cliff. Move −7 spaces."

Activity 3: Designing

Add details to your game board that require multiplication of integers. Use illustrations and color, and put a cardboard backing on the game board.

Activity 4: Organizing

Finish your game board, and write the rules of your game. Organize everything needed to play your game.

Chapter 1 Project: Board Walk (continued)

Finishing the Project

Present your game to the class. Explain the rules of the game. Answer any questions from your classmates.

Be sure your work is neat and clear. The game rules should be easy to understand.

Reflect and Revise

Work (or play) in small groups to test each other's games. Point out to each other the features of the games that you think are well designed. What part of the mathematics of the game works well? What do you like about playing the game? Revise your game based on comments from your group.

Extending the Project

Make a list of sports that use integers in some way. Create or adapt your game to help your classmates learn integer operations. Share your game with a coach in your school, for example, the baseball, football, golf, swimming or tennis coach.

Research how to have a new game produced to sell in a store. Write a report explaining what you learned.

Visit PHSchool.com for information and links you might find helpful as you complete your project.

Chapter Project Manager

Getting Started

Read about the project. As you work on it, you will need several sheets of paper. If available, a spreadsheet program can be used. Keep all your work for the project in a folder, along with this Project Manager.

Checklist	**Suggestions**
❑ Activity 1: planning	❑ Make a list of the features you like in some of your favorite games to give you ideas.
❑ Activity 2: developing	❑ Use graph paper to sketch your design.
❑ Activity 3: designing	❑ Review how to operate with integers.
❑ Activity 4: organizing	❑ Play your game so you can make final revisions before bringing it to school. Verify that the rules include every possible situation that a player might encounter
❑ Recommendations	❑ When writing the rules, be sure to check your spelling, grammar, and punctuation.

Scoring Rubric

3 You provided work to show that you thought about your game before putting it together. Your game includes opportunities to use addition, subtraction, and multiplication of positive and negative integers. Your finished game board is attractive, and your project includes rules that are easy to understand and follow.

2 You created a game that includes opportunities to add, subtract, and multiply positive and negative integers, but your finished product is not as well planned or constructed as it could have been.

1 Your finished game is not well thought out nor does it provide opportunities to add, subtract, and multiply positive and negative integers.

0 You did not make a game, or you did not include the use of both positive and negative integers in your game.

Your Evaluation of Project   Evaluate your work, based on the Scoring Rubric.

Teacher's Evaluation of Project

Chapter Project Teacher Notes

About the Project

Students will have an opportunity to apply their knowledge of integers to design a game.

Introducing the Project

Ask students:

- *Do you know what negative numbers are?*

- *Have you ever used a game board to practice a skill?*

Activity 1: Planning

Have students brainstorm a list of decisions they need to make in order to design their game.

Activity 2: Developing

Hint to students that they may want to determine the total number of spaces to include on the game board before they create rules for movement. For example, if there are only 12 spaces, they may not want to use "Fly in an airplane. Move +10 spaces."

Activity 3: Designing

Encourage students to share ways to use multiplication of integers to make their game more interesting. For example: "You wrote three checks for $9 each, but you did not have any money in your checking account. Multiply $3 \cdot -9$."

Activity 4: Organizing

Make sure students have all of the supplies they need to play the game. Have students trade rules with a partner to make sure the rules are easy to understand.

Finishing the Project

You may wish to plan a project day on which students share their completed projects. Encourage students to explain their process in creating their game as well as their product.

Visit PHSchool.com for information and links you might find helpful as you complete your project.

✔ Checkpoint Quiz 1

Use with Lessons 1-1 through 1-3.

Use any estimation strategy to estimate.

1. $79.06 - 38.64$

2. $\$5.78 + \$3.64$

3. $7.875 \div 3.91$

_____

Find each sum or difference.

4. $53.23 - 24.89$

5. $4.89 + 34.5 + 2.17$

6. $7.895 - 3.449$

_____

Find each product.

7. 7.5×3

8. $1.8 \cdot 0.3$

9. $0.71 \cdot 50$

_____

- - - ✂ -

✔ Checkpoint Quiz 2

Use with Lessons 1-4 through 1-6.

Compare using >, <, or ≠.

1. $-15 \ \square \ 25$

2. $0 \ \square \ -7$

3. $21 \ \square \ -3$

4. $|-6| \ \square \ |6|$

Find each quotient.

5. $11.2 \div 1.6$

6. $\dfrac{6.24}{4}$

7. $41.6 \div 5.2$

_____

8. $\dfrac{144}{0.6}$

9. $3.1\overline{)8.61}$

10. $0.0714 \div 4.2$

_____

11. An Olympic-sized swimming pool is 50 meters long. What is its length in centimeters?

_____

12. Choose a reasonable estimate for the volume of a flower bud vase from these choices: 40 kL, 40 L, 40 mL, 40 g.

_____

Name _____ Class _____ Date _____

Chapter Test

Form A

Chapter 1

1. Estimate the product by rounding to the nearest whole number.
   110.5×10.2

   _____

2. Use front-end estimation to estimate the sum to the nearest whole number. $5.312 + 3.726$

   _____

Find each sum or difference.

3. $8.27 + 6.9 + 5$

4. $19 - 12.735$

5. $21.6 - 9.24$

6. $0.68 + 5.681$

7. $52.1 - 51.06$

8. $74.5 + 0 + 17.3$

Find each product or quotient.

9. $\frac{57.96}{2.8}$

10. $\frac{408.48}{8}$

11. $5.9 \cdot 0.32$

12. $6.73 \cdot 0.04$

13. $3.2 \div 0.128$

14. $(2.6)(0.02)$

Change each measurement to the given unit.

15. 24 m 5 cm to centimeters

16. 5 kg 240 g to kilograms

17. 11 L 17 mL to liters

Write the metric unit that makes each statement true.

18. $12{,}451 \text{ dL} = 1{,}245.1$ _____

19. $2.48 \text{ cm} = 24.8$ _____

20. In last Saturday's parade, Tom counted all of the bicycles and tricycles, for a total of 227 wheels. His count included 76 bicycles. How many tricycles were in the parade?

   _____

Chapter Test (continued)   **Form A**

Chapter 1

Order the numbers from least to greatest.

21. $-6, -10, 7, 0, -3, -4$

22. $-100, -1,000, 0, -1, -10, 100$

_____   _____

Compare. Use <, >, or =.

23. $2 \;\square\; -8$ **24.** $-6 \;\square\; -6$ **25.** $-13 \;\square\; -3$

26. At midnight the temperature was $-2°C$. By noon the following day the temperature was $8°C$. Find the temperature change.

_____

Find the value of each expression.

27. $4 + 5 - 9$

28. $26 - (-9) - 6$

_____   _____

29. $5 - 5 - 5$

30. $-4 - 4 + (-15)$

_____   _____

Find each product or quotient.

31. $\frac{-72}{9}$

32. $-64 \div 4$

_____   _____

33. $(-8) \cdot (-11)$

34. $25 \cdot (-10)$

_____   _____

35. Which operation should be done first in the expression $9 - 30 \div 2$?

_____

Here are scores for six bowlers. Use the data to answer Exercises 36 and 37.
$156, 145, 162, 215, 148, 163$

36. Find the range and mean of the data set.

_____

37. How many modes are in the data set?

_____

Name _____ Class _____ Date _____

Chapter Test   Form B

Chapter 1

1. Round to the nearest whole number to estimate the product.
   110.5×10.2

   _____

2. Use front-end estimation to estimate the sum to the nearest
   whole number. $5.312 + 3.726$

   _____

Find each sum or difference.

3. $8.27 + 6.9 + 5$ 4. $19 - 12.735$

   _____   _____

5. $21.6 - 9.24$ 6. $0.68 + 5.681$

   _____   _____

Find each product or quotient.

7. $\dfrac{57.96}{2.8}$ 8. $6.73 \cdot 0.04$

   _____   _____

9. $3.2 \div 0.128$ 10. $(2.6)(0.02)$

   _____   _____

Change each measurement to the given unit.

11. 24 m 5 cm to centimeters _____

12. 5 kg 240 g to kilograms _____

Write the metric unit that makes each statement true.

13. $12{,}451 \text{ dL} = 1{,}245.1$ 14. $2.48 \text{ cm} = 24.8$

    _____   _____

Solve.

15. In last Saturday's parade, Tom counted all of the bicycles and
    tricycles, for a total of 227 wheels. His count included 76 bicycles.
    How many tricycles were in the parade?

    _____

Chapter Test (continued)   Form B

Chapter 1

Order the numbers from least to greatest.

16. $-6, -10, 7, 0, -3, -4$

17. $-100, -1,000, 0, -1, -10, 100$

_____   _____

Compare. Use <, >, or =.

18. $2 \ \square \ -8$ **19.** $-6 \ \square \ -6$ **20.** $-13 \ \square \ -3$

Find the value of each expression.

21. $4 + 5 - 9$ **22.** $26 - (-9) - 6$ **23.** $5 - 5 - 5$

_____   _____   _____

Find each product or quotient.

24. $\dfrac{-72}{9}$ **25.** $-64 \div 4$ **26.** $(-8) \cdot (-11)$

_____   _____   _____

Solve.

27. Which operation should be done first in the expression $9 - 30 \div 2$?

_____

Here are scores for six bowlers. Use the data to answer exercises 28 and 29.

156, 145, 162, 215, 148, 163

28. Find the range and mean of the data set.

_____

29. How many modes are in the data set?

_____

Alternative Assessment

Form C

Chapter 1

MOVIES FOR LESS

Carla and Christian Mendoza, seventh-grade twins, love going to the movies. Their neighborhood theater was selling special summer passes for $90.00. The pass can be used to see any movies at the theater for 10 weeks. Without a pass, tickets bought before 5:00 P.M. are $4.50 each. Tickets bought at or after 5:00 P.M. are $7.00 each.

Show all of your work on a separate sheet of paper.

1. Carla and Christian want to convince their parents that they should each have a summer movie pass. Write a good presentation that they could use to convince their parents. Be sure to include some realistic data in your presentation.

2. Do you think the twins' parents should buy each twin a summer movie pass? Explain why or why not.

3. Billy and Bobbie Carter go to the movies with the Mendoza twins, but Billy and Bobbie do *not* have movie passes. Mr. and Mrs. Carter have set these guidelines:

   • Their children may see only one movie each week.

   • They may attend only early afternoon showings.

   • Each child may buy two items from the snack bar during each movie.

SNACK BAR MENU					
Popcorn	small:	$2.50	**Peanuts**	small:	$1.75
	large:	$3.50		medium:	$2.00
				large:	$2.50
Drinks	small:	$2.00			
	large:	$3.00			

Approximately how much should Mr. and Mrs. Carter budget for movie expenses for both children? Explain your answer and show your work.

Alternative Assessment (continued)   Form C

Chapter 1

4. Mr. Carter has decided he wants his children to do chores to help pay for movie expenses. Explain in detail how Billy and Bobbie could help pay for part of the cost. Describe some tasks and the amount the children should be paid for each task. Remember, the amount they're paid must be realistic. For example, Bobbie might be paid $5.00 to cut and trim the grass.

Excursion

Suppose that television costs the same as movies. For example, an afternoon movie-length time period of TV costs $4.50; an evening movie-length time period costs $7.00.

If you had to pay these rates to watch television, about how much would you spend in a month? Show your work or explain your answer. (If you do not watch television, estimate the amount of time and money your teacher would spend on television in a month.)

Use a data display to present your findings to your class. Compare your costs with that of your classmates. Write a paragraph explaining the similarities and differences of your costs and those of your classmates.

Name _____ Class _____ Date _____

Cumulative Review

Chapter 1

Multiple Choice. Choose the letter of the best answer.

1. Which of the following shows the order from least to greatest for the mean, the median, and the mode of this set of data?
0, 1, 2, 2, 2, 3, 4, 7, 10, 11

   A. mode, median, mean

   B. median, mode, mean

   C. mode, mean, median

   D. mean, median, mode

2. You have saved $35.75. How many CDs can you buy if each CD costs $11.47, tax included?

   F. 2 CDs   **G.** 3 CDs

   H. 4 CDs   **J.** 5 CDs

3. Identify the property of addition shown.
$(1.5 + 2.5) + 3 = 1.5 + (2.5 + 3)$

   A. associative   **B.** distributive

   C. commutative   **D.** identity

4. Which expression is *not* the same as $2.7 \times 3.6 \div 9$?

   F. $2.7 \div 9 \times 3.6$

   G. $3.6 \times 9 \div 2.7$

   H. $3.6 \times 2.7 \div 9$

   J. $3.6 \div 9 \times 2.7$

5. In the quotient $120 \div 11$, what digit is in the tenths place?

   A. 0   **B.** 1

   C. 8   **D.** 9

6. Sara saved $12.50 for five weeks. Her brother saved $13.75 for five weeks. How much more did her brother save?

   F. $6.25   **G.** $62.50

   H. $6.88   **J.** $68.75

7. Which list shows the following integers ordered from least to greatest?
$0, -1, 2, -3, -8$

   A. $-1, -3, -8, 0, 2$

   B. $-8, -3, -1, 0, 2$

   C. $0, -8, -3, -1, 2$

   D. $0, -1, 2, -3, -8$

8. For a dance, the student government bought 198 carnations at $.49 each. What is the best estimate of the total amount paid for the carnations?

   F. $60   **G.** $80

   H. $100   **J.** $120

9. The temperature on Mars reaches 27°C during the day and −125°C at night. What is the average temperature?

   A. −49°C

   B. +76°C

   C. +49°C

   D. −76°C

10. Divide. $-10 \div (-2)$

   F. -5 **G.** $-\frac{1}{5}$

   H. $\frac{1}{5}$ **J.** 5

11. Which of the following statements is *always* true?
   I. A negative integer plus a negative integer equals a negative integer.
   II. A negative integer minus a negative integer equals a negative integer.

   A. II only   **B.** Both I and II

   C. I only   **D.** Neither I nor II

Cumulative Review (continued)

Chapter 1

12. Which of the following uses the Distributive Property to find 7×57?

   F. $7 \times 5 \times 7$

   G. $7(50 \times 7)$

   H. $(7 \times 50) + 7$

   J. $(7 \times 50) + (7 \times 7)$

13. Which equation is true?

   A. $17 - 3 \times 5 = 2$

   B. $20 - 5 \times 3 = 45$

   C. $10 + 3 \times 2 = 26$

   D. $6 + 5 \times 9 = 99$

14. Which integer is between -6 and -2?

   F. 0   **G.** -1

   H. -3 **J.** -8

15. Which symbol makes the sentence true?
$7 + 3 \times 2 = 5 \times 3 \underline{} 2$

   A. $-$ **B.** $\div$

   C. $\times$ **D.** $+$

16. What number makes this statement true?
$28.2 \text{ cm} = \underline{} \text{ m}$

   F. 0.282   **G.** 2.82

   H. 28.2   **J.** 282

17. Which of these is the smallest weight?

   A. 24.378 kg   **B.** 24.387 kg

   C. 24.390 kg   **D.** 2.499 kg

18. Bertha, Burt, Barb, and Brenda entered a swimming contest. Burt finished last. Brenda finished between Burt and Barb. Bertha placed first. Who came in third?

   F. Brenda   **G.** Barb

   H. Bertha   **J.** Burt

Extended Response

19. The water level indicator measures the rise and fall in meters of the water level at a reservoir. The 0 on the gauge indicates the normal water level in the reservoir. What was the water level at the end of the summer? at the end of the winter? Find the difference between the two levels.

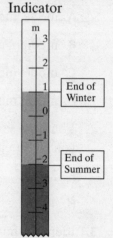

Water Level Indicator

End of Winter

End of Summer

_____

_____

_____

Practice 2-1

Exponents and Order of Operations

Write using exponents.

1. $3 \times 3 \times 3 \times 3 \times 3$ _____

2. $2.7 \times 2.7 \times 2.7$ _____

3. $11.6 \times 11.6 \times 11.6 \times 11.6$ _____

4. $2 \times 2 \times 2 \times 2 \times 2 \times 2$ _____

5. $8.3 \times 8.3 \times 8.3 \times 8.3 \times 8.3$ _____

6. $4 \times 4 \times 4 \times 4 \times 4 \times 4 \times 4 \times 4$ _____

Write as the product of repeated factors. Then simplify.

7. $(0.5)^3$ _____

8. $(-4)^5$ _____

9. $(2.7)^2$ _____

10. 2^3 _____

11. $(-5)^6$ _____

12. $(8.1)^3$ _____

Simplify. Use a calculator, paper and pencil, or mental math.

13. -4^3

14. $11 + (-6^3)$

15. $14 + 16^2$

16. $8 + 6^4$

17. $3^2 \cdot 5^4$

18. $6^2 - 2^{4F}$

19. $4(0.9 + 1.3)^3$

20. $35 - (4^2 + 5)$

21. $(3^3 + 6) - 7$

22. $5(0.3 \cdot 1.2)^2$

23. $5(4 + 2)^2$

24. $(8 - 6.7)^3$

25. A cubic aquarium has edges measuring 4.3 ft each. Find the volume of the aquarium in cubic feet.

26. Lana is 2^3 in. taller than her little sister. How many inches taller is Lana than her sister?

2-1 • Guided Problem Solving

GPS Student Page 71, Exercise 36:

A Scanning Electron Microscope (SEM) can magnify an image to as much as 10^5 times the actual size. How many times is this?

Understand

1. What are you being asked to do?

   _____

   _____

2. What do you call the 5 in 10^5?

   _____

3. What do you call the 10 in 10^5?

   _____

Plan and Carry Out

4. The number 10^5 is what number? _____

5. How many zeros are in the number 10^5? _____

6. How many times does the SEM magnify? _____

Check

7. Does your answer follow the pattern of powers of 10? Explain.

   _____

   _____

   _____

Solve Another Problem

8. Lucy has a microscope that magnifies an image to as much as 10^3 times the actual size. Aaron has a microscope that magnifies an image to as much as 10^4 times the actual size. What is the difference in these two numbers?

   _____

   _____

Practice 2-1

Exponents and Order of Operations

Write using exponents.

1. $3 \times 3 \times 3 \times 3 \times 3$

   _____

2. $2.7 \times 2.7 \times 2.7$

   _____

3. $11.6 \times 11.6 \times 11.6 \times 11.6$

   _____

4. $2 \times 2 \times 2 \times 2 \times 2 \times 2$

   _____

5. $8.3 \times 8.3 \times 8.3 \times 8.3 \times 8.3$

   _____

6. $4 \times 4 \times 4 \times 4 \times 4 \times 4 \times 4 \times 4$

   _____

Write as the product of repeated factors. Then simplify.

7. $(0.5)^3$ _____

8. $(-4)^5$ _____

9. $(2.7)^2$ _____

10. 2^3 _____

Simplify. Use a calculator, paper and pencil, or mental math.

11. -4^3

    _____

12. $11 + (-6^3)$

    _____

13. $14 + 16^2$

    _____

14. $8 + 6^4$

    _____

15. $3^2 \cdot 5^4$

    _____

16. $6^2 - 2^4$

    _____

17. $4(0.9 + 1.3)^3$

    _____

18. $35 - (4^2 + 5)$

    _____

19. $(3^3 + 6) - 7$

    _____

Solve.

20. A cubic aquarium has edges measuring 4.3 ft each. Find the volume of the aquarium in cubic feet.

    _____

21. Lana is 2^3 in. taller than her little sister. How many inches taller is Lana than her sister?

    _____

Activity Lab 2-1

Exponents and Order of Operations

Materials needed: scientific calculator

Example 1: Simplify 12^2.

When you simplify expressions that have a quantity squared, you will use the x^2 key.

① Enter 12. Press x^2 and ENTER .

② The answer is 144.

Example 2: Simplify 8^5.

When you simplify expressions with exponents greater than 2, use the ∧ key.

① Enter 8 ∧ 5, and press ENTER .

② The answer is 32,768.

Example 3: Simplify $2(3^7 + 9)^2$.

① Enter 2 (3 ∧ 7 + 9) x^2 , and press ENTER .

② The answer is 9,644,832.

Exercises

Simplify each expression.

1. 19^2

2. 41^2

3. 107^2

4. 17^5

5. 68^3

6. 2^{21}

7. $(3^6 - 18)^2$

8. $2(5^9 - 2^8)$

9. $(3 + 11)^4 \div 2$

Reteaching 2-1

Exponents and Order of Operations

You can use a shortcut to indicate repeated multiplication. The **exponent** tells how many times the **base** is used as a factor.

$$5 \times 5 \times 5 \times 5 = 5^4 = 625$$

exponent

base

5^4 is called an **exponential expression** and 625 is the **value of the expression.**

You can use this sentence ⟶ **P**lease **E**xcuse **M**y **D**ear **A**unt **S**ally.
to remember the order of operations
for expressions with exponents.

$2^2 + 4(7 - 3) + 6 = 2^2 + 4(4) + 6$

P	Do all operations within **P**arentheses first.

$= 4 + 4(4) + 6$ **E**   Evaluate any terms with **E**xponents.

$= 4 + 16 + 6$ **M-D**   **M**ultiply and **D**ivide in order from left to right.

$= 26$ **A-S**   **A**dd and **S**ubtract in order from left to right.

Write each expression using exponents.

1. $6 \times 6 \times 6 \times 6 \times 6$ _____

2. $0.2 \times 0.2 \times 0.2$ _____

Write each expression as a product of its factors. Then evaluate each expression.

3. 12^2

4. 8^3

_____

_____

5. $(0.4)^3$

6. 1.4^2

_____

_____

Simplify each expression.

7. $7^2 + 3^3$

8. $5(0.2 + 0.8)^{10}$

9. $(9 - 7)^2$

_____

_____

_____

10. $(8^2 + 16) \div 2$

11. $(4 + 7)^2 - 8$

12. $(9 - 3)^2 + 6 \times 2$

_____

_____

_____

Enrichment 2-1

Exponents and Order of Operations

Critical Thinking

Rewrite each of the numbers as an expression using addition, subtraction, multiplication, division, and exponents. Use only the numbers 1, 2, 3, and 4 or a combination of these numbers. Use the numbers only once each. You must use at least one operation. Don't forget the order of operations!

1		16	
2		17	
3		18	
4		19	
5		20	
6		21	
7		22	
8		23	
9		24	
10		25	
11		26	
12		27	
13		28	
14		29	
15		30	

2A: Graphic Organizer

For use before Lesson 2-1

Study Skill Develop consistent study habits. Block off the same amount of time each evening for schoolwork. Plan ahead by setting aside extra time when you have a big project or test coming up.

Write your answers.

1. What is the chapter title? _____

2. How many lessons are there in this chapter? _____

3. What is the topic of the Test-Taking Strategies page? _____

4. Complete the graphic organizer below as you work through the chapter.
   - In the center, write the title of the chapter.
   - When you begin a lesson, write the lesson name in a rectangle.
   - When you complete a lesson, write a skill or key concept in a circle linked to that lesson block.
   - When you complete the chapter, use this graphic organizer to help you review.

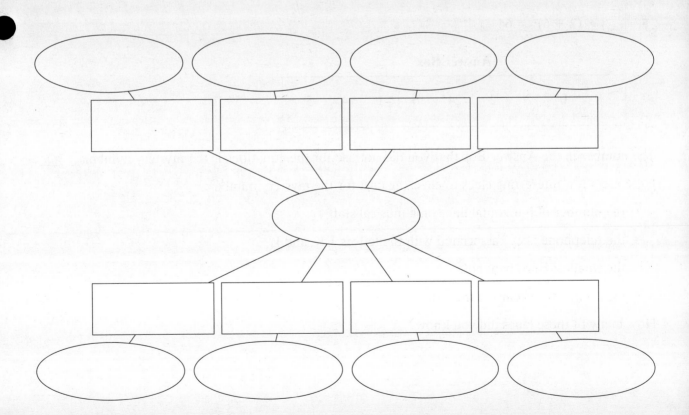

Puzzle 2-1

Exponents and Order of Operations

Each equation can be made true by filling in the missing number with one of the numbers in the answer box.

1. $3^{\square} = 81$

2. $2 + 5^{\square} = 127$

3. $\square(2^3 + 7) = 90$

4. $-36 + (14 - \square)^2 = 0$

5. $(-3)^{\square} = 9$

6. $(-2)^{\square} \times 4 = -8$

7. $6(4 - 2)^2 = \square$

8. $\square + (2 + 6)^2 = 64$

Answer Box

| 8 | 0 | 3 | 2 | 24 | 6 | 1 | 4 | 5 |

The number in the Answer Box that you did not use for the equations is the mystery number _____.

Here are a few interesting clues to check against for the mystery number:

- the number of horizontal lines on a musical staff
- the telephone "key" associated with the letters J, K, and L
- the smallest Euro banknote
- the number of oceans in the world

How many of these clues did you know?

Practice 2-2

Find the LCM of each pair of numbers.

1. 11, 5 _____   **2.** 5, 12 _____   **3.** 12, 7 _____

4. 5, 9 _____   **5.** 5, 18 _____   **6.** 5, 20 _____

7. 7, 10 _____   **8.** 17, 13 _____   **9.** 14, 8 _____

10. 11, 23 _____   **11.** 14, 5 _____   **12.** 16, 9 _____

13. Cameron is making bead necklaces. He has 90 green beads and 108 blue beads. What is the greatest number of identical necklaces he can make if he wants to use all of the beads?

_____

14. One radio station broadcasts a weather forecast every 18 minutes and another station broadcasts a commercial every 15 minutes. If the stations broadcast both a weather forecast and a commercial at noon, when is the next time that both will be broadcast at the same time?

_____

Determine whether each number is prime or composite.

15. 97 _____   **16.** 63 _____   **17.** 29 _____   **18.** 120 _____

Write the prime factorization. Use exponents where possible.

19. 42 _____   **20.** 130 _____

21. 78 _____   **22.** 126 _____

23. 125 _____   **24.** 90 _____

25. 92 _____   **26.** 180 _____

Find the GCF of each pair of numbers.

27. 45, 60 _____   **28.** 18, 42 _____   **29.** 32, 80 _____

30. 20, 65 _____   **31.** 24, 90 _____   **32.** 17, 34 _____

33. 14, 35 _____   **34.** 51, 27 _____   **35.** 42, 63 _____

2-2 • Guided Problem Solving

GPS Student Page 78, Exercise 48:

A movie theatre just added two rooms. One room is large enough for 125 people, and the other can seat up to 350 people. In each room, the seating is arranged in horizontal rows with the same number of seats in each row. What is the greatest number of seats that can make up each row?

Understand

1. Circle the information you will need to solve.

2. What do you need to do to answer the question?

   _____

   _____

Plan and Carry Out

3. List the prime factors of 350.   _____

4. List the prime factors of 125.   _____

5. List the factors that 350 and
   125 have in common.   _____

6. What is the greatest common
   factor of 350 and 125?   _____

7. What is the largest number of seats
   that can make up each row?   _____

Check

8. What is 350 ÷ 25? What is 125 ÷ 25? Do these quotients have any common factors besides 1?

   _____

   _____

Solve Another Problem

9. For graduation, the left side of the gymnasium can seat 228 people and the right side can seat 144 people. The principal wants the same number of chairs in each row on both sides. How many chairs does the setup committee need to put in each row?

   _____

Practice 2-2

Prime Factorization

Find the LCM of each pair of numbers.

1. 11, 5

_____

2. 5, 12

_____

3. 12, 7

_____

4. 5, 9

_____

5. 5, 18

_____

6. 5, 20

_____

7. 7, 10

_____

8. 17, 13

_____

9. 14, 8

_____

10. Cameron is making bead necklaces. He has 90 green beads and 108 blue beads. What is the greatest number of identical necklaces he can make if he wants to use all of the beads?

_____

Determine whether each number is prime or composite.

11. 97 _____ **12.** 63 _____ **13.** 29 _____ **14.** 120 _____

Write the prime factorization. Use exponents where possible.

15. 42 _____

16. 130 _____

17. 78 _____

18. 126 _____

19. 125 _____

20. 90 _____

Find the GCF of each pair of numbers.

21. 45, 60

_____

22. 18, 42

_____

23. 20, 65

_____

24. 24, 90

_____

25. 14, 35

_____

26. 51, 27

_____

Activity Lab 2-2

Materials needed: paper; red, blue, and black ink pens

Work in groups of three.

1. On a sheet of paper, create four grids with the numbers 1 through 50 like the one shown below. Draw three boxes beside each grid.

1	2	3	4	5	6	7	8	9	10
11	12	13	14	15	16	17	18	19	20
21	22	23	24	25	26	27	28	29	30
31	32	33	34	35	36	37	38	39	40
41	42	43	44	45	46	47	48	49	50

2. The player with the longest last name is Player 1, next longest is Player 2, and shortest is Player 3. If your last names are the same length, use your first names to determine players.

3. Player 3 calls out a number between 11 and 20 and writes the number in one of the boxes beside the first grid. Using a red pen, Player 1 marks out all of the factors of that number in the grid. For example, 14 has factors 1, 2, 7, and 14.

4. If Player 1 correctly marks out all of the factors of the number, he or she receives one point. If any factors were left out, Player 2 receives one point for each missing factor that he or she can identify. If Player 1 marks out any numbers that are not factors, Player 2 receives two points for each incorrect factor that he or she can identify. (Player 3 should help determine whether factors are correctly identified.) Keep a tally of your points.

5. Switch roles. Player 1 will call out a number between 11 and 20 and write the number in the second box beside the grid. Using a blue pen and the same grid, Player 2 will mark out all of the factors of the number. Player 3 will then try to identify any incorrect or missing factors. Use the same scoring method and record your points in your table.

6. Switch roles again, so Player 2 calls out a number between 11 and 20 Player 3 crosses out its factors using a black pen. Player 1 then tries to identify any missing or incorrect factors. Use the same scoring method and record your points.

7. Use a new grid for Round 2. Call out numbers between 21 and 30.

8. Complete Round 3 using numbers between 31 and 40. Complete Round 4 using numbers between 41 and 50. The player with the most points at the end of four rounds wins.

Reteaching 2-2

A **prime number** has exactly
two factors, 1 and itself.
2 and 7 are prime numbers.
2 is the smallest prime number.

$2 \times 1 = 2 \qquad 7 \times 1 = 7$

Every **composite number** can be
written as a product of two or more
prime numbers. This is called the
prime factorization of the number.

$60 = 2 \cdot 2 \cdot 3 \cdot 5 = 2^2 \cdot 3 \cdot 5$
$40 = 2 \cdot 2 \cdot 2 \cdot 5 = 2^3 \cdot 5$

You can use a *factor tree* and division to find the prime factorization
of a number.

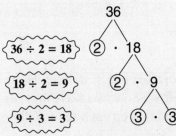

① Divide by a factor other than 1 and
the number itself. Record the divisor
and the quotient in the factor tree.

② Continue dividing until all the
factors are prime numbers.

③ Use exponents to write the
prime factorization.

$36 = 2^2 \cdot 3^2$

**Complete each factor tree. Then write the prime factorization using
exponents where possible.**

1.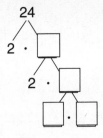
    24

    _____

2. 30

    _____

3. 27

    _____

**Write the prime factorization of each number. Use exponents where
possible.**

4. 20 = _____

5. 54 = _____

6. 40 = _____

7. 48 = _____

8. 56 = _____

9. 150 = _____

Enrichment 2-2

Decision Making

Mr. Jones wants to arrange 24 desks into groups so that students can work together. He wants each group to be the same size.

1. What different sizes of groups can Mr. Jones use?

   _____

2. What does Mr. Jones need to consider when he moves the desks into the groups?

   _____

   _____

3. The current project is a class debate. There will be four teams. In the space below, show two ways that Mr. Jones can arrange the desks so that students on each team will be sitting together.

   | Chalkboard |

   | Chalkboard |

4. For the next project, each group will perform a skit showing a typical day in the life of a teenager in another country. What would be the best group sizes for this project? Explain.

   _____

   _____

   _____

5. How can Mr. Jones arrange the desks for students to work on the skit? Use the space to the right to show the arrangement. Why is this the best seating arrangement?

   | Chalkboard |

   _____

   _____

   _____

Puzzle 2-2

Prime Factorization

Holmes and Watson needed to find the combination to unlock a
locker at Charing Cross Station. Here are the clues they had.

1. One number is the GCF of 12 and 15.

_____

2. Another number is the GCF of 19 and 57.

_____

3. The third number is the GCF of 27, 36, and 45.

_____

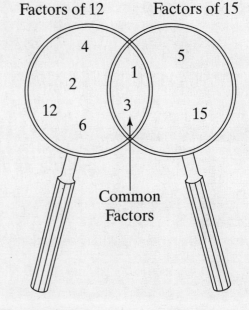

Factors of 12   Factors of 15

Common
Factors

To put the numbers in the proper order, Holmes and Watson had one
more clue.

4. The first number is the square of the third.

Combination: _____ _____ _____

Write your own lock combination problem and clues to share with
Holmes or a friend.

5. _____

_____

_____

Practice 2-3

Write each fraction in simplest form.

1. $\frac{8}{12}$ _____

2. $\frac{9}{15}$ _____

3. $\frac{16}{20}$ _____

4. $\frac{20}{25}$ _____

5. $\frac{15}{18}$ _____

6. $\frac{14}{30}$ _____

7. $\frac{11}{44}$ _____

8. $\frac{24}{36}$ _____

Write each fraction in simplest form. Give the GCF of the numerator and denominator.

9. $\frac{125}{200}$ ____ GCF = ____

10. $\frac{36}{64}$ ____ GCF = ____

11. $\frac{65}{90}$ ____ GCF = ____

12. $\frac{45}{72}$ ____ GCF = ____

13. $\frac{35}{85}$ ____ GCF = ____

14. $\frac{30}{42}$ ____ GCF = ____

Solve.

15. Emily exercised from 4:05 P.M. to 4:32 P.M. For what part of an hour did Emily exercise? Write the fraction in simplest form.

_____

16. Luis rode his bike after school for 48 min. For what part of an hour did he ride his bike? Write the fraction in simplest form.

_____

17. Philip played video games for 55 min before dinner. For what part of an hour did he play?

_____

18. What part of an hour is your school lunch time?

_____

19. Survey 12 people to find their favorite kind of pizza from the following choices. Write the results in fraction form. Then shade the pizza shapes using different colors to indicate their choices.

Pizza Favorites

Cheese _____

Green Pepper _____

Olive _____

Mushroom _____

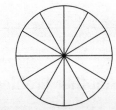

Name _____ Class _____ Date _____

2-3 • Guided Problem Solving

Student Page 84, Exercise 28:

Weather The city of Houston, Texas, typically has 90 clear days out of the 365 days in a year. Houston's clear days represent what fraction of a year? Write your answer in simplest form.

Understand

1. Circle the information you will need to solve.

2. What are you being asked to do?

_____

_____

Plan and Carry Out

3. Write the fraction for the expression 90 out of 365.

_____

4. List the prime factors of 90.

_____

5. List the prime factors of 365.

_____

6. List the factors that 90 and 365 have in common.

_____

7. Divide both 90 and 365 by the common factors.

_____

8. Write the fraction in simplest form. _____

Check

9. Is 365 ÷ 90 the same as 73 ÷ 18? Explain.

_____

_____

Solve Another Problem

10. Gerald received a score of 66 out of 72 on his vocabulary test. Write his score as a fraction in simplest form.

_____

Practice 2-3

Simplifying Fractions

Write each fraction in simplest form.

1. $\frac{8}{12}$ _____

2. $\frac{9}{15}$ _____

3. $\frac{16}{20}$ _____

4. $\frac{15}{18}$ _____

5. $\frac{14}{30}$ _____

6. $\frac{11}{44}$ _____

Write each fraction in simplest form. Give the GCF of the numerator and denominator.

7. $\frac{125}{200}$ _____ GCF = _____

8. $\frac{36}{64}$ _____ GCF = _____

9. $\frac{45}{72}$ _____ GCF = _____

10. $\frac{35}{85}$ _____ GCF = _____

Solve.

11. Luis rode his bike after school for 48 min. For what part of an hour did he ride his bike? Write the fraction in simplest form.

_____

12. Philip played video games for 55 min before dinner. For what part of an hour did he play?

_____

13. What part of an hour is your school lunch time? Write the fraction in simplest form.

_____

14. Survey 12 people to find their favorite kind of pizza from the following choices. Write the results in fraction form. Then shade the pizza shapes using different colors to indicate their choices.

Pizza Favorites

Cheese _____

Green Pepper _____

Olive _____

Mushroom _____

Activity Lab 2-3

Simplifying Fractions

Critical Thinking

The fraction $\frac{3}{4}$ can be modeled in a variety of ways. Two ways are shown below.

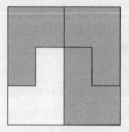 

Divide the squares in column one into fourths. Show a different way to divide the square into fourths for each problem. Shade some parts. Write a fraction. Then use your model in column one to show an equivalent fraction in column two. Write equivalent fraction.

Fourths   **Equivalent Fraction**

1.

   fraction _____   fraction _____

2.

   fraction _____   fraction _____

3.

   fraction _____   fraction _____

4.

   fraction _____   fraction _____

Name _____ Class _____ Date _____

Reteaching 2-3

A fraction is in **simplest form** when the numerator and denominator have no common factors other than 1.

To write $\frac{18}{24}$ in the simplest form:

① Divide the numerator and denominator $\frac{18 \div 2}{24 \div 2} = \frac{9}{12}$ by a common factor.

② Continue dividing by common factors $\frac{9 \div 3}{12 \div 3} = \frac{3}{4}$ until the only common factor is 1.   The only factor common to 3 and 4 is 1.

In simplest form, $\frac{18}{24}$ is $\frac{3}{4}$.

You can use the greatest common factor (GCF) to write a fraction in simplest form. Divide the numerator and the denominator by the GCF.

The GCF of 18 and 24 is 6.

$\frac{18}{24} = \frac{18 \div 6}{24 \div 6} = \frac{3}{4}$

Complete to write each fraction in simplest form.

1. $\frac{10}{20} = \frac{10 \div}{20 \div 2} = \frac{\div}{10 \div} =$ _____

2. $\frac{24}{60} = \frac{24 \div 6}{60 \div} = \frac{\div}{10 \div} =$ _____

Find the GCF of the numerator and denominator of each fraction. Then write each fraction in simplest form.

3. $\frac{12}{14} =$ _____

GCF = _____

4. $\frac{9}{15} =$ _____

GCF = _____

5. $\frac{35}{42} =$ _____

GCF = _____

6. $\frac{40}{50} =$ _____

GCF = _____

Write each fraction in simplest form.

7. $\frac{42}{60} =$ _____

8. $\frac{20}{36} =$ _____

9. $\frac{18}{20} =$ _____

10. $\frac{9}{27} =$ _____

11. $\frac{25}{75} =$ _____

12. $\frac{65}{75} =$ _____

13. $\frac{40}{60} =$ _____

14. $\frac{50}{95} =$ _____

Enrichment 2-3

Decision Making

A grab bag at a school rummage sale costs $15.00. Only the packers know what is inside each bag. Ferdinand and Rachel want to buy one grab bag. Ferdinand has $10.50 and Rachel has $6.75.

1. How much should each person contribute to the purchase? Why?

   _____

   _____

2. Based on how much each person contributed, what fraction of the surprises in the grab bag should each person receive? Why?

   _____

   _____

   _____

3. The grab bag contents are listed below.

1 wallet-size calculator	4 pocket combs
2 tickets to a matinee	5 bus tokens
3 school pencils	2 school sports buttons

   What would be a way for Ferdinand and Rachel to divide the contents so that each gets a fair share?

   _____

   _____

   _____

4. Using the way you decided, who gets which items? Explain why you chose the items for each to receive.

   _____

   _____

   _____

Puzzle 2-3

Simplifying Fractions

Write each fraction in simplest form to find equivalent fractions, then draw
a line in the diagram below to connect the pairs of equivalent fractions.

1. $\frac{21}{28} = \frac{21 \div 7}{28 \div 7} = \frac{3}{4}$

2. $\frac{65}{91} =$

3. $\frac{45}{48} =$

4. $\frac{2}{10} =$

5. $\frac{15}{40} =$

6. $\frac{36}{48} =$

7. $\frac{10}{14} =$

8. $\frac{165}{176} =$

9. $\frac{27}{72} =$

10. $\frac{6}{30} =$

$\frac{21}{28}$ •   • $\frac{65}{91}$

$\frac{27}{72}$
•

$\frac{45}{48}$
•

$\frac{6}{30}$ •

• $\frac{2}{10}$

$\frac{165}{176}$ •

• $\frac{15}{40}$

• $\frac{10}{14}$

$\frac{36}{48}$ •

Practice 2-4

Comparing and Ordering Fractions

Write the two fractions for these models and compare them with <, >, or =.

1.

2.

3.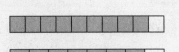

_____   _____   _____

Find the LCD of each pair of fractions.

4. $\frac{5}{8}, \frac{5}{6}$ _____

5. $\frac{5}{12}, \frac{7}{8}$ _____

6. $\frac{9}{10}, \frac{1}{2}$ _____

7. $\frac{1}{6}, \frac{3}{10}$ _____

8. $\frac{1}{4}, \frac{2}{15}$ _____

9. $\frac{5}{6}, \frac{8}{15}$ _____

Compare each pair of fractions. Use <, >, or =.

10. $\frac{7}{8} \; \square \; \frac{3}{10}$

11. $\frac{6}{12} \; \square \; \frac{4}{8}$

12. $\frac{7}{15} \; \square \; \frac{11}{15}$

13. $\frac{4}{5} \; \square \; \frac{6}{10}$

14. $\frac{8}{15} \; \square \; \frac{1}{2}$

15. $\frac{10}{15} \; \square \; \frac{8}{12}$

16. $\frac{4}{9} \; \square \; \frac{7}{9}$

17. $\frac{1}{2} \; \square \; \frac{11}{20}$

18. $\frac{7}{16} \; \square \; \frac{1}{2}$

Order from least to greatest.

19. $\frac{1}{4}, \frac{1}{3}, \frac{1}{6}$ _____

20. $\frac{1}{2}, \frac{5}{6}, \frac{7}{8}$ _____

21. $\frac{1}{4}, \frac{2}{5}, \frac{3}{8}$ _____

22. $\frac{7}{8}, \frac{5}{9}, \frac{2}{3}$ _____

23. $\frac{3}{8}, \frac{5}{6}, \frac{1}{2}$ _____

24. $\frac{9}{10}, \frac{11}{12}, \frac{15}{16}$ _____

25. $\frac{3}{4}, \frac{1}{2}, \frac{7}{8}$ _____

26. $\frac{5}{9}, \frac{2}{3}, \frac{7}{12}$ _____

27. $\frac{15}{16}, \frac{7}{8}, \frac{1}{2}$ _____

Solve.

28. A pattern requires a seam of at least $\frac{5}{8}$ in. Rachel sewed a seam $\frac{1}{2}$ in. wide. Did she sew the seam wide enough? Explain.

_____

29. Marc needs $\frac{3}{4}$ cup of milk for a recipe. He has $\frac{2}{3}$ cup. Does he have enough? Explain.

_____

30. Monica is growing three bean plants as part of a science experiment. Plant A is $\frac{1}{2}$ in. tall. Plant B is $\frac{3}{4}$ in tall. Plant C is $\frac{3}{8}$ in. tall. Order the plants from shortest to tallest.

_____

31. During a rainstorm Willow received $\frac{7}{16}$ in. of rain and Riverton received $\frac{5}{8}$ in. of rain. Which community received more rain?

_____

2-4 • Guided Problem Solving

GPS Student Page 89, Exercise 29:

Carpentry You want to nail a board that is $\frac{1}{2}$ in. thick onto a wall. You can choose from nails that are $\frac{3}{8}$ in. long and $\frac{3}{4}$ in. long. Which size nail is the better choice? Explain.

Understand

1. Circle the information you will need to solve.

2. What are you being asked to do?

   _____

   _____

3. In order to compare fractions what must you do?

   _____

   _____

Plan and Carry Out

4. What is the common denominator for $\frac{1}{2}, \frac{3}{8}, \frac{3}{4}$? _____

5. Write an equivalent fraction for $\frac{1}{2}$ and $\frac{3}{4}$
   with the denominator found in Step 4.   _____

6. Which nail is longer than $\frac{4}{8}$ in.?   _____

7. Which size nail is the better
   choice, the $\frac{3}{8}$ in. nail or the $\frac{3}{4}$ in. nail?   _____

8. Explain why you chose the nail you did in Step 8.

   _____

   _____

   _____

Check

9. What is $\frac{3}{4} - \frac{1}{2}$? What is $\frac{3}{8} - \frac{1}{2}$?

Solve Another Problem

10. Louise used the $\frac{1}{2}$ in., the $\frac{11}{16}$ in., and the $\frac{5}{8}$ in. wrench from her
    dad's toolbox. Now he wants her to put them back in his toolbox
    from smallest to largest. What order should the wrenches be in?

    _____

Practice 2-4

Comparing and Ordering Fractions

Write the two fractions for these models and compare them with <, >, or =.

1.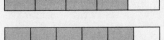

2.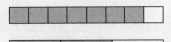

_____   _____

Find the LCD of each pair of fractions.

3. $\frac{5}{8}, \frac{5}{6}$ _____

4. $\frac{5}{12}, \frac{7}{8}$ _____

5. $\frac{9}{10}, \frac{1}{2}$ _____

6. $\frac{1}{6}, \frac{3}{10}$ _____

7. $\frac{1}{4}, \frac{2}{15}$ _____

8. $\frac{5}{6}, \frac{8}{15}$ _____

Compare each pair of fractions. Use <, >, or =.

9. $\frac{7}{8}$ ☐ $\frac{3}{10}$

10. $\frac{6}{12}$ ☐ $\frac{4}{8}$

11. $\frac{7}{15}$ ☐ $\frac{11}{15}$

12. $\frac{4}{5}$ ☐ $\frac{6}{10}$

13. $\frac{8}{15}$ ☐ $\frac{1}{2}$

14. $\frac{10}{15}$ ☐ $\frac{8}{12}$

Order from least to greatest.

15. $\frac{1}{4}, \frac{1}{3}, \frac{1}{6}$ _____

16. $\frac{1}{2}, \frac{5}{6}, \frac{7}{8}$ _____

17. $\frac{1}{4}, \frac{2}{5}, \frac{3}{8}$ _____

18. $\frac{7}{8}, \frac{5}{9}, \frac{2}{3}$ _____

19. $\frac{3}{8}, \frac{5}{6}, \frac{1}{2}$ _____

20. $\frac{3}{4}, \frac{1}{2}, \frac{7}{8}$ _____

Solve.

21. A pattern requires a seam of at least $\frac{5}{8}$ in. Rachel sewed a seam $\frac{1}{2}$ in. wide. Did she sew the seam wide enough? Explain.

_____

22. Marc needs $\frac{3}{4}$ cup of milk for a recipe. He has $\frac{2}{3}$ cup. Does he have enough? Explain.

_____

23. Monica is growing three bean plants as part of a science experiment. Plant A is $\frac{1}{2}$ in. tall. Plant B is $\frac{3}{4}$ in tall. Plant C is $\frac{3}{8}$ in. tall. Order the plants from shortest to tallest.

_____

Activity Lab 2-4
Comparing and Ordering Fractions

Materials needed: fraction calculator

1. Subtraction can help you compare any numbers. First, see what happens when you subtract a larger number from a smaller number on your calculator. You know that 16 < 25. Press 16 ▅ 25 ▤. What does the display show?

_____

You will study about negative numbers later. For now it is helpful to know that any time you subtract a larger number from a smaller number, the difference is a negative number.

2. Compare $\frac{4}{5}$ and $\frac{6}{7}$. Subtract the fractions in order following this key sequence: $\frac{4}{5}$ ▅ $\frac{6}{7}$ ▤. What does the display show?

_____

_____

3. Compare $\frac{3}{7}$ and $\frac{1}{3}$ by subtracting the fractions in order. What does the display show?

_____

Note: The numbers you work with most of the time are positive numbers. In subtraction, when the difference is positive, the first number in the subtraction is larger than the second number: $\frac{3}{7} > \frac{1}{3}$.

4. Compare $\frac{18}{24}$ and $\frac{9}{12}$ by subtracting the fractions in order.

   a. What does the display show? _____

   b. Zero is the only number that is neither positive nor negative.

   What do you think this tells you about $\frac{18}{24}$ and $\frac{9}{12}$? _____

Use your calculator to compare the fractions. Write <, >, or = in the boxes.

5. $\frac{5}{9}$ ☐ $\frac{6}{11}$ 6. $\frac{1}{8}$ ☐ $\frac{1}{6}$

7. $\frac{7}{10}$ ☐ $\frac{3}{4}$ 8. $\frac{12}{20}$ ☐ $\frac{30}{50}$

9. $\frac{1}{2}$ ☐ $\frac{17}{42}$ 10. $\frac{5}{6}$ ☐ $\frac{7}{9}$

11. $\frac{13}{16}$ ☐ $\frac{3}{4}$ 12. $\frac{4}{15}$ ☐ $\frac{3}{8}$

13. $\frac{9}{45}$ ☐ $\frac{6}{30}$ 14. $\frac{9}{11}$ ☐ $\frac{11}{12}$

Name _____ Class _____ Date _____

Reteaching 2-4

Follow these steps to *compare* $\frac{2}{5}$ and $\frac{3}{10}$ (unlike denominators).

①Find the **least common denominator** (LCD).

The denominators are 5 and 10. The LCD of 5 and 10 is their least common multiple.

②Write the equivalent fractions using the LCD.

$\frac{2}{5} = \frac{4}{10}$ and $\frac{3}{10} = \frac{3}{10}$

③Compare the numerators.

$4 > 3$

So, $\frac{4}{10} > \frac{3}{10}$ and $\frac{2}{5} > \frac{3}{10}$.

Follow these steps to *order* the fractions $\frac{1}{2}, \frac{3}{5}$, and $\frac{2}{3}$.

①Find the LCD.

The LCD of 2, 5, and 3 is 30.

②Write equivalent fractions using the LCD.

$\frac{1}{2} = \frac{1 \cdot 15}{2 \cdot 15} = \frac{15}{30}$

$\frac{3}{5} = \frac{3 \cdot 6}{5 \cdot 6} = \frac{18}{30}$

$\frac{2}{3} = \frac{2 \cdot 10}{3 \cdot 10} = \frac{20}{30}$

③Order the fractions using their numerators.

$\frac{15}{30} < \frac{18}{30} < \frac{20}{30}$

So, $\frac{1}{2} < \frac{3}{5} < \frac{2}{3}$.

Find each missing number. Then compare the fractions.
Use <, >, or =.

1. $\frac{2}{3}$ and $\frac{3}{5}$

   a. $\frac{2}{3} = \frac{\boxed{}}{15}, \frac{3}{5} = \frac{\boxed{}}{15}$

   b. $\frac{2}{3} \boxed{} \frac{3}{5}$

2. $\frac{1}{2}$ and $\frac{5}{8}$

   a. $\frac{1}{2} = \frac{\boxed{}}{8}, \frac{5}{8} = \frac{\boxed{}}{8}$

   b. $\frac{1}{2} \boxed{} \frac{5}{8}$

3. $\frac{3}{4}$ and $\frac{9}{12}$

   a. $\frac{3}{4} = \frac{\boxed{}}{12}, \frac{9}{12} = \frac{\boxed{}}{12}$

   b. $\frac{3}{4} \boxed{} \frac{9}{12}$

Compare each pair of fractions. Use <, >, or =.

4. $\frac{3}{5} \boxed{} \frac{4}{5}$

5. $\frac{3}{4} \boxed{} \frac{7}{8}$

6. $\frac{8}{12} \boxed{} \frac{2}{3}$

7. $\frac{1}{2} \boxed{} \frac{9}{16}$

8. $\frac{2}{3} \boxed{} \frac{1}{2}$

9. $\frac{5}{9} \boxed{} \frac{10}{18}$

10. $\frac{6}{7} \boxed{} \frac{5}{6}$

11. $\frac{3}{8} \boxed{} \frac{3}{5}$

Order from least to greatest.

12. $\frac{1}{2}, \frac{4}{5}, \frac{1}{4}$ _____

13. $\frac{2}{3}, \frac{3}{8}, \frac{1}{2}$ _____

14. $\frac{5}{6}, \frac{7}{8}, \frac{1}{4}$ _____

15. $\frac{1}{2}, \frac{5}{8}, \frac{5}{6}$ _____

16. $\frac{7}{10}, \frac{2}{3}, \frac{1}{5}$ _____

17. $\frac{2}{3}, \frac{1}{4}, \frac{11}{12}$ _____

Enrichment 2-4

Comparing and Ordering Fractions

Critical Thinking

You can compare fractions using *cross products*.

Compare $\frac{3}{7}$ and $\frac{4}{9}$.

$\frac{3}{7}$? $\frac{4}{9}$

① Write the cross products.

$27 = \frac{3}{7} \diagdown\!\!\!\!\!\diagup \frac{4}{9} = 28$

② Compare the cross products.

$27 < 28$

③ Compare the fractions.

so $\frac{3}{7} < \frac{4}{9}$

Use the cross-product method to order the five fractions below from least to greatest.

$$\frac{7}{9}, \quad \frac{8}{11}, \quad \frac{4}{7}, \quad \frac{13}{19}, \quad \frac{3}{4}$$

1. Compare the first two fractions on the left. List them in order with the smaller fraction first.

   _____

2. Compare the middle fraction with the smaller fraction you found in Exercise 1. Is it smaller or larger?

   _____

3. Starting from the left, list the first three fractions in order.

   _____

4. How will you determine the position of the fraction $\frac{13}{19}$? Show your work.

   _____

5. List all five of the fractions in order from least to greatest.

   _____

6. When would it be easier to use cross products to compare fractions than to find equivalent fractions with a common denominator?

   _____

   _____

7. Would you ever use both methods to order a list of fractions? Explain.

   _____

   _____

   _____

Puzzle 2-4

Comparing and Ordering Fractions

A close relative to the guinea pig is native to Central and South America. This animal can be over four feet long, and weigh more than one hundred pounds. What is it? To find out, circle the letter of the fraction with the highest value in each row. Then write the letter in the space above the exercise number in the code at the bottom.

1. L $\frac{7}{12}$ C $\frac{2}{3}$ J $\frac{6}{15}$

2. A $\frac{33}{45}$ J $\frac{9}{15}$ E $\frac{3}{5}$

3. F $\frac{1}{8}$ G $\frac{1}{9}$ P $\frac{1}{5}$

4. Y $\frac{2}{3}$ G $\frac{3}{6}$ M $\frac{5}{8}$

5. D $\frac{5}{18}$ B $\frac{5}{9}$ S $\frac{5}{27}$

6. K $\frac{3}{4}$ A $\frac{10}{12}$ C $\frac{2}{3}$

7. T $\frac{1}{3}$ A $\frac{22}{42}$ R $\frac{4}{7}$

8. A $\frac{3}{4}$ D $\frac{3}{8}$ P $\frac{1}{2}$

$$\overline{} \ \overline{} \ \overline{} \ \overline{} \ \overline{} \ \overline{} \ \overline{} \ \overline{}$$
$$\ \ 1 \quad 2 \quad 3 \quad 4 \quad 5 \quad 6 \quad 7 \quad 8$$

Practice 2-5

Mixed Numbers and Improper Fractions

1. Write a mixed number and an improper fraction for the model below.

   _____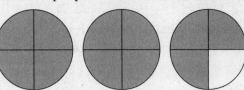

Write each mixed number as an improper fraction.

2. $2\frac{3}{8}$ _____

3. $5\frac{1}{3}$ _____

4. $1\frac{7}{10}$ _____

5. $4\frac{5}{8}$ _____

6. $3\frac{5}{12}$ _____

7. $1\frac{15}{16}$ _____

Write each improper fraction as a mixed number in simplest form.

8. $\frac{25}{3}$ _____

9. $\frac{42}{7}$ _____

10. $\frac{18}{4}$ _____

11. $\frac{27}{12}$ _____

12. $\frac{11}{6}$ _____

13. $\frac{20}{3}$ _____

14. $\frac{125}{5}$ _____

15. $\frac{34}{7}$ _____

16. $\frac{40}{6}$ _____

The distance around the inside of a shopping mall is $\frac{12}{16}$ mi.

17. Juan jogged around the mall 4 times. How far did he jog?

   _____

18. Aaron walked around the mall 3 times. How far did he walk?

   _____

The distance around an indoor running track is $\frac{1}{6}$ mile.

19. Aruna jogged around the track 16 times. How far did she jog?

   _____

20. Theresa walked around the track 22 times. How far did she walk?

   _____

21. Shade the figures below to represent $3\frac{5}{8}$. How many eighths are shaded?

   _____

   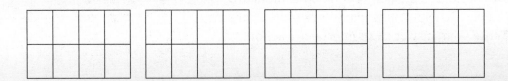

2-5 • Guided Problem Solving

GPS Student Page 94, Exercise 38:

A tailor designs a skirt that is $25\frac{1}{4}$ in. long. What is the length in eighths of an inch? Write your answer as an improper fraction.

Understand

1. What are you being asked to do?

   _____

   _____

2. What is an improper fraction?

   _____

   _____

3. How many eighths of an inch are in one inch? _____

Plan and Carry Out

4. Write an expression that will be used to solve the problem.

   _____

5. In order to combine these two numbers, what must you do first?

   _____

6. How many eighths of an inch are in $25\frac{1}{4}$ in. ? _____

7. What is the length in eighths of an inch?

   _____

Check

8. Rewrite the answer to Step 7 as a mixed number.

   _____

Solve Another Problem

9. There are $8\frac{3}{4}$ cups of flour in a batch of cookies. If there are 6 servings in a batch of cookies, how many cups of flour are in each serving? Write your answer as an improper fraction.

   _____

Name _____ Class _____ Date _____

Practice 2-5

Mixed Numbers and Improper Fractions

1. Write a mixed number and an improper fraction for the model below.

_____

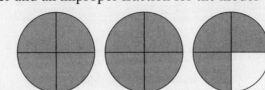

Write each mixed number as an improper fraction.

2. $2\frac{3}{8}$ _____

3. $5\frac{1}{3}$ _____

4. $4\frac{5}{8}$ _____

5. $3\frac{5}{12}$ _____

Write each improper fraction as a mixed number in simplest form.

6. $\frac{25}{3}$ _____

7. $\frac{42}{7}$ _____

8. $\frac{27}{12}$ _____

9. $\frac{11}{6}$ _____

The distance around the inside of a shopping mall is $\frac{12}{16}$ mi.

10. Juan jogged around the mall 4 times. How far did he jog?

_____

11. Aaron walked around the mall 3 times. How far did he walk?

_____

The distance around an indoor running track is $\frac{1}{6}$ mile.

12. Aruna jogged around the track 16 times. How far did she jog?

_____

13. Theresa walked around the track 22 times. How far did she walk?

_____

14. Shade the figures below to represent $3\frac{5}{8}$. How many eighths are shaded?

_____

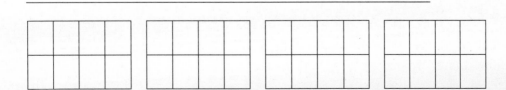

Activity Lab 2-5

Mixed Numbers and Improper Fractions

Materials needed: fraction calculator

Example 1: Write $4\frac{5}{8}$ as an improper fraction.

① Enter 4 **UNIT** 5 **/** 8 **2nd** [A^{b}/$_{c}$ ◀▶ ^{d}/$_{e}$] **ENTER** .

② The calculator displays **37 / 8**, which means that $4\frac{5}{8}$ written as an improper fraction is $\frac{37}{8}$.

Example 2: Write $\frac{26}{5}$ as a mixed number.

① Enter 26 **/** 5 **2nd** [A^{b}/$_{c}$ ◀▶ ^{d}/$_{e}$] **ENTER** .

② The calculator displays **5 ⎵ 1 / 5**, which means that $\frac{26}{5}$ written as a mixed number is $5\frac{1}{5}$.

Exercises

Write each mixed number as an improper fraction, and each improper fraction as a mixed number in simplest form.

1. $7\frac{2}{3}$ 2. $\frac{28}{9}$

3. $9\frac{7}{8}$ 4. $\frac{31}{20}$

5. $15\frac{5}{16}$ 6. $\frac{43}{32}$

7. $21\frac{11}{12}$ 8. $\frac{50}{27}$

9. $35\frac{24}{25}$ 10. $\frac{67}{8}$

11. $58\frac{33}{40}$ 12. $\frac{85}{3}$

13. $49\frac{52}{63}$ 14. $\frac{163}{82}$

15. $20\frac{21}{446}$ 16. $\frac{1024}{7}$

Reteaching 2-5

Mixed Numbers and Improper Fractions

An *improper fraction* is greater than or equal to 1. Its numerator is greater than or equal to its denominator.

Improper fractions

$\frac{6}{4}$ $\frac{8}{8}$ $\frac{10}{8}$ $\frac{7}{2}$

A *mixed number* is the sum of a whole number and a fraction.

Mixed numbers

$1\frac{2}{3}$ $5\frac{4}{9}$ $3\frac{1}{2}$

To write a mixed number as an improper fraction:

① Write the mixed number as a sum.

$3\frac{1}{2} = 3 + \frac{1}{2}$

② Write both numbers as fractions.

$= \frac{6}{2} + \frac{1}{2}$

③ Add the fractions.

$= \frac{7}{2}$

To write an improper fraction as a mixed number:

① Divide the numerator by the denominator.

$\frac{7}{2}$ ⟨Think: 7 ÷ 2⟩ $\begin{array}{r} 3 \\ 2\overline{)7} \\ \underline{-6} \\ 1 \end{array}$

② Write the whole number, then the remainder over the divisor.

$\frac{7}{2} = 3\frac{1}{2}$

Write each mixed number as an improper fraction.

1. $3\frac{1}{4} =$ _____

2. $2\frac{2}{3} =$ _____

3. $1\frac{3}{8} =$ _____

4. $5\frac{2}{7} =$ _____

5. $6\frac{3}{4} =$ _____

6. $1\frac{1}{9} =$ _____

7. $4\frac{1}{2} =$ _____

8. $3\frac{4}{5} =$ _____

9. $5\frac{1}{6} =$ _____

10. $3\frac{1}{3} =$ _____

11. $5\frac{7}{8} =$ _____

12. $4\frac{1}{8} =$ _____

Write each improper fraction as a mixed number in simplest form.

13. $\frac{14}{4} =$ _____

14. $\frac{12}{2} =$ _____

15. $\frac{22}{5} =$ _____

16. $\frac{16}{3} =$ _____

17. $\frac{47}{8} =$ _____

18. $\frac{56}{7} =$ _____

19. $\frac{17}{4} =$ _____

20. $\frac{21}{6} =$ _____

21. $\frac{13}{5} =$ _____

22. $\frac{23}{4} =$ _____

23. $\frac{13}{9} =$ _____

24. $\frac{14}{2} =$ _____

Enrichment 2-5

Mixed Numbers and Improper Fractions

Patterns in Numbers

The fractions shown below are called *continued fractions*. A continued fraction is the sum of a number and a fraction whose numerator is 1 and whose denominator is the sum of a number and a fraction, and so on as shown in this model.

Number Fraction $\quad 1 + \dfrac{1}{1+\frac{1}{1}} = 1 + \dfrac{1}{1+1} = 1 + \dfrac{1}{2} = 1\frac{1}{2} = \dfrac{3}{2}$

$1+ \boxed{\dfrac{1}{1+\frac{1}{1}}}$ is a continued fraction.

$\quad\quad \longrightarrow 1 \; \leftarrow$ Numerator

Number$\rightarrow 1 + \boxed{\frac{1}{1}} \leftarrow$ Fraction

Write each continued fraction as a mixed number and as an improper fraction. To evaluate a continued fraction, find the denominator of the last fraction written and work backward.

	Mixed	**Improper**

1. $1 + \dfrac{1}{1+\dfrac{1}{1+\frac{1}{1}}}$ _____ _____

2. $1 + \dfrac{1}{1+\dfrac{1}{1+\dfrac{1}{1+\frac{1}{1}}}}$ _____ _____

3. $1 + \dfrac{1}{1+\dfrac{1}{1+\dfrac{1}{1+\frac{1}{1}}}}$ _____ _____

4. Write the next fraction as a mixed number and an improper fraction.

_____

5. What pattern do you see in the improper fractions?

_____

_____

6. What would be the value of the tenth continued fraction?

_____

2B: Reading Comprehension

Study Skill Never go to class unprepared. List your assignments, books needed, and supplies to help you prepare.

Read the paragraph and answer the questions.

> Old Faithful is the most famous geyser at Yellowstone National Park. It erupts approximately every $1\frac{1}{4}$ hours for up to 5 minutes. When it erupts, a mixture of water and steam shoots into the air as high as 170 feet. The amount of water expelled during each eruption ranges from 10,000 to 12,000 gallons. Giant Geyser and Steamboat Geyser, two other geysers at Yellowstone, shoot water to heights of 200 feet and 380 feet, respectively.

1. What is the paragraph about?

   _____

2. Which number in the paragraph is written as a mixed number?

   _____

3. For what fraction of an hour does Old Faithful erupt?

   _____

4. Which of the geysers shoots water to the greatest height when it erupts?

   _____

5. What is the rate, in gallons per minute, of Old Faithful's eruptions?

   _____

   _____

6. **High-Use Academic Words** In the study skill given at the top of the page, what does it mean to *list*?

   a. to enumerate   b. to locate on a map

Puzzle 2-5

Mixed Numbers and Improper Fractions

Fraction Shuffle

Use these cards to make each statement true. Each number card can only be used once in each problem.

$$\boxed{1} \quad \boxed{2} \quad \boxed{3} \quad \boxed{4}$$

1. $\dfrac{\boxed{}}{3} = \boxed{}\,\dfrac{1}{\boxed{}}$

2. $\dfrac{\boxed{}}{\boxed{}} = 1\,\dfrac{\boxed{}}{2}$

3. $\dfrac{17}{5} = \boxed{}\,\dfrac{\boxed{}}{5}$

4. $\dfrac{14}{6} = \boxed{}\,\dfrac{\boxed{}}{\boxed{}}$

Use the cards 2, 5, 6, and 8 to make each statement true. Each number card can only be used once in each problem.

$$\boxed{2} \quad \boxed{5} \quad \boxed{6} \quad \boxed{8}$$

5. $9\,\dfrac{7}{8} = \dfrac{79}{\boxed{}}$

6. $\boxed{}\,\dfrac{\boxed{}}{\boxed{}} = \dfrac{21}{8}$

7. $\boxed{}\,\dfrac{4}{\boxed{}} = \dfrac{44}{5}$

8. $11\,\dfrac{\boxed{}}{7} = \dfrac{83}{7}$

Practice 2-6

Write each fraction as a decimal.

1. $\frac{3}{5}$ _____

2. $\frac{7}{8}$ _____

3. $\frac{7}{9}$ _____

4. $\frac{5}{16}$ _____

5. $\frac{1}{6}$ _____

6. $\frac{5}{8}$ _____

7. $\frac{1}{3}$ _____

8. $\frac{2}{3}$ _____

9. $\frac{9}{10}$ _____

10. $\frac{7}{11}$ _____

11. $\frac{9}{20}$ _____

12. $\frac{3}{4}$ _____

13. $\frac{4}{9}$ _____

14. $\frac{9}{11}$ _____

15. $\frac{11}{20}$ _____

Write each decimal as a mixed number or fraction in simplest form.

16. 0.6 _____

17. 0.45 _____

18. 0.62 _____

19. 0.8 _____

20. 0.325 _____

21. 0.725 _____

22. 4.75 _____

23. 0.33 _____

24. 0.925 _____

25. 3.8 _____

26. 4.7 _____

27. 0.05 _____

28. 0.65 _____

29. 0.855 _____

30. 0.104 _____

31. 0.47 _____

32. 0.894 _____

33. 0.276 _____

Order from least to greatest.

34. $0.\overline{2}, \frac{1}{5}, 0.02$

35. $1.\overline{1}, 1\frac{1}{10}, 1.101$

_____

_____

36. $\frac{6}{5}, 1\frac{5}{6}, 1.\overline{3}$

37. $4.\overline{3}, \frac{9}{2}, 4\frac{3}{7}$

_____

_____

38. A group of gymnasts were asked to name their favorite piece of equipment. 0.33 of the gymnasts chose the vault, $\frac{4}{9}$ chose the beam, and $\frac{1}{7}$ chose the uneven parallel bars. List their choices in order of preference from greatest to least.

_____

2-6 • Guided Problem Solving

GPS Student Page 99, Exercise 28:

Biology DNA content in a cell is measured in picograms (pg). A sea star cell has $\frac{17}{20}$ pg of DNA, a scallop cell has $\frac{19}{25}$ pg, a red water mite cell has 0.19 pg, and a mosquito cell has 0.024 pg. Order the DNA contents from greatest to least.

Understand

1. What are you being asked to do?

   _____

2. To order fractions and decimals, what must you do first?

   _____

   _____

Plan and Carry Out

3. Write the fraction $\frac{17}{20}$ as a decimal. _____

4. Write the fraction $\frac{19}{25}$ as a decimal. _____

5. Which organism has the smallest DNA content? _____

6. Which organism has the largest DNA content? _____

7. Order the DNA contents from greatest to least.

   _____

   _____

Check

8. Write 0.19 and 0.024 as fractions in simplest form. Order the DNA contents from greatest to least. Does your order check with that of Step 7?

   _____

   _____

Solve Another Problem

9. A solution calls for 0.25 oz of water, $\frac{2}{3}$ oz of vinegar, 0.6 oz of carbonate, and $\frac{9}{16}$ oz of lemon juice. Order the amounts from least to greatest.

   _____

   _____

Practice 2-6

Fractions and Decimals

Write each fraction as a decimal.

1. $\frac{3}{5}$ _____

2. $\frac{7}{8}$ _____

3. $\frac{7}{9}$ _____

4. $\frac{5}{16}$ _____

5. $\frac{1}{6}$ _____

6. $\frac{5}{8}$ _____

7. $\frac{1}{3}$ _____

8. $\frac{2}{3}$ _____

9. $\frac{9}{10}$ _____

Write each decimal as a mixed number or fraction in simplest form.

10. 0.6 _____

11. 0.45 _____

12. 0.62 _____

13. 0.8 _____

14. 0.325 _____

15. 0.725 _____

16. 4.75 _____

17. 0.33 _____

18. 0.925 _____

19. 3.8 _____

20. 4.7 _____

21. 0.05 _____

Order from least to greatest.

22. $0.\overline{2}, \frac{1}{5}, 0.02$

23. $1.\overline{1}, 1\frac{1}{10}, 1.101$

_____

_____

24. $\frac{6}{5}, 1\frac{5}{6}, 1.\overline{3}$

25. $4.\overline{3}, \frac{9}{2}, 4\frac{3}{7}$

_____

_____

26. A group of gymnasts were asked to name their favorite piece of equipment. 0.33 of the gymnasts chose the vault, $\frac{4}{9}$ chose the beam, and $\frac{1}{7}$ chose the uneven parallel bars. List their choices in order of preference from greatest to least.

_____

_____

Activity Lab 2-6

Fractions and Decimals

Materials needed: calculator

Use your calculator to find a decimal for each fraction.

1. $\frac{3}{8}$ _____

2. $\frac{5}{6}$ _____

3. $\frac{7}{12}$ _____

4. $\frac{4}{5}$ _____

5. $\frac{8}{9}$ _____

6. $\frac{3}{10}$ _____

7. $\frac{4}{15}$ _____

8. $\frac{11}{16}$ _____

9. List the denominators for the fractions that produced terminating decimals.

   _____

10. Find the prime factors of the denominators in Exercise 9.

    _____

11. List the denominators for the fractions that produced repeating decimals.

    _____

12. Find the prime factors of the denominators in Exercise 11.

    _____

13. What pattern do you notice?

    _____

14. Without dividing, tell whether each of the following fractions will produce a terminating or a repeating decimal.

    a. $\frac{7}{24}$ _____

    b. $\frac{35}{64}$ _____

    c. $\frac{14}{125}$ _____

    d. $\frac{1}{20}$ _____

    e. $\frac{17}{111}$ _____

    f. $\frac{14}{148}$ _____

15. Write a fraction that, as a decimal, will terminate. Use a 2-digit or a 3-digit number as the denominator.

    _____

16. Write a fraction that, as a decimal, will repeat. Use a 2-digit or a 3-digit number as the denominator.

    _____

Name _____ Class _____ Date _____

Reteaching 2-6

Fractions and Decimals

To change a fraction to a decimal, divide the numerator by the denominator.

$\frac{3}{5}$ Think: $3 \div 5$

$$\begin{array}{r} 0.6 \\ 5\overline{)3.0} \\ -30 \\ \hline 0 \end{array}$$

$\frac{3}{5} = 0.6$

To change a decimal to a fraction:

① Read the decimal to find the denominator. Write the decimal digits over 10, 100, or 1,000.

② 0.65 is 65 *hundredths* → $\frac{65}{100}$

Use the GCF to write the fraction in simplest form.

The GCF of 65 and 100 is 5.

$\frac{65}{100} = \frac{65 \div 5}{100 \div 5} = \frac{13}{20}$

Write each fraction as a decimal.

1. $\frac{4}{5} =$ _____

2. $\frac{3}{4} =$ _____

3. $\frac{1}{6} =$ _____

4. $\frac{1}{4} =$ _____

5. $\frac{2}{3} =$ _____

6. $\frac{7}{10} =$ _____

7. $\frac{5}{9} =$ _____

8. $\frac{1}{5} =$ _____

9. $\frac{3}{8} =$ _____

Write each decimal as a mixed number or fraction in simplest form.

10. $0.4 =$ _____

11. $0.75 =$ _____

12. $1.5 =$ _____

13. $0.35 =$ _____

14. $2.7 =$ _____

15. $1.8 =$ _____

16. $0.625 =$ _____

17. $0.78 =$ _____

18. $0.88 =$ _____

Order from least to greatest.

19. $2.\overline{6}, \frac{13}{6}, 2\frac{5}{6}$

20. $2.\overline{02}, 2\frac{1}{200}, 2.0202$

21. $\frac{5}{4}, 1\frac{4}{5}, 1.\overline{4}$

_____ _____ _____

Enrichment 2-6

Fractions and Decimals

Patterns in Numbers

Find a decimal for each fraction. Use your calculator to check your work.

1. $\frac{3}{8}$ _____

2. $\frac{5}{6}$ _____

3. $\frac{7}{12}$ _____

4. $\frac{4}{5}$ _____

5. $\frac{8}{9}$ _____

6. $\frac{3}{10}$ _____

7. List the denominators for the fractions that produced terminating decimals.

_____

8. Find the prime factors of the denominators in exercise 7.

_____

9. List the denominators for the fractions that produced repeating decimals.

_____

10. Find the prime factors of the denominators in exercise 9.

_____

11. What pattern do you notice?

_____

_____

12. Without dividing, tell whether each of the following fractions will produce a terminating or a repeating decimal.

a. $\frac{7}{24}$ _____

b. $\frac{35}{64}$ _____

c. $\frac{17}{111}$ _____

d. $\frac{14}{148}$ _____

13. Write a fraction that, as a decimal, will terminate. Use a 2-digit or a 3-digit number as the denominator.

_____

14. Write a fraction that, as a decimal, will repeat. Use a 2-digit or a 3-digit number as the denominator.

_____

2E: Vocabulary Check

For use after Lesson 2-6

Study Skill Strengthen your vocabulary. Use these pages and add cues and summaries by applying the Cornell Notetaking style.

Write the definition for each word or term at the right. To check your work, fold the paper back along the dotted line to see the correct answers.

_____ exponent

_____

_____

_____ composite number

_____

_____ mixed number

_____

_____

_____ terminating decimal

_____

_____

_____ simplest form

_____

_____

2E: Vocabulary Check (continued)

Write the vocabulary word or term for each definition. To check your work, fold the paper forward along the dotted line to see the correct answers.

how many times a number, or base, is used as a factor

_____

a whole number that has more than two factors

_____

the sum of a whole number and a fraction

_____

a decimal that stops, or terminates

_____

a fraction where the numerator and denominator have no common factors other than 1

_____

Name _____ Class _____ Date _____

Puzzle 2-6

Fractions and Decimals

How Many Parakeets?

To find the number of parakeets you will need the following clues.

1. Sam's shoe size is one-quarter the number of minutes it took Li Hua to wash her sheepdog.

2. The number of players on the Lizard City tiddlywinks team is 7 more than the number of rutabaga plants in Carlos's window box.

3. Talasi's golf score was 1 less than 3 times the number of parakeets in the Lizard City Zoo.

4. The number of sour notes Marie hit while playing "Ramona" on her sousaphone was 6 less than 6 times the number of avocados that Max used in his guacamole.

5. If Talasi's golf score is increased by 10, the result is 3 times the number of minutes it took Li Hua to wash her sheepdog.

6. The number of players on the Lizard City tiddlywinks team is 1 less than 4 times the number of avocados that Max used in his guacamole.

7. The number of rutabaga plants in Carlos's window box is 5 less than twice Sam's shoe size.

QUESTION: If Marie hits 24 sour notes while playing "Ramona" on her sousaphone, then how many parakeets are there in the Lizard City Zoo?

To solve, follow these steps:

1. Use clue #4 to find the number of avocados that Max used in his guacamole.

2. Use clue #6 and your answer to the preceding question to find how many players there are on the Lizard City tiddlywinks team.

3. Use clue #2 and your answer to the preceding question to find how many rutabaga plants there are in Carlos's window box.

4. Use clue #7 and your answer to the preceding question to find Sam's shoe size.

5. Use clue #1 and your answer to the preceding question to find how long it took Li Hua to wash her sheepdog.

6. Use clue #5 and your answer to the preceding question to learn Talasi's golf score.

7. Use clue #3 and your answer to the preceding question to find how many parakeets there are in the Lizard City Zoo.

Practice 2-7

Compare. Use <, >, or =.

1. $-\frac{2}{9}$ ☐ $-\frac{4}{9}$

2. $-\frac{1}{6}$ ☐ $-\frac{2}{3}$

3. $-\frac{5}{12}$ ☐ $-\frac{3}{4}$

4. -1.2 ☐ -2.1

5. -0.6 ☐ -0.52

6. -1.23 ☐ -1.25

7. -5.3 ☐ $-5.\overline{3}$

8. $-3\frac{1}{4}$ ☐ -3.25

9. $-4\frac{2}{5}$ ☐ -4.12

Order from least to greatest.

10. $\frac{5}{4}, 1.5, -\frac{3}{2}, -0.5$

11. $\frac{1}{11}, -0.9, 0.09, \frac{1}{10}$

_____

_____

12. $0.1\overline{2}, -\frac{11}{12}, -\frac{1}{6}, -0.1$

13. $\frac{2}{3}, 0.6, -\frac{5}{6}, -6.6$

_____

_____

14. $1.312, 1\frac{3}{8}, -1\frac{3}{10}, -1.33$

15. $1, \frac{4}{5}, -\frac{8}{9}, -1$

_____

_____

Evaluate. Write in simplest form.

16. $\frac{y}{z}$, for $y = -6$ and $z = -20$ _____

17. $\frac{2y}{-z}$, for $y = -5$ and $z = -12$ _____

18. $\frac{y + z}{2z}$, for $y = -4$ and $z = 8$ _____

19. $\frac{-2y + 1}{-z}$, for $y = 3$ and $z = 10$ _____

Compare.

20. The temperature at 3:00 A.M. was $-17.3°$F. By noon the temperature was $-17.8°$F. At what time was it the coldest?

_____

21. Samuel is $\frac{5}{8}$ in. taller than Jackie. Shelly is 0.7 in. taller than Jackie. Who is the tallest?

_____

2-7 • Guided Problem Solving

GPS **Student Page 105, Exercise 29:**

Animals About $\frac{1}{25}$ of a toad's eggs survive to adulthood. About 0.25 of a frog's eggs and $\frac{1}{5}$ of a green turtle's eggs survive to adulthood. Which animal's eggs have the highest survival rate?

Understand

1. Circle the information you will need to solve.

2. What are you being asked to do?

   _____

   _____

3. In order to find the greatest number, what must you do first?

   _____

Plan and Carry Out

4. Write $\frac{1}{25}$ as a decimal. _____

5. Write $\frac{1}{5}$ as a decimal. _____

6. Which is the largest decimal, 0.04, 0.2, or 0.25? _____

7. Which animal's eggs have the highest survival rate? _____

Check

8. What fraction is 0.25 equal to? Is it the greatest value?

   _____

Solve Another Problem

9. In order to organize the nails in a garage, Anne and Jeff measured the nails. Anne used fractions to measure her 3 groups of nails and found that they were $\frac{3}{5}$ in., $\frac{7}{12}$ in., and $\frac{4}{9}$ in. Jeff used decimals to measure his two groups and found that they were 0.62 in., and 0.31 in. Which nail is the longest?

   _____

Practice 2-7

Rational Numbers

Compare. Use <, >, or =.

1. $-\frac{2}{9} \;\square\; -\frac{4}{9}$

2. $-\frac{1}{6} \;\square\; -\frac{2}{3}$

3. $-\frac{5}{12} \;\square\; -\frac{3}{4}$

4. $-1.2 \;\square\; -2.1$

5. $-0.6 \;\square\; -0.52$

6. $-1.23 \;\square\; -1.25$

Order from least to greatest.

7. $\frac{5}{4}, 1.5, -\frac{3}{2}, -0.5$

8. $\frac{1}{11}, -0.9, 0.09, \frac{1}{10}$

_____

_____

9. $0.1\overline{2}, -\frac{11}{12}, -\frac{1}{6}, -0.1$

10. $\frac{2}{3}, 0.6, -\frac{5}{6}, -6.6$

_____

_____

Evaluate. Write in simplest form.

11. $\frac{y}{z}$, for $y = -6$ and $z = -20$

_____

12. $\frac{2y}{-z}$, for $y = -5$ and $z = -12$

_____

13. $\frac{y + z}{2z}$, for $y = -4$ and $z = 8$

_____

Compare.

14. The temperature at 3:00 A.M. was $-17.3°F$. By noon the temperature was $-17.8°F$. At what time was it the coldest?

_____

15. Samuel is $\frac{5}{8}$ in. taller than Jackie. Shelly is 0.7 in. taller than Jackie. Who is the tallest?

_____

Activity Lab 2-7 .... **Rational Numbers**

Patterns in Numbers

You can find patterns in these division problems.

1. Find each quotient.

   a. $80 \div 40 =$ _____   **a.** $60{,}000 \div 12{,}000 =$ _____

   b. $80 \div 20 =$ _____   **b.** $6{,}000 \div 1{,}200 =$ _____

   c. $80 \div 10 =$ _____   **c.** $600 \div 120 =$ _____

   d. $80 \div 5 =$ _____   **d.** $60 \div 12 =$ _____

   e. $80 \div 2.5 =$ _____   **e.** $6 \div 1.2 =$ _____

   f. $80 \div 1.25 =$ _____   **f.** $0.6 \div 0.12 =$ _____

2. What pattern do you see in the first column?

   _____

   _____

3. What pattern do you see in the second column?

   _____

   _____

4. Use what you know about the patterns above to find each quotient.

   a. $72 \div 36 =$ _____   **a.** $400 \div 200 =$ _____

   b. $72 \div 18 =$ _____   **b.** $40 \div 20 =$ _____

   c. $72 \div 9 =$ _____   **c.** $4 \div 2 =$ _____

   d. $72 \div 4.5 =$ _____   **d.** $0.4 \div 0.2 =$ _____

   e. $72 \div 2.25 =$ _____   **e.** $0.04 \div 0.02 =$ _____

5. In Exercise 4, when did you stop calculating and start using what you know about patterns? Why did you stop at that place?

   _____

   _____

Reteaching 2-7

Rational Numbers

A **rational number** is a number that can be written as a quotient of two integers, where the divisor is not zero.

A negative rational number can be written in three different ways.

$$-\frac{2}{3} = \frac{-2}{3} = \frac{2}{-3}$$

Comparing Negative Rational Numbers

Compare $-\frac{2}{3}$ and $-\frac{1}{4}$.

Method 1 Use a number line. Graph both points on a number line and see which is farther to the left.

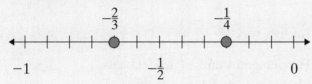

Since $-\frac{2}{3}$ is farther to the left, $-\frac{2}{3} < -\frac{1}{4}$.

Method 2 Use the lowest common denominator.

$$-\frac{2}{3} = \frac{-2}{3} = \frac{-2 \times 4}{3 \times 4} = \frac{-8}{12} \qquad -\frac{1}{4} = \frac{-1}{4} = \frac{-1 \times 3}{4 \times 3} = \frac{-3}{12}$$

Since $\frac{-8}{12} < \frac{-3}{12}$, then $-\frac{2}{3} < -\frac{1}{4}$.

Compare. Use <, >, or =.

1. $-\frac{4}{9} \;\square\; -\frac{2}{3}$

2. $-1 \;\square\; -\frac{4}{5}$

3. $-\frac{7}{8} \;\square\; -\frac{1}{8}$

4. $-\frac{1}{3} \;\square\; -\frac{5}{6}$

5. $-\frac{2}{5} \;\square\; -\frac{1}{10}$

6. $-\frac{2}{8} \;\square\; -\frac{1}{4}$

Order from least to greatest.

7. $-\frac{1}{3}, 0.3, -0.35, -\frac{3}{10}$

8. $\frac{1}{5}, -0.25, 0.21, \frac{3}{10}$

_____

_____

9. You and your brother invested an equal amount of money in a college savings plan. In the last quarter your investment was worth $1\frac{5}{6}$ of its original value. Your brother's investment was worth 1.85 of its original value. Whose investment is worth more?

_____

Enrichment 2-7

Critical Thinking

You can use the same rules to compare and order positive and
negative fractions and decimals that you learned when comparing and
ordering integers on the number line. Remember:

> On a number line, the farther to the right an integer is, the greater
> it is. The farther to the left an integer is, the less it is.

Beth and Leroy used a number line to order $\frac{1}{2}$, $-\frac{1}{8}$, and -0.75 from
least to greatest.

Beth's way

She changed -0.75 to a fraction
$(-0.75 = -\frac{75}{100} = -\frac{3}{4})$. Then she
located fractions on a number line.

She listed the fractions from left to right to order
them from least to greatest and changed $-\frac{3}{4}$ back
to -0.75.

$$-\frac{3}{4}, \quad -\frac{1}{8}, \frac{1}{2}$$
$$\downarrow \quad \downarrow \ \downarrow$$
$$-0.75, -\frac{1}{8}, \frac{1}{2}$$

Leroy's way

He changed $\frac{1}{2}$ and $-\frac{1}{8}$ to decimals
$(\frac{1}{2} = 0.5$ and $-\frac{1}{8} = -0.125)$. Then he
located the decimals on a number line.

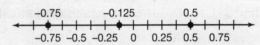

He listed the decimals from left to right to order
them from least to greatest and changed -0.125
and 0.5 back to fractions.

$$-0.75, -0.125, 0.5$$
$$\downarrow \qquad \downarrow \quad \downarrow$$
$$-0.75, \quad -\frac{1}{8}, \quad \frac{1}{2}$$

1. Choose either Beth's or Leroy's way to order each set of
   numbers from least to greatest. Draw a number line if necessary.

   a. $0.25, -\frac{1}{2}, -\frac{5}{8}$ _____

   b. $\frac{1}{3}, 0.7, -\frac{5}{6}$ _____

   c. $-\frac{25}{41}, \frac{13}{50}, -\frac{14}{22}, -0.516$ _____

2. In which exercises did you use Beth's way? Leroy's way? Explain.

   _____

   _____

   _____

2C: Reading/Writing Math Symbols

For use after Lesson 2-7

Study Skill Use flashcards to help you memorize math symbols and their meanings.

Write each statement in words.

1. $-7 < 6$ _____

2. $4^3 = 64$ _____

3. $-3 > -5$ _____

4. $|-5| = 5$ _____

5. $3^2 = 9$ _____

6. $3.01 \approx 3$ _____

7. $\frac{8}{4} = 2$ _____

8. $\frac{1}{3} < \frac{3}{5}$ _____

9. $4.\overline{6} > 0$ _____

10. $5^4 = 625$ _____

Write each statement using mathematical symbols.

11. Three and seven tenths is less than 4 and one–half.

    _____

12. The absolute value of 2.6 is 2.6.

    _____

13. Negative three-fourths is greater than negative ten.

    _____

14. Four and three tenths is approximately equal to four point three repeating.

    _____

15. Two raised to the fifth power is thirty-two.

    _____

16. Six cubed is two hundred sixteen.

    _____

Course 2 Chapter 2 **153**

Puzzle 2-7

Order the following sets of rational numbers from least to greatest to solve the puzzles below.

1. The first peanuts in the United States were grown in

    — — — — — — — —

$\frac{5}{6}$	2.3	0.5	$\frac{5}{8}$	$2\frac{2}{5}$	0.75	$\frac{6}{7}$	1.1
G	I	V	I	A	R	I	N

2. The first American performance of a Beethoven symphony

    was in Lexington, ___ ___ ___ ___ ___ ___ ___ ___ in 1817.

$\frac{2}{9}$	2.5	0.5	1.1	-0.2	$\frac{3}{4}$	4.7	2.4
E	K	N	U	K	T	Y	C

3. ___ ___ ___ ___ ___ ___ ___ ___ ___ is nicknamed the
    Badger State.

$4\frac{7}{10}$	1.1	0.75	2.4	$\frac{1}{4}$	$4\frac{1}{5}$	4.9	0	$\frac{7}{10}$
I	O	C	N	I	S	N	W	S

4. The first automobile law was passed by the state of

    ___ ___ ___ ___ ___ ___ ___ ___ ___ ___ ___ in 1901.

    The speed limit was set at 12 miles per hour.

$\frac{3}{4}$	$\frac{1}{8}$	2.3	$-\frac{2}{9}$	0.25	$\frac{1}{7}$	$\frac{1}{32}$	2.4	0.5	4.2	1.1
T	N	C	C	E	N	O	U	C	T	I

Practice 2-8

Scientific Notation

Write each number in scientific notation.

1. 73,000,000

2. 4,300

3. 510

4. 56,870

_____

5. 68,900

6. 98,000,000,000

7. 4,890,000

8. 38

_____

9. 120,000

10. 543,000

11. 27

12. 54,000

_____

Write in standard form.

13. 5.7×10^6

14. 2.45×10^8

15. 4.706×10^{11}

_____

16. 8×10^1

17. 7.2×10^3

18. 1.63×10^{12}

_____

19. 8.03×10^{14}

20. 3.26×10^4

21. 5.179×10^5

_____

Write each number in scientific notation.

22. One type of roundworm can lay 200,000 eggs each day.

_____

23. The nose of a German shepherd dog has about 220 million cells that are used in picking out smells.

_____

24. The brain contains about 100 trillion nerve connections.

_____

25. During an average life span, the human heart will beat about 2,800,000,000 times.

_____

26. The volume of the water behind the Grand Coulee Dam is about 10.6 million cubic yards.

_____

27. A second has been defined as the time it takes for an atom of a particular metal to vibrate 9,192,631,770 times.

_____

2-8 • Guided Problem Solving

GPS Student Page 109, Exercise 31:

Plants There are about 350,000 species of plants on Earth. Write this number in scientific notation.

Understand

1. What are you being asked to do?

   _____

   _____

2. How do you write a number in scientific notation?

   _____

   _____

   _____

   _____

Plan and Carry Out

3. How many places do you move the decimal point so that you obtain a factor greater than 1 and less than 10?

   _____

4. What is the exponent on the power of 10?

   _____

5. What are the two factors? _____

6. Write the number in scientific notation. _____

Check

7. Multiply $3.5 \times 100,000$. Does your answer check?

   _____

   _____

Solve Another Problem

8. In July 2002, the population of the United States was 287,509,286. Write this number in scientific notation.

   _____

   _____

Practice 2-8

Scientific Notation

Write each number in scientific notation.

1. 73,000,000   **2.** 4,300   **3.** 510   **4.** 56,870

_____   _____   _____   _____

5. 68,900   **6.** 98,000,000,000   **7.** 4,890,000   **8.** 38

_____   _____   _____   _____

Write in standard form.

9. 5.7×10^6 **10.** 2.45×10^8 **11.** 4.706×10^{11}

_____   _____   _____

12. 8×10^1 **13.** 7.2×10^3 **14.** 1.63×10^{12}

_____   _____   _____

Write each number in scientific notation.

15. One type of roundworm can lay 200,000 eggs each day.

_____

16. The nose of a German shepherd dog has about 220 million cells that are used in picking out smells.

_____

17. During an average life span, the human heart will beat about 2,800,000,000 times.

_____

18. A second has been defined as the time it takes for an atom of a particular metal to vibrate 9,192,631,770 times.

_____

Activity Lab 2-8

Scientific notation is very useful when you are dealing with very large or very small values. The Solar System is large compared to the scales we use on Earth. The table below shows the average distance of each planet from the Sun.

Average Distance From the Sun (km)

Mercury	57,090,000
Venus	108,200,000
Earth	149,600,000
Mars	227,940,000
Jupiter	778,400,000
Saturn	1,423,600,000
Uranus	2,867,000,000
Neptune	4,448,400,000
Pluto	5,909,600,000

1. Use the information from the table above. Rewrite each distance in scientific notation and complete the table below.

Average Distance From the Sun (km)

Mercury	
Venus	
Earth	
Mars	
Jupiter	
Saturn	
Uranus	
Neptune	
Pluto	

2. Look at the differences in scientific notation. Compare them to the standard form in the first table. Does one method make it easier to compare the values? If so, which one?

_____

_____

Reteaching 2-8

Scientific notation is an efficient way to write very large numbers. A number is written as the product of a number between 1 and 10 and a power of 10.

Write 4,000,000,000 in scientific notation.

① Count the number of places that you need to move the decimal point to the left to get a factor between 1 and 10.

$$4,000,000,000 \rightarrow 4.000\ 000\ 000$$

9 places

② Use the number of places as the exponent of 10.

$$4,000,000,000 = 4 \times 10^9$$

To change a number from scientific notation to standard form, undo the steps at the left.

Write 3.5×10^8 in standard form.

① Note the exponent of 10. (Here it is 8.)

② Move the decimal point to the right the number of places that is equal to the exponent.

$$3.5 \times 10^8 \rightarrow 350,000,000$$

8 places

$$3.5 \times 10^8 = 350,000,000$$

Write in scientific notation.

1. 3,500

   Move the decimal point _____ places

   to the _____.

   3,500 = _____ × _____

2. 1,400,000

   Move the decimal point _____ places

   to the _____.

   1,400,000 = _____ × _____

3. 93,000,000 _____

4. 1,200,000 _____

5. 17,000 _____

6. 750,000 _____

7. 560,000,000,000 _____

8. 34,800,000 _____

Write in standard form.

9. 2.58×10^3 _____

10. 8×10^6 _____

11. 4.816×10^5 _____

12. 8.11×10^2 _____

13. 8.003×10^1 _____

14. 5.66×10^9 _____

15. 4.23×10^2 _____

16. 9.992×10^{10} _____

Enrichment 2-8

Critical Thinking

Our place-value system is based on tens. Each place value is 10 times greater than the one at its right. The number 34,567 is shown in a **base ten** place-value chart.

10,000s $(10 \times 10 \times 10 \times 10)$	1000s $(10 \times 10 \times 10)$	100s (10×10)	10s (10)	1s (1)
3	4	5	6	7

To find the value of the number 34,567, add the values of each of its digits:

$(3 \times 10,000) + (4 \times 1,000) + (5 \times 100) + (6 \times 10) + (7 \times 1) = 34,567$

Other place-value systems are based on numbers other than ten. The place-value chart below is based on fours. Notice that each value is 4 times greater than the one at its right. The number in the **base four** place-value chart below can be written as 31232_{four}.

Base of system

256s $(4 \times 4 \times 4 \times 4)$	64s $(4 \times 4 \times 4)$	16s (4×4)	4s (4)	1s (1)
3	1	2	3	2

To find the value of the number 31232_{four}, add the values of each of its digits:

$(3 \times 256) + (1 \times 64) + (2 \times 16) + (3 \times 4) + (2 \times 1) = 878$

Sketch a place-value chart for the indicated base of each number. Then find the value of the number.

	Place-Value Chart		Value
1. 4503_{seven}	a.	b.	_____
2. 71462_{eight}	a.	b.	_____
3. 10110111_{two}	a.	b.	_____

2D: Visual Vocabulary Practice

For use after Lesson 2-8

Study Skill Mathematics builds on itself, so build a strong foundation.

Concept List

equivalent fractions   greatest common factor   improper fraction

least common denominator   least common multiple   prime factorization

repeating decimal   scientific notation   simplest form

Write the concept that best describes each exercise. Choose from the concept list above.

1.	2.	3.
$\dfrac{6}{4}$ _____	The number 24 represents this for the numbers 48 and 72. _____	$0.312312312\ldots = 0.\overline{312}$ _____
4. $\dfrac{1}{2} \quad = \quad \dfrac{3}{6}$ _____	5. The number 12 represents this for the fractions $\dfrac{1}{6}$ and $\dfrac{3}{4}$. _____	6. $0.00034 = 3.4 \times 10^{-4}$ _____
7. The number 60 represents this for the numbers 12 and 15. _____	8. $\dfrac{3}{20}$ _____	9. $108 = 2^2 \cdot 3^3$ _____

2F: Vocabulary Review Puzzle

For use with the Chapter Review

Study Skill Use a notebook or a section of a loose-leaf binder for math assignments. Review problems that gave you trouble.

Unscramble each of the key words from the chapter to help you fill in the famous quote by Lewis Carroll. Match the letters in the numbered cells with the numbered cells at the bottom.

NENPTEXO `[ ][X][ ][ ][ ][ ]` 5

FECINCITSI NATNOOTI `[S][ ][ ][ ][ ][ ][ ][ ]` `[ ][ ][ ][T][ ][ ]` 9 15

OPWER `[ ][O][ ][ ]` 1

LORNIATA RUNMEB `[R][ ][ ][ ][ ][ ]` `[ ][ ][B][ ]` 22 2 17 25

SIVIEBIDL `[ ][V][ ][ ][ ][ ]` 16 20 7

TARTEEGS COOMNM RAOFTC `[ ][ ][ ][ ][ ][T][ ]` `[C][ ][ ][ ][ ]` `[A][ ][ ][ ]` 6 13 19

MIEPLLUT `[U][ ][ ][ ][ ][ ]` 11 4

LESAT COOMNM METLULPI `[E][ ][ ]` `[M][ ][ ]` `[ ][ ][ ][ ][ ][P][ ]` 21 8 14

RIPME MUNREB `[ ][ ][M][ ]` `[ ][M][ ][ ]` 10 23

MIEDX MUEBRN `[ ][X][ ]` `[ ][ ][ ][ ]` 24 12

ROMPIERP FRTAINOC `[ ][P][ ][ ][ ]` `[ ][R][ ][ ][ ][ ]` 18 3

`[ ][H][ ]` `[ ]` `[ ][ ][ ][ ]` `[Y][ ]`
1 2 3 4 5 6 7 8 9 10

`[ ][H][ ][ ][ ]` `[ ][ ][ ][ ][ ]` `[ ][ ]` `[ ][ ][ ][ ]`
11 12 13 14 15 16 17 18 19 20 21 22 23 24 25

Puzzle 2-8

Scientific Notation

The values shown below are written in scientific notation. Rewrite them in standard form. Use the puzzle to check your work.

1. $2 \times 10^{-4} =$ _____

2. $3.6987 \times 10^8 =$ _____

3. $6.3 \times 10^{-7} =$ _____

4. $5.012 \times 10^7 =$ _____

5. $3.0165 \times 10^5 =$ _____

6. $4.75 \times 10^8 =$ _____

7. $5.61 \times 10^2 =$ _____

8. $2.6672 \times 10^5 =$ _____

9. $9.602 \times 10^3 =$ _____

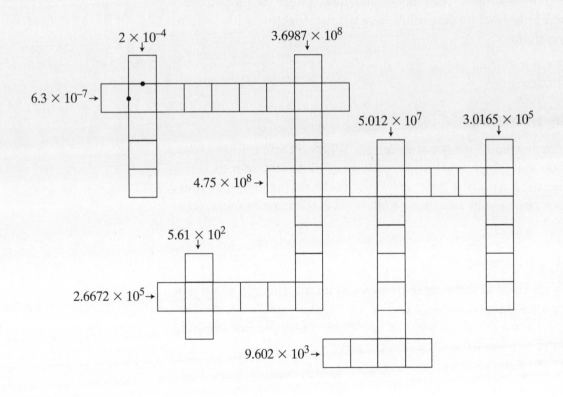

Chapter 2 Project: Making the Measure

Invent Your Own Ruler

Beginning the Chapter Project

In the high jump, as in most sports, a consistent system of measurement allows athletes to make comparisons. It took the decree of a king to create one such system!

Back in the 12th century, King Henry I of England decided that a yard was the distance from the tip of his nose to the end of his thumb. How far is it from the tip of your nose to the end of your thumb? Is it more than a yard or less? Is it the same distance for everyone?

In this chapter project, you will design a new system for measuring distance. Your final project will be a new ruler, together with a report on its usefulness.

Activities

Activity 1: Designing

Design a new unit for measuring length. What will you call it? Make a ruler one unit long based on your new measurement. Use it to measure the length of a classroom door. Estimate the length of your classroom using your measuring unit. What is the length of a bicycle or a car?

Activity 2: Measuring

Mark your ruler to show equal fractions of a unit. This will allow you to measure lengths less than a unit. What fractions do the marks on your ruler show? Explain why you chose them. Use the fractions on your ruler to measure several small objects.

Between the number of objects you measured in Activity 1 and the number of objects you measured in Activity 2, you should have measured at least 8 objects of varying sizes.

Activity 3: Analyzing

Is your system as good as the other systems you have used to measure lengths? What are the advantages and disadvantages of your system and the other systems?

Chapter 2 Project: Making the Measure (continued)

Finishing the Project

Your final product will be a demonstration of your ruler to the class. Show how to measure a wide range of lengths using your ruler. Include some actual measurements to show how useful your system is.

Be sure your work is neat and clear. Write any explanations you think are necessary.

Reflect and Revise

Discuss the usefulness of your ruler with a classmate, friend, or family member. Does it allow you to measure long and short lengths? Can you measure in fractions of units? If necessary, make changes to improve your project.

Extending the Project

Create another ruler that has a measurement two times bigger than the basic unit on your ruler.

- Predict what your ruler would look like if it was three times larger, or if it was three times smaller.

- Compare your predictions with a classmate.

Visit PHSchool.com for information and links you might find helpful as you complete your project.

Chapter Project Manager

Getting Started

Read about the project. As you work on it, you will need several
sheets of paper. If available, a spreadsheet program also can be used.
Keep all your work for the project in a folder, along with this Project
Manager.

Checklist

☐ Activity 1: designing

☐ Activity 2: measuring

☐ Activity 3: analyzing

☐ Recommendations

Suggestions

☐ Be creative when it comes to naming your ruler, but be sure it
is a name other people can pronounce and use easily.

☐ Take each measurement 3 times to ensure accuracy.

☐ Have a classmate use your ruler to measure certain items and
ask your classmate for his/her opinion on your ruler.

☐ When demonstrating your ruler, be sure to measure both large
and small objects to show its diversity.

Scoring Rubric

3 You constructed and labeled your ruler carefully, and it
accurately shows fractions of your basic measurement unit. You
used your ruler to accurately measure at least 8 objects over a
wide range of lengths. You described how your ruler could be
used to measure fractional units, or you compared your
measurement system to other measurement systems.

2 You constructed a ruler that includes fractional units, but it is not
as accurate as it could have been. You measured and listed the
lengths of several short objects and several long objects.

1 You constructed a ruler without fractional units, or you made and
recorded inaccurate measurements.

0 You did not create your own unit of measure, you didn't use
fractional units, or you made very few measurements.

Your Evaluation of Project   Evaluate your work, based on the Scoring Rubric.

Teacher's Evaluation of Project

Chapter Project Teacher Notes

About the Project Students will have an opportunity to use their knowledge of fractions and number theory to make a unique ruler.

Introducing the Project

Ask students:

- Have you ever compared units of measure?

- How did the units of measure we use now develop?

- What are some advantages and disadvantages of using the yard as a primary unit of measure?

Activity 1: Designing

Have students brainstorm what materials to use and what size to make their rulers.

Activity 2: Measuring

Point out to students that on an inch ruler, the one-half inch marks are longer than the one-quarter inch marks to make reading the ruler easier. Encourage the students to use marks of different sizes to measure the objects.

Activity 3: Analyzing

Encourage students to organize their information into a table of two lists, one that lists the advantages and one that lists the disadvantages.

Finishing the Project

You may wish to plan a project day on which students share their completed projects. Encourage students to explain their processes as well as their products.

- Have students review their ruler.

- Ask students to share any insight they gained when completing the project, such as the difficulty in creating a system of measurement.

Visit PHSchool.com for information and links you might find helpful as you complete your project.

Name _____ Class _____ Date _____

✔ Checkpoint Quiz 1

Use with Lessons 2-1 through 2-2.

Simplify each expression.

1. $20 - 3^2$ _____ **2.** $2^3 + 10^2$ _____ **3.** $(8 - 1)^2$ _____ **4.** $(-3)^3$ _____

Tell whether each number is prime or composite. Then find the GCF of each pair of numbers.

5. 2, 14 **6.** 15, 18 **7.** 20, 35 **8.** 7, 13

_____ _____ _____ _____

_____ _____ _____ _____

9. Two groups are marching together in a parade and must divide into equal-sized rows. There are 36 people in the first group and 90 people in the second group. What is the greatest possible number of people in each row?

_____

- - - - ✂ -

Name _____ Class _____ Date _____

✔ Checkpoint Quiz 2

Use with Lessons 2-3 through 2-6.

1. Which fraction is greatest, $\frac{8}{10}$, $\frac{7}{8}$, $\frac{5}{6}$, or $\frac{12}{18}$? _____

Write each mixed number as an improper fraction and each improper fraction as a mixed number.

2. $\frac{34}{6}$ **3.** $4\frac{1}{5}$ **4.** $\frac{65}{8}$ **5.** $1\frac{3}{10}$ **6.** $3\frac{6}{7}$

_____ _____ _____ _____ _____

Write each fraction in simplest form.

7. $\frac{12}{20}$ **8.** $\frac{15}{18}$ **9.** $\frac{24}{36}$ **10.** $\frac{45}{60}$ **11.** $\frac{20}{48}$

_____ _____ _____ _____ _____

Name _____ Class _____ Date _____

Chapter Test

Form A

Chapter 2

Simplify each expression.

1. $(1 + 7)^2 + 2$

2. $(-5)^2$

_____

3. $\frac{63}{81}$

4. $\frac{35}{42}$

_____

Order from least to greatest.

5. $\frac{7}{11}, \frac{5}{6}, \frac{2}{8}$

6. $\frac{1}{2}, -0.51, 0.\overline{5}, -\frac{1}{2}$

_____

Write the prime factorization of each number.

7. 52

8. 60

_____

Write each improper fraction as a mixed number and each mixed number as an improper fraction.

9. $3\frac{3}{10}$

10. $\frac{52}{6}$

_____

11. Write 1,325,000 in scientific notation.

12. Write 8.35×10^4 in standard form.

_____

13. Is 982 divisible by 3? Explain.

_____

_____

14. Write three fractions that are equivalent to $\frac{1}{3}$.

_____

_____

_____

Chapter Test (continued)

Form A

Chapter 2

15. What factors do 12 and 15 have in common?

16. Write $6 \cdot 6 \cdot 6 \cdot 6$ using an exponent.

_____

17. Compare using $<, >,$ or $=$. $\frac{7}{12} \underline{\ ?\ } \frac{5}{9}$.

18. Find the GCF of 27 and 36.

_____

19. Find two prime numbers that are larger than 17.

20. Find two composite numbers that are greater than 17.

_____

21. Write 16 as the sum of two prime numbers.

22. Evaluate the expression $(s + t)^2$ for $s = 7$ and $t = 4$.

_____

22. Evaluate the expression $(s + t)^2$ for $s = 7$ and $t = 4$.

23. Write $\frac{6}{15}$ as a decimal.

_____

23. Write $\frac{6}{15}$ as a decimal.

24. Write 0.56 as a fraction in simplest form.

_____

25. Which of the following is *not* equivalent to $\frac{78}{45}$? $1\frac{11}{15}$ $\frac{26}{15}$ $1\frac{33}{45}$ $\frac{13}{9}$

_____

26. Find the 100th decimal digit in the decimal equivalent of $\frac{12}{37}$.

_____

Chapter Test

Form B

Chapter 2

Simplify each expression.

1. $(1 + 7)^2 + 2$

2. $(-5)^2$

_____

3. $\frac{63}{81}$

4. $\frac{35}{42}$

_____

Order from least to greatest.

5. $\frac{1}{2}, -0.51, 0.\overline{5}, -\frac{1}{2}$

_____

Write the prime factorization of each number.

6. 52

7. 60

_____

Write each improper fraction as a mixed number and each mixed number as an improper fraction.

8. $3\frac{3}{10}$

9. $\frac{52}{6}$

_____

Solve.

10. Write 1,325,000 in scientific notation. _____

11. Write 8.35×10^4 in standard form. _____

12. Is 982 divisible by 3? Explain.

_____

13. Write two fractions that are equivalent to $\frac{1}{3}$.

_____

Chapter Test (continued)   Form B

Chapter 2

14. What factors do 12 and 15 have in common?

_____

15. Write $6 \cdot 6 \cdot 6 \cdot 6$ using an exponent.

_____

16. Compare using $<, >$, or $=$. $\frac{7}{12}$ __?__ $\frac{5}{9}$

_____

17. Find the GCF of 27 and 36.

_____

18. Find two prime numbers that are larger than 17.

_____

19. Evaluate the expression $(s + t)^2$ for $s = 7$ and $t = 4$.

_____

20. Write $\frac{6}{15}$ as a decimal.   **21.** Write 0.56 as a fraction in simplest form.

_____   _____

22. Which of the following is *not* equivalent to $\frac{78}{45}$?
$\frac{26}{15}$; $1\frac{33}{45}$; $\frac{13}{9}$

_____

23. Find the 100th decimal digit in the decimal equivalent of $\frac{12}{37}$.

_____

Name _____ Class _____ Date _____

Alternative Assessment

Form C

Chapter 2

ALL IN A DAY

Everyone has 24 hours in a day, but we each use our 24 hours differently. For example, everyone spends some time asleep, but the number of hours we sleep varies from one person to another.

The table below shows the average number of hours people spend sleeping at different ages.

Age in Years	Hours Spent Sleeping
Newborn	19
6	11
12	9
25	8
40	7
48	6

Show all of your work on a separate sheet of paper.

1. Write the fraction of a day that each of the following people is likely to spend sleeping. Write each fraction in simplest form.

    a. young adult

    b. newborn

    c. first-grader

    d. seventh-grader

    e. 48-year-old man

2. Estimate the fraction of a day that you spend sleeping. Explain.

3. There are 1,440 minutes in a day. List how many minutes each day you spend doing the activities listed below. Then write a fraction that tells what part of a day you spend on each activity. Write each fraction in simplest form.

    a. eating

    b. brushing teeth

    c. doing homework

    d. talking on phone

    e. watching TV

4. Everybody has some activities that they must do, like eating and sleeping. Most people also have free time each week to do things they enjoy, such as playing a particular sport, playing with pets, practicing a musical instrument, reading a book, playing video games, going to scout meetings, shopping at a mall, listening to music, and so on.

There are 168 hours in a week. Figure out how many hours of free time you have each week. Free time includes only those hours when you are not asleep, in school, eating, or doing homework and chores. Show your work.

5. Think of at least 4 things that you like to do in your free time. Copy the table below. List the activities and estimate the hours per week you spend doing each. Then write the fraction of your free time you spend on each activity.

Activity	Hours per Week	Fraction of Free Time

Excursion

Imagine that you could spend a day as someone else. The person may be someone famous, somebody in your family, a police officer, or a character from a story or TV show. Explain why you chose the person you have listed.

Now think about how this person probably spends his or her day. What job-related tasks does he or she perform? Using fractions, tell what part of a day he or she probably spends doing each task.

What might the person do during free time? List at least three activities you would choose to do in your free time if you were that person. Use fractions to estimate how much of your day you would spend on each activity.

Name _____ Class _____ Date _____

Cumulative Review

Chapter 1–2

Multiple choice. Choose the letter of the best answer.

1. Which numbers are in order from least to greatest?

   A. 1.1, 1.2, 1.25, 1.415

   B. 0.2, 0.02, 2.2, 0.22

   C. 0.3, 0.6, 0.51, 0.65

   D. 3.5, 3.41, 3.02, 3.6

2. Karl's scores for five video games were 38, 57, 48, 62, and 55. What is his mean score?

   F. 24   **G.** 38

   H. 52   **J.** 55

3. Which difference is greatest?

   A. 2.5 − 2.3

   B. 5.5 − 4.15

   C. 3.75 − 2.95

   D. 8.05 − 7.85

4. Which number is the outlier?

   25   34   63   27   31

   F. 34   **G.** 25

   H. 63   **J.** 36

5. Ten identical coins weigh 34.5 g. How much does one coin weigh?

   A. 0.345 g   **B.** 3.45 g

   C. 345 g   **D.** not here

6. What is the mode of this data?

   0.12   0.21   0.15   0.51
   0.51   0.25   0.52

   A. 0.25   **B.** 0.40

   C. 0.51   **D.** 0.52

7. Which sum is positive?

   F. −56 + (−4)   **G.** 81 + (−90)

   H. −48 + 55   **J.** −76 + 45

8. Which of the following is equal to 16?

   A. $(-2)^4$

   B. -2^3

   C. -4^2

   D. 8^2

9. Which fraction below is not equivalent to any of the other choices?

   F. $\frac{3}{8}$

   G. $\frac{9}{24}$

   H. $\frac{24}{72}$

   J. $\frac{15}{40}$

10. What is the product of 2.3 and 3.45?

    A. 0.7935

    B. 1.15

    C. 1.5

    D. 7.935

Cumulative Review (continued)

Chapter 1–2

11. Which of the following is equivalent to $4^2 - 2^4$?

  A. $2^6 - 6^2$ **B.** $5^3 - 3^5$

  C. $8^2 - 2^8$ **D.** $2^4 - 4^2$

12. Which of the following is equivalent to $\frac{7}{8}$?

  F. $\frac{14}{18}$ **G.** $\frac{28}{30}$

  H. $\frac{35}{40}$ **J.** $\frac{21}{28}$

13. Which fraction is greatest?

  A. $\frac{2}{5}$ **B.** $\frac{1}{6}$

  C. $\frac{6}{10}$ **D.** $\frac{14}{18}$

14. What is the GCF of 84 and 126?

  F. 42   **G.** 21

  H. 18   **J.** 7

15. What is $5\frac{2}{3}$ as an improper fraction?

  A. $\frac{10}{3}$ **B.** $\frac{15}{3}$

  C. $\frac{17}{3}$ **D.** $\frac{52}{3}$

Short Response

16. A choreographer designs a dance performance that has three acts. In Act One, dancers are divided into groups of 4. In Act Two, dancers are divided into groups of 5. In Act Three, dancers are divided into groups of 6. What is the least number of dancers required to perform all three acts, with no dancers left out?

_____

_____

17. Mia rode her bike 1.6 km on Saturday. Max rode his bike $1\frac{2}{3}$ km on Sunday. Who rode farther? Explain.

_____

_____

Extended Response

18. Explain the difference between a prime number and a composite number. Give an example of each.

_____

_____

_____

_____

_____

_____

Practice 3-1

Estimating With Fractions and Mixed Numbers

Estimate each sum or difference.

1. $\frac{1}{6} + \frac{5}{8}$ _____

2. $\frac{7}{8} - \frac{1}{16}$ _____

3. $\frac{9}{10} + \frac{7}{8}$ _____

4. $\frac{1}{10} + \frac{5}{6}$ _____

5. $\frac{4}{5} - \frac{1}{6}$ _____

6. $\frac{11}{12} - \frac{5}{16}$ _____

7. $2\frac{1}{6} + 7\frac{1}{9}$ _____

8. $4\frac{9}{10} - 3\frac{5}{8}$ _____

9. $4\frac{7}{8} + 8\frac{1}{5}$ _____

10. $14\frac{3}{4} + 9\frac{7}{8}$ _____

11. $7\frac{11}{15} - 6\frac{7}{16}$ _____

12. $3\frac{11}{15} - 2\frac{9}{10}$ _____

Estimate each product or quotient.

13. $13\frac{1}{8} \div 6\frac{1}{5}$ _____

14. $5\frac{1}{6} \cdot 8\frac{4}{5}$ _____

15. $8\frac{1}{6} \div 1\frac{9}{10}$ _____

16. $27\frac{6}{7} \div 3\frac{2}{3}$ _____

17. $20\frac{4}{5} \cdot 2\frac{2}{7}$ _____

18. $9\frac{1}{3} \div 2\frac{7}{8}$ _____

19. $19\frac{4}{5} \div 4\frac{5}{8}$ _____

20. $9\frac{2}{13} \div 3\frac{1}{18}$ _____

21. $42\frac{1}{6} \div 6\frac{1}{16}$ _____

22. $15\frac{1}{20} \cdot 3\frac{1}{10}$ _____

23. $72\frac{2}{15} \div 8\frac{3}{4}$ _____

24. $3\frac{5}{6} \cdot 10\frac{1}{12}$ _____

Solve each problem.

25. Each dress for a wedding party requires $7\frac{1}{8}$ yd of material. Estimate the amount of material you would need to make 6 dresses.

_____

26. A fabric store has $80\frac{3}{8}$ yd of a particular fabric. About how many pairs of curtains could be made from this fabric if each pair requires $4\frac{1}{8}$ yd of fabric?

_____

27. Adam's car can hold $16\frac{1}{10}$ gal of gasoline. About how many gallons are left if he started with a full tank and has used $11\frac{9}{10}$ gal?

_____

28. Julia bought stock at $\$28\frac{1}{8}$ per share. The value of each stock increased by $\$6\frac{5}{8}$. About how much is each share of stock now worth?

_____

Estimate each answer.

29. $6\frac{2}{9} - 2\frac{7}{8}$ _____

30. $\frac{1}{8} + \frac{9}{10}$ _____

31. $8\frac{2}{9} \cdot 10\frac{4}{9}$ _____

32. $6\frac{1}{4} \div 2\frac{3}{11}$ _____

33. $5\frac{1}{11} \cdot 8\frac{13}{15}$ _____

34. $\frac{21}{40} - \frac{5}{89}$ _____

35. $\frac{81}{100} - \frac{1}{2}$ _____

36. $11\frac{5}{9} \div 2\frac{1}{2}$ _____

37. $\frac{3}{5} + \frac{7}{8}$ _____

3-1 • Guided Problem Solving

GPS **Student Page 123, Exercise 43:**

Writing in Math You need $9\frac{9}{16}$ lb of chicken. The store sells chicken in half-pound packages. How much chicken should you order? Explain.

Understand

1. What are you being asked to do?

   _____

2. How do you know when to round up or when to round down with a fraction?

   _____

   _____

   _____

Plan and Carry Out

3. What is the numerator of the fraction? _____

4. What is half of the denominator of the fraction? _____

5. Is the numerator bigger or smaller than half of the denominator? _____

6. Do you round the fraction up or down? _____

7. How many pounds of chicken do you need? _____

8. How many packages of chicken will you need to buy? _____

Check

9. What is $9 \div 16$? Round to the nearest whole number. Does your answer make sense?

   _____

   _____

   _____

Solve Another Problem

10. You are making curtains to cover the top of four windows. Each window is $15\frac{5}{8}$ in. wide. You buy material by the whole yard. How many yards should you buy?

   _____

Practice 3-1   **Estimating With Fractions and Mixed Numbers**

Estimate each sum or difference.

1. $\frac{1}{6} + \frac{5}{8}$

2. $\frac{7}{8} - \frac{1}{16}$

3. $\frac{1}{10} + \frac{5}{6}$

4. $\frac{4}{5} - \frac{1}{6}$

5. $2\frac{1}{6} + 7\frac{1}{9}$

6. $4\frac{9}{10} - 3\frac{5}{8}$

Estimate each product or quotient.

7. $13\frac{1}{8} \div 6\frac{1}{5}$

8. $5\frac{1}{6} \cdot 8\frac{4}{5}$

9. $27\frac{6}{7} \div 3\frac{2}{3}$

10. $20\frac{4}{5} \cdot 2\frac{2}{7}$

11. $19\frac{4}{5} \div 4\frac{5}{8}$

12. $9\frac{2}{13} \div 3\frac{1}{18}$

Solve each problem.

13. Each dress for a wedding party requires $7\frac{1}{8}$ yd of material. Estimate the amount of material you would need to make 6 dresses.

14. Adam's car can hold $16\frac{1}{10}$ gal of gasoline. About how many gallons are left if he started with a full tank and has used $11\frac{9}{10}$ gal?

Estimate each answer.

15. $6\frac{2}{9} - 2\frac{7}{8}$

16. $\frac{1}{8} + \frac{9}{10}$

17. $6\frac{1}{4} \div 2\frac{3}{11}$

18. $5\frac{1}{11} \cdot 8\frac{13}{15}$

19. $\frac{81}{100} - \frac{1}{2}$

20. $11\frac{5}{9} \div 2\frac{1}{2}$

Activity Lab 3-1   **Estimating With Fractions and Mixed Numbers**

The perimeter of a shape is determined by finding the sum of the lengths of all of its sides. For example, the perimeter of the rectangle below is: $2 + 4 + 2 + 4 = 12$

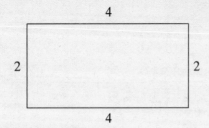

The McColin family has decided to build a fence. Below is a diagram showing the length of each edge of their property measured in kilometers. Using estimates for each fractional length, determine approximately how much fencing they will need to purchase.

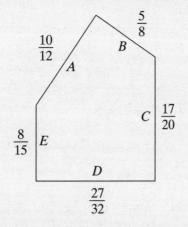

1. Use the benchmarks to estimate each length:

   $A = \frac{5}{8} \approx$ $D = \frac{8}{15} \approx$

   $B = \frac{17}{20} \approx$ $E = \frac{10}{12} \approx$

   $C = \frac{27}{32} \approx$

2. How much fencing should the McColins purchase?

   _____

3. Is the amount of fencing from part 2 the exact amount necessary to build the fence?

   _____

4. The original measurements were given in kilometers. How would you change the way the property was measured in order to take a more accurate estimate of its perimeter?

   _____

Reteaching 3-1   **Estimating With Fractions and Mixed Numbers**

You can estimate sums, differences, and products by using benchmarks. A *benchmark* is a value that can be used as a reference point.

- You can use the benchmarks to estimate fractions.

- Round mixed numbers to the nearest whole number.

Estimate the sum:

$\frac{5}{6} + \frac{7}{12}$

$1 + \frac{1}{2} = 1\frac{1}{2}$

Estimate the difference:

$3\frac{5}{6} - 2\frac{1}{3}$

$4 - 2 = 2$

Estimate the product:

$4\frac{1}{3} \times 2\frac{2}{3}$

$4 \times 3 = 12$

You can estimate a quotient by using compatible numbers.

Estimate: $15\frac{3}{8} \div 4\frac{1}{8}$ **Think:** $15\frac{3}{8}$ is close to 16.

16 is divisible by 4.

$15\frac{3}{8} \div 4\frac{1}{8} \approx 16 \div 4 = 4$

Circle the better estimate.

1. $\frac{1}{2} + \frac{3}{8}$ 1 or $\frac{1}{2}$

2. $\frac{9}{10} - \frac{7}{8}$ 0 or $\frac{1}{2}$

3. $\frac{5}{8} + \frac{3}{7}$ $\frac{1}{2}$ or 1

4. $\frac{8}{9} - \frac{1}{9}$ $\frac{1}{2}$ or 1

5. $\frac{5}{8} + \frac{8}{9}$ 1 or $1\frac{1}{2}$

6. $\frac{5}{6} + \frac{11}{12}$ $1\frac{1}{2}$ or 2

Estimate each sum or difference.

7. $\frac{1}{2} + \frac{3}{7}$ _____

8. $\frac{5}{9} - \frac{3}{7}$ _____

9. $4\frac{2}{3} - \frac{1}{2}$ _____

10. $6\frac{7}{8} + 4\frac{4}{9}$ _____

11. $5\frac{8}{9} + 3\frac{1}{3}$ _____

12. $11\frac{1}{5} - 4\frac{1}{12}$ _____

Circle the better choice to estimate each product or quotient.

13. $5\frac{1}{4} \cdot 2\frac{1}{8}$

$5 \cdot 2$ or $5 \cdot 3$

14. $13\frac{1}{4} \div 3\frac{7}{8}$

$12 \div 4$ or $15 \div 3$

15. $21\frac{1}{2} \div 4\frac{1}{4}$

$20 \div 4$ or $24 \div 4$

16. $4\frac{13}{15} \cdot 7\frac{2}{9}$

$5 \cdot 7$ or $4 \cdot 8$

Estimate each product or quotient.

17. $6\frac{1}{4} \cdot 3\frac{5}{6}$ _____

18. $9\frac{1}{2} \div 2\frac{5}{8}$ _____

19. $2\frac{1}{7} \cdot 3\frac{5}{7}$ _____

20. $9\frac{4}{5} \cdot 4\frac{5}{6}$ _____

21. $15\frac{1}{2} \div 3\frac{5}{7}$ _____

22. $11\frac{1}{9} \cdot 2\frac{7}{8}$ _____

Enrichment 3-1

Estimating With Fractions and Mixed Numbers

Geometric Properties

Use benchmarks to estimate the perimeter of each figure.

1. _____

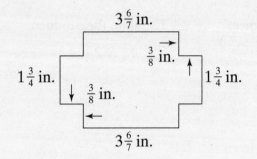

$3\frac{6}{7}$ in.

$\frac{3}{8}$ in.

$1\frac{3}{4}$ in. $1\frac{3}{4}$ in.

$\frac{3}{8}$ in.

$3\frac{6}{7}$ in.

2. _____

$2\frac{5}{6}$ cm

$3\frac{1}{5}$ cm

$3\frac{1}{5}$ cm

$2\frac{5}{6}$ cm

3. _____

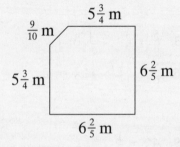

$\frac{9}{10}$ m

$5\frac{3}{4}$ m

$5\frac{3}{4}$ m

$6\frac{2}{5}$ m

$6\frac{2}{5}$ m

4. _____

$10\frac{1}{8}$ yd $10\frac{1}{8}$ yd

$9\frac{5}{8}$ yd $9\frac{5}{8}$ yd

$12\frac{3}{6}$ yd

5. _____

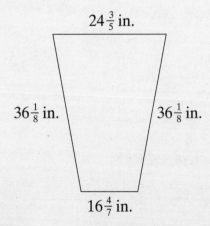

$24\frac{3}{5}$ in.

$36\frac{1}{8}$ in. $36\frac{1}{8}$ in.

$16\frac{4}{7}$ in.

6. _____

$3\frac{2}{9}$ in. $3\frac{2}{9}$ in.

$3\frac{2}{9}$ in. $3\frac{2}{9}$ in.

$3\frac{2}{9}$ in.

3A: Graphic Organizer

Study Skill You should fully understand the basic concepts in each chapter before moving on to more complex material. Be sure to ask questions when you are not comfortable with what you have learned.

Write your answers.

1. What is the chapter title? _____

2. How many lessons are there in this chapter? _____

3. What is the topic of the Test-Taking Strategies page? _____

4. Complete the graphic organizer below as you work through the chapter.
   - In the center, write the title of the chapter.
   - When you begin a lesson, write the lesson name in a rectangle.
   - When you complete a lesson, write a skill or key concept in a circle linked to that lesson block.
   - When you complete the chapter, use this graphic organizer to help you review.

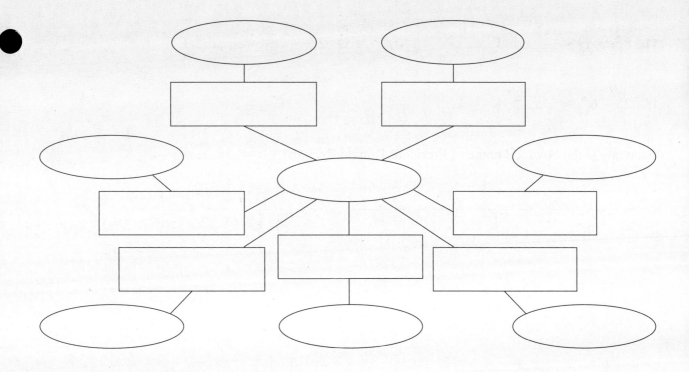

Puzzle 3-1
Estimating With Fractions and Mixed Numbers

Estimate each sum or difference. Use the benchmarks $0, \frac{1}{2},$ and 1.
Write the letter next to each answer in order from least to greatest to
answer the question.

1. $1\frac{3}{8} + 2\frac{7}{8} \approx$ _____ L

2. $5\frac{1}{4} - 3\frac{1}{4} \approx$ _____ X

3. $2\frac{2}{9} + 4\frac{7}{8} \approx$ _____ N

4. $6\frac{2}{3} - 5\frac{3}{4} \approx$ _____ D

5. $4\frac{5}{6} + 2\frac{4}{5} \approx$ _____ O

6. $5\frac{3}{10} - 1\frac{4}{5} \approx$ _____ I

7. $1\frac{1}{5} + 2\frac{1}{4} \approx$ _____ N

8. $7\frac{11}{12} - 6\frac{5}{9} \approx$ _____ I

9. $3\frac{3}{8} - 1\frac{1}{4} \approx$ _____ O

10. $6\frac{4}{5} + 1\frac{17}{20} \approx$ _____ I

11. $8\frac{5}{12} - 1\frac{5}{6} \approx$ _____ I

12 $2\frac{9}{10} + 2\frac{1}{20} \approx$ _____ L

13. $2\frac{7}{8} + 6\frac{8}{17} \approx$ _____ S

What city is the boyhood home of President Ronald Reagan?

____ ____ ____ ____ ____, ____ ____ ____ ____ ____ ____ ____ ____

Name _____ Class _____ Date _____

Practice 3-2

Adding and Subtracting Fractions

Write a number statement for each model.

1.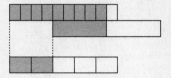

2.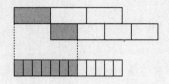

3.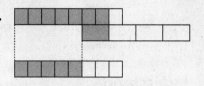

_____   _____   _____

Find each sum or difference.

4. $\frac{1}{6} + \frac{7}{8}$ _____

5. $\frac{9}{10} - \frac{1}{6}$ _____

6. $\frac{1}{6} + \frac{1}{6}$ _____

7. $\frac{1}{10} + \frac{2}{5}$ _____

8. $\frac{5}{6} + \frac{1}{12}$ _____

9. $\frac{2}{3} - \frac{1}{2}$ _____

10. $\frac{7}{9} - \frac{1}{3}$ _____

11. $\frac{3}{4} - \frac{1}{4}$ _____

12. $\frac{1}{5} + \frac{3}{4}$ _____

13. $\frac{1}{3} + \frac{1}{2}$ _____

14. $\frac{1}{8} + \frac{1}{12}$ _____

15. $\frac{7}{10} - \frac{1}{3}$ _____

Use the table at the right for Exercises 16–21. Tell which two snacks combine to make each amount.

16. $\frac{5}{6}$ c _____

17. $\frac{1}{2}$ c _____

18. $\frac{3}{4}$ c _____

19. $\frac{11}{12}$ c _____

20. 1 c _____

21. $\frac{19}{24}$ c _____

Snack	Serving Amount
Raisins	$\frac{1}{4}$ c
Walnuts	$\frac{3}{8}$ c
Almonds	$\frac{1}{8}$ c
Sesame sticks	$\frac{2}{3}$ c
Mini pretzels	$\frac{5}{8}$ c
Dried apricots	$\frac{1}{6}$ c

Solve each equation.

22. $\frac{2}{3} + x = \frac{4}{6}$

23. $s - \frac{1}{5} = \frac{2}{10}$

24. $b - \frac{4}{12} = \frac{8}{12}$

_____   _____   _____

25. $c + \frac{1}{6} = \frac{5}{12}$

26. $\frac{3}{8} + d = \frac{7}{8}$

27. $f - \frac{1}{10} = \frac{2}{5}$

_____   _____   _____

3-2 • Guided Problem Solving

GPS **Student Page 129, Exercise 40:**

You rowed $\frac{2}{3}$ mi. Your friend rowed $\frac{8}{10}$ mi. Who rowed farther?
How much farther?

Understand

1. Circle the information you will need to solve.

2. What are you being asked to do?

   _____

   _____

3. In order to subtract fractions what needs to be true about the
   denominators?

   _____

   _____

Plan and Carry Out

4. How far did you row? _____

5. How far did your friend row? _____

6. What is the common denominator for
   the two fractions in Steps 4 and 5? _____

7. Write the two numbers with a common
   denominator. _____

8. Who rowed farther? _____

9. How much farther? _____

Check

10. Write a sum you can use to check the answer.

   _____

Solve Another Problem

11. A cherry cheesecake was cut into 15 pieces. You ate $\frac{4}{15}$ of the
   cheesecake and your brother ate $\frac{1}{3}$ of the cheesecake. How much
   was left?

   _____

   _____

Name _____ Class _____ Date _____

Practice 3-2

Adding and Subtracting Fractions

Write a number statement for each model.

1.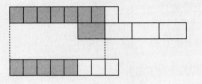

2.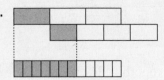

_____   _____

Find each sum or difference.

3. $\frac{1}{6} + \frac{7}{8}$

4. $\frac{9}{10} - \frac{1}{6}$

_____   _____

5. $\frac{1}{10} + \frac{2}{5}$

6. $\frac{5}{6} + \frac{1}{12}$

_____   _____

7. $\frac{7}{9} - \frac{1}{3}$

8. $\frac{3}{4} - \frac{1}{4}$

_____   _____

9. $\frac{1}{3} + \frac{1}{2}$

10. $\frac{1}{8} + \frac{1}{12}$

_____   _____

Use the table at the right for Exercises 11–15. Tell which two snacks combine to make each amount.

11. $\frac{1}{2}$ c _____

12. $\frac{3}{4}$ c _____

13. $\frac{11}{12}$ c _____

14. 1 c _____

15. $\frac{19}{24}$ c _____

Snack	Serving Amount
Raisins	$\frac{1}{4}$ c
Walnuts	$\frac{3}{8}$ c
Almonds	$\frac{1}{8}$ c
Sesame sticks	$\frac{2}{3}$ c
Mini pretzels	$\frac{5}{8}$ c

Solve each equation.

16. $\frac{2}{3} + x = \frac{4}{6}$

17. $s - \frac{1}{5} = \frac{2}{10}$

_____   _____

18. $c + \frac{1}{6} = \frac{5}{12}$

19. $\frac{3}{8} + d = \frac{7}{8}$

_____   _____

Activity Lab 3-2

Adding and Subtracting Fractions

Materials needed: fraction bars, snap cubes (red and blue)

Work with a partner.

1. Snap 6 red cubes together. Then add 3 blue cubes to one end.

   a. Write a fraction that names the blue part of the bar.

   b. Write the fraction in simplest form.

   c. Build 3 more fraction bars with snap cubes. Write fractions to represent them. Simplify the fractions, if possible.

2. One partner builds a fraction bar from 5 red and 3 blue cubes; the other partner builds one from 4 red and 4 blue cubes.

   a. Add the 2 fractions.

   b. Add the 2 fractions using the cubes.

   c. Build 3 fraction bars and use them to add or subtract the fractions. Simplify your answers, if necessary.

3. Make a fraction bar. Then make 3 more fraction bars that are equivalent to the amount shaded on the first fraction bar. Write a fraction for each bar picked. Circle the fraction that is in simplest form.

4. Put the fraction bars in order from smallest amount to greatest amount shaded. Write the fractions in order using simplest form.

5. Group the fraction bars according to common denominators. Write a fraction for each bar. Tell which fraction has the least common denominator.

6. Use fraction bars to find each sum or difference. Show your answer in simplest form.

   a. $\frac{7}{12} - \frac{5}{12}$

   b. $\frac{3}{8} + \frac{3}{8}$

   c. $\frac{1}{6} + \frac{5}{6}$

   d. $\frac{4}{5} - \frac{1}{2}$

   e. $\frac{5}{6} + \frac{1}{2}$

   f. $\frac{9}{10} - \frac{1}{2}$

Reteaching 3-2
Adding and Subtracting Fractions

Follow these steps to add or subtract fractions with different denominators.

	Add: $\frac{1}{3} + \frac{1}{6}$	Subtract: $\frac{11}{12} - \frac{1}{6}$
① Write the fractions with the same denominator.	$\frac{2}{6} + \frac{1}{6}$	$\frac{11}{12} - \frac{2}{12}$
② Add or subtract the numerators.	$\frac{2}{6} + \frac{1}{6} = \frac{3}{6}$	$\frac{11}{12} - \frac{2}{12} = \frac{9}{12}$
③ Simplify the fraction.	$\frac{3}{6} = \frac{1}{2}$	$\frac{9}{12} = \frac{3}{4}$

Complete to find each sum or difference.

1. $\frac{3}{10} + \frac{2}{5}$

   $\frac{3}{10} + \frac{\square}{10} = \frac{\square}{\square}$

2. $\frac{1}{4} + \frac{3}{6}$

   $\frac{\square}{12} + \frac{\square}{12} = \frac{\square}{\square} = \frac{\square}{\square}$

3. $\frac{5}{8} + \frac{1}{4}$

   $\frac{5}{8} + \frac{\square}{8} = \frac{\square}{\square}$

4. $\frac{3}{4} - \frac{1}{2}$

   $\frac{3}{4} - \frac{\square}{4} = \frac{\square}{\square}$

5. $\frac{5}{9} - \frac{1}{3}$

   $\frac{5}{9} - \frac{\square}{9} = \frac{\square}{\square}$

6. $\frac{3}{5} - \frac{1}{3}$

   $\frac{\square}{15} - \frac{\square}{15} = \frac{\square}{\square}$

Find each sum or difference. Write it in simplest form.

7. $\frac{4}{5} + \frac{4}{5}$

8. $\frac{7}{8} - \frac{5}{8}$

9. $\frac{5}{6} - \frac{2}{3}$

10. $\frac{5}{12} - \frac{1}{4}$

11. $\frac{7}{8} + \frac{1}{4}$

12. $\frac{3}{4} - \frac{1}{8}$

13. $\frac{2}{5} + \frac{1}{10}$

14. $\frac{7}{12} - \frac{1}{3}$

15. $\frac{1}{2} + \frac{9}{10}$

16. $\frac{5}{6} - \frac{1}{4}$

17. $\frac{5}{8} + \frac{1}{2}$

18. $\frac{2}{5} - \frac{3}{10}$

Enrichment 3-2

Adding and Subtracting Fractions

Critical Thinking

Using each number only once, use the numbers 2, 4, 6, and 8 to write an expression with two proper fractions that have:

a. The largest possible sum

b. The largest possible difference

c. The smallest possible sum

d. The smallest possible difference

1. What is a proper fraction?

   _____

2. How many proper fractions will you write in each expression?

   _____

3. How many different digits are in each pair of fractions?

   _____

4. List all the proper fractions you can make using the numbers 2, 4, 6, and 8.

   _____

5. What are the pairs of fractions you can use when writing the expressions?

   _____

6. For each pair of fractions, find the sum and the difference.

7. Write an expression for each part of the problem.

   Part a. _____   **Part b.** _____

   Part c. _____   **Part d.** _____

8. How can you tell that your answers are reasonable without calculating?

   _____

   _____

Fraction Pairs	Sum	Difference

9. Use the numbers 2, 3, 6, and 8 to write an expression with two proper fractions that have:

   a. The largest possible sum

   b. The largest possible difference

   c. The smallest possible sum

   d. The smallest possible difference

   _____   _____   _____   _____

Puzzle 3-2

Adding and Subtracting Fractions

Simplify each expression and match your answers to the numbers in the chart below. The remaining number is the solution to the puzzle.

1. $\frac{3}{4} + \frac{7}{4} + \frac{1}{4}$ _____

2. $\frac{9}{8} - \frac{3}{8} + \frac{1}{8} - \frac{3}{8}$ _____

3. $\frac{3}{16} - \frac{1}{16} + \frac{5}{16} - \frac{1}{16}$ _____

4. $\frac{11}{4} + \frac{3}{4} + \frac{7}{4} - \frac{1}{4}$ _____

5. $\frac{9}{16} - \frac{5}{16} - \frac{3}{16}$ _____

Florida $\frac{1}{16}$	Tennessee 5	Louisiana $\frac{3}{16}$
Mississippi $2\frac{3}{4}$	Arkansas $\frac{3}{8}$	Texas $\frac{1}{2}$

Which state's bird is *not* the mockingbird? _____

Practice 3-3

Adding and Subtracting Mixed Numbers

Find each sum.

1. $5\frac{1}{3} + 3\frac{2}{3}$

2. $7\frac{1}{4} + 4\frac{3}{8}$

3. $2\frac{1}{8} + 6\frac{5}{8}$

_____

_____

_____

4. $8\frac{1}{5} + 4\frac{3}{10}$

5. $9\frac{1}{6} + 6\frac{1}{4}$

6. $3\frac{2}{3} + 10\frac{5}{6}$

_____

_____

_____

Find each difference.

7. $6\frac{11}{12} - 4\frac{5}{12}$

8. $12 - 5\frac{3}{10}$

9. $14\frac{1}{2} - 7\frac{1}{5}$

_____

_____

_____

10. $9 - 5\frac{5}{6}$

11. $13\frac{3}{4} - 10\frac{1}{2}$

12. $15\frac{1}{6} - 6\frac{5}{12}$

_____

_____

_____

Find each sum or difference.

13. $1\frac{1}{6} - \frac{3}{4}$

14. $4\frac{1}{2} - 2\frac{7}{8}$

15. $9\frac{3}{4} + 7\frac{7}{8}$

_____

_____

_____

16. $5\frac{1}{6} - 4\frac{7}{12}$

17. $9\frac{8}{15} + 11\frac{5}{12}$

18. $\frac{14}{15} - \frac{1}{2}$

_____

_____

_____

Write a mixed number for each time period. Be sure each fraction is in lowest terms.

19. 8:00 A.M. to 9:20 A.M.

20. 9:00 A.M. to 2:45 P.M.

_____

_____

21. 11:00 A.M. to 3:55 P.M.

22. 8:30 A.M. to 10:40 P.M.

_____

_____

3-3 • Guided Problem Solving

GPS **Student Page 133, Exercise 29:**

On Saturday you hiked $4\frac{3}{8}$ mi. On Sunday, you hiked $3\frac{1}{2}$ mi. How far did you hike during the weekend?

Understand

1. Circle the information you will need to solve.

2. What are you being asked to do?

    _____

3. Estimate the sum of the distances.

    _____

Plan and Carry Out

4. Add the whole numbers.   _____

5. In order to add $\frac{3}{8} + \frac{1}{2}$, what do you need to find first?

    _____

6. What is the common denominator for $\frac{3}{8} + \frac{1}{2}$? _____

7. Add. $\frac{3}{8} + \frac{1}{2}$ _____

8. Add. $7 + \frac{7}{8}$ _____

9. How far did you hike during the weekend?   _____

Check

10. Is your answer reasonable according to the estimate you made in Step 3?

    _____

    _____

Solve Another Problem

11. On a white-water rafting trip you paddled $1\frac{3}{4}$ mi the first day and $2\frac{3}{8}$ mi the second day. How many miles did you raft on both days?

    _____

    _____

Practice 3-3

Adding and Subtracting Mixed Numbers

Find each sum.

1. $5\frac{1}{3} + 3\frac{2}{3}$

2. $7\frac{1}{4} + 4\frac{3}{8}$

_____

3. $8\frac{1}{5} + 4\frac{3}{10}$

4. $9\frac{1}{6} + 6\frac{1}{4}$

_____

Find each difference.

5. $6\frac{11}{12} - 4\frac{5}{12}$

6. $12 - 5\frac{3}{10}$

_____

7. $9 - 5\frac{5}{6}$

8. $13\frac{3}{4} - 10\frac{1}{2}$

_____

Find each sum or difference.

9. $1\frac{1}{6} - \frac{3}{4}$

10. $4\frac{1}{2} - 2\frac{7}{8}$

_____

11. $5\frac{1}{6} - 4\frac{7}{12}$

12. $9\frac{8}{15} + 11\frac{5}{12}$

_____

Write a mixed number for each time period. Be sure each fraction is in lowest terms.

13. 8:00 A.M. to 9:20 A.M.

14. 9:00 A.M. to 2:45 P.M.

_____

15. 11:00 A.M. to 3:55 P.M.

16. 8:30 A.M. to 10:40 P.M.

_____

Activity Lab 3-3

Adding and Subtracting Mixed Numbers

> **Materials needed:** yardsticks

Work with a partner.

1. Copy the table below on a separate sheet of paper.

A in inches	A in feet	B in inches	B in feet	A+B in feet	C in inches	C in feet	(A+B)−C in feet

Measurement *A:*

2. **a.** Measure the height of your classroom chair. Round your measurement to the nearest inch and record the result in your table.

   b. Rewrite measurement *A* as a mixed number in feet. Be sure to write your answer in simplest terms. For example, if measurement *A* is 14 inches, this would be $1\frac{2}{12} = 1\frac{1}{6}$ ft. Record the answer in your table.

Measurement *B:*

3. **a.** Measure the height of your classroom desk or table. Round your measurement to the nearest inch and record the result in your table.

   b. In simplest terms, rewrite measurement *B* as a mixed number in feet. Record the answer in your table.

   c. Find the sum of measurements *A* and *B* and record the answer in simplest terms in your table.

Measurement *C:*

4. **a.** Measure the height of the classroom. Round your measurement to the nearest inch and record the result in your table.

   b. In simplest terms, rewrite measurement *C* as a mixed number in feet. Record the answer in your table.

   c. Is the sum of measurements *A* and *B* less than, greater than, or equal to measurement *C*? By how much? Record the difference in your table.

5. If you stacked your chair on top of the table or desk, would the total height be less than, greater than, or equal to the height of the classroom? How do you know?

6. If a mobile was hanging $2\frac{3}{4}$ ft above your desk, and you stacked your chair on top of your desk to vacuum the carpeting, might the chair hit the mobile? Explain.

Reteaching 3-3

Adding and Subtracting Mixed Numbers

Follow these steps to add or subtract mixed numbers with different denominators.

		Add: $2\frac{2}{5} + 1\frac{3}{4}$	Subtract: $4\frac{1}{3} - 2\frac{5}{6}$
①	Write the equivalent fractions with the LCD.	$2\frac{8}{20} + 1\frac{15}{20}$	$4\frac{2}{6} - 2\frac{5}{6}$
②	Rename, if necessary.		$4\frac{2}{6} = 3 + 1\frac{2}{6} = 3\frac{8}{6}$
③	Add or subtract the whole numbers. Add or subtract the fractions.	$2\frac{8}{20} + 1\frac{15}{20} = 3\frac{23}{20}$	$3\frac{8}{6} - 2\frac{5}{6} = 1\frac{3}{6}$
④	Simplify.	$3\frac{23}{20} = 4\frac{3}{20}$	$1\frac{3}{6} = 1\frac{1}{2}$

Complete to find each sum or difference.

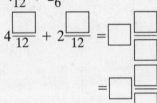

1. $4\frac{3}{4} - 2\frac{3}{8}$

$4\frac{\square}{8} - 2\frac{\square}{8} = \square\frac{\square}{\square}$

2. $4\frac{7}{12} + 2\frac{5}{6}$

$4\frac{\square}{12} + 2\frac{\square}{12} = \square\frac{\square}{\square}$

$= \square\frac{\square}{\square}$

3. $4\frac{1}{3} - 1\frac{3}{5}$

$4\frac{\square}{15} - 1\frac{\square}{15}$

$= \square\frac{\square}{\square} - \square\frac{\square}{\square}$

$= \square\frac{\square}{\square}$

Find each sum or difference. Write it in simplest form.

4. $2\frac{3}{5} + 1\frac{1}{10}$ _____

5. $2\frac{5}{6} + 3\frac{4}{9}$ _____

6. $5 - 3\frac{7}{10}$ _____

7. $3\frac{1}{6} - 2\frac{1}{3}$ _____

8. $4\frac{3}{4} - 1\frac{2}{3}$ _____

9. $3\frac{1}{2} + 4\frac{1}{3}$ _____

10. $3\frac{3}{10} + 1\frac{3}{5}$ _____

11. $6\frac{1}{3} + 7\frac{1}{4}$ _____

12. $4\frac{3}{5} + 6\frac{7}{10}$ _____

13. $7\frac{15}{16} - 2\frac{3}{8}$ _____

14. $4 - 2\frac{3}{10}$ _____

15. $2\frac{1}{2} + 5\frac{3}{5}$ _____

16. $7\frac{1}{4} - 3\frac{3}{5}$ _____

17. $9\frac{3}{5} + 1\frac{7}{10}$ _____

18. $6 - 5\frac{5}{6}$ _____

19. Shea cut $2\frac{1}{8}$ in. material off of the bottom of a $21\frac{1}{4}$ in. skirt. How long is the skirt now?

_____

Enrichment 3-3

Adding and Subtracting Mixed Numbers

Visual Thinking

The combined area of Shapes A and B is $4\frac{2}{3}$ m². The area of Shape B is $1\frac{1}{3}$ m² more than the area of Shape A. Find the areas of both shapes.

1. What are you asked to find?

   _____

2. What is the combined area of the shapes? _____

3. How much larger is Shape B than Shape A? _____

The diagram represents the combined area of the two shapes. Use the diagram to answer the questions.

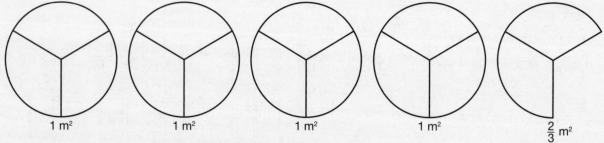

1 m²   1 m²   1 m²   1 m² $\frac{2}{3}$ m²

4. Write a "B" in the sections of the diagram that are equal to difference in the areas of Shape B and Shape A.

5. With the difference accounted for, the area of Shape A equals the area of Shape B. Write an "A" for Shape A and a "B" for Shape B in the remaining sections.

6. Use the sections labeled "A" in the diagram to write the area of Shape A.

   _____

7. Use the sections labeled "B" in the diagram to write the area of Shape B.

   _____

8. Write and solve an addition equation to check your answer.

   _____

9. The combined area of Shapes C and D is $8\frac{3}{4}$ in.² The area of Shape D is $2\frac{1}{4}$ in.² more than the area of Shape C. Find the areas of both shapes.

   _____

Name _____ Class _____ Date _____

Puzzle 3-3

Adding and Subtracting Mixed Numbers

The rows and columns in each addition square have the same sum.
Complete each addition square.

1. The sum is $7\frac{4}{11}$.

$2\frac{6}{11}$	$2\frac{7}{11}$	
		$2\frac{9}{11}$
$2\frac{8}{11}$		

2. The sum is $3\frac{11}{16}$.

$1\frac{1}{8}$	$1\frac{3}{16}$	
		$1\frac{1}{16}$
$1\frac{1}{4}$		

3. What is the sum?

$3\frac{1}{3}$	$2\frac{7}{18}$	$1\frac{1}{9}$
$2\frac{1}{6}$		$1\frac{1}{6}$

4. What is the sum?

$2\frac{1}{5}$		$\frac{2}{5}$
$\frac{7}{10}$	$2\frac{1}{2}$	
$1\frac{3}{5}$		

5. What is the sum?

$3\frac{1}{4}$		$5\frac{1}{8}$
	$2\frac{3}{4}$	$\frac{7}{8}$
		$4\frac{1}{8}$

6. Make an addition square of your own with a sum of $8\frac{2}{3}$.

Practice 3-4

Multiplying Fractions and Mixed Numbers

Find each product.

1. $\frac{5}{6} \cdot \frac{3}{5}$ _____

2. $\frac{7}{8} \cdot \frac{4}{5}$ _____

3. $\frac{9}{10} \cdot \frac{5}{12}$ _____

4. $\frac{5}{8} \cdot \frac{3}{5}$ _____

5. $\frac{1}{6}$ of 36 _____

6. $\frac{5}{9} \cdot 36$ _____

7. $\frac{3}{4} \cdot 36$ _____

8. $2 \cdot \frac{9}{10}$ _____

9. $8 \cdot \frac{9}{10}$ _____

10. $\frac{1}{3} \cdot 3\frac{1}{3}$ _____

11. $\frac{5}{6}$ of $1\frac{3}{5}$ _____

12. $\frac{1}{8}$ of $1\frac{4}{5}$ _____

13. $3 \cdot 4\frac{1}{2}$ _____

14. $5 \cdot 2\frac{1}{4}$ _____

15. $3 \cdot 2\frac{2}{3}$ _____

16. $3\frac{2}{3} \cdot 1\frac{1}{2}$ _____

17. $4\frac{1}{6} \cdot 2\frac{2}{5}$ _____

18. $3\frac{1}{4} \cdot 2\frac{1}{6}$ _____

Solve.

19. A sheet of plywood is $\frac{5}{8}$ in. thick. How tall is a stack of 21 sheets of plywood?

_____

20. A poster measures 38 cm across. If a photocopy machine is used to make a copy that is $\frac{3}{5}$ of the original size, what is the width of the copy?

_____

21. A one-kilogram object weighs about $2\frac{1}{5}$ pounds. Find the weight, in pounds, of a computer monitor with mass $7\frac{3}{8}$ kilograms.

_____

22. The population of Sweden is about $1\frac{11}{16}$ times as great as the population of Denmark. Find the population of Sweden if the population of Denmark is about 5,190,000.

_____

3-4 • Guided Problem Solving

GPS Student Page 139, Exercise 39:

The length of a track around a field is $\frac{1}{4}$ mi. You jog $3\frac{1}{2}$ times around the track. How far do you jog?

Understand

1. Circle the information you will need to solve.

2. What are you being asked to do?

_____

3. What operation will you use to solve the problem?

_____

Plan and Carry Out

4. What is the length of the track? _____

5. How many times did you run
   around the track? _____

6. Write a multiplication expression
   to solve the problem. _____

7. How far do you jog? _____

Check

8. How many times would you have to run around the track to run
   one mile? Is your answer reasonable? Explain.

_____

_____

Solve Another Problem

9. One can of paint covers $2\frac{1}{2}$ walls. You have $\frac{3}{4}$ of a can of paint.
   How many walls can you paint?

_____

_____

Practice 3-4

Multiplying Fractions and Mixed Numbers

Find each product.

1. $\frac{5}{6} \cdot \frac{3}{5}$

2. $\frac{7}{8} \cdot \frac{4}{5}$

3. $\frac{5}{8} \cdot \frac{3}{5}$

4. $\frac{1}{6}$ of 36

5. $\frac{3}{4} \cdot 36$

6. $2 \cdot \frac{9}{10}$

7. $\frac{1}{3} \cdot 3\frac{1}{3}$

8. $\frac{5}{6}$ of $1\frac{3}{5}$

9. $3 \cdot 4\frac{1}{2}$

10. $5 \cdot 2\frac{1}{4}$

11. $3\frac{2}{3} \cdot 1\frac{1}{2}$

12. $4\frac{1}{6} \cdot 2\frac{2}{5}$

Solve.

13. A poster measures 38 cm across. If a photocopy machine is used to make a copy that is $\frac{3}{5}$ of the original size, what is the width of the copy?

14. A one-kilogram object weighs about $2\frac{1}{5}$ pounds. Find the weight, in pounds, of a computer monitor with mass $7\frac{3}{8}$ kilograms.

15. The population of Sweden is about $1\frac{11}{16}$ times as great as the population of Denmark. Find the population of Sweden if the population of Denmark is about 5,190,000.

Activity Lab 3-4
Multiplying Fractions and Mixed Numbers

Materials needed: decimal grids

1. Model the problem $\frac{1}{2} \times \frac{1}{2}$ by following these steps:

   a. Shade the first five vertical columns of a decimal grid as shown. Why would this represent the fraction $\frac{1}{2}$?

   b. On the same grid, shade the top five horizontal rows. What fraction does the horizontal shading represent?

   c. Now look at the shaded portions of the grid. The squares that have been shaded twice represent the solution to the problem. How many squares have been shaded twice?

   d. To solve the multiplication problem, write your answer to part *c* as a fraction of the total number of squares in the grid (in simplest form). What is the solution to the problem $\frac{1}{2} \times \frac{1}{2}$?

2. Use a decimal grid to find the product $\frac{1}{10} \times \frac{2}{5}$.

   a. How many vertical columns should you shade to represent $\frac{1}{10}$?

   b. How many horizontal rows should you shade to represent $\frac{2}{5}$?

   c. How many squares are shaded twice?

   d. What is the solution?

3. **a.** You cannot find the product $\frac{1}{3} \times \frac{1}{6}$ using a standard decimal grid. Why not?

   b. How can you change the grid to find the product? Use your new grid to find the solution.

4. Based on your answers above, what do you observe about the value of the solution of a fraction multiplication problem compared to the values of the two factors?

Reteaching 3-4
Multiplying Fractions and Mixed Numbers

Follow these steps to multiply fractions and mixed numbers.

Multiply: $\frac{3}{4} \cdot \frac{2}{5}$ Multiply: $2\frac{2}{3} \cdot 1\frac{5}{8}$

(1) Write the mixed numbers as improper fractions if necessary.

$\frac{8}{3} \cdot \frac{13}{8}$

(2) Multiply numerators. Multiply denominators.

$\frac{3 \cdot 2}{4 \cdot 5} = \frac{6}{20}$ $\frac{8 \cdot 13}{3 \cdot 8} = \frac{104}{24}$

(3) Simplify, if necessary.

$\frac{6}{20} = \frac{3}{10}$ $\frac{104}{24} = 4\frac{1}{3}$

Complete to find each product.

1. $\frac{1}{5} \cdot \frac{2}{3}$

$\frac{1 \cdot 2}{5 \cdot 3} = \dfrac{\boxed{}}{\boxed{}}$

Product _____

2. $\frac{1}{4} \cdot 4\frac{1}{8}$

$\frac{1}{4} \cdot \dfrac{\boxed{}}{8} = \dfrac{\boxed{}}{32}$

Product _____

3. $2\frac{3}{4} \cdot 1\frac{2}{3}$

$\dfrac{\boxed{}}{4} \cdot \dfrac{\boxed{}}{3} = \dfrac{\boxed{}}{12}$

Product _____

Find each product. Write the product in simplest form.

4. $\frac{5}{8} \cdot \frac{2}{5}$ _____

5. $\frac{5}{12} \cdot \frac{3}{10}$ _____

6. $\frac{1}{2} \cdot 5\frac{1}{6}$ _____

7. $1\frac{2}{3} \cdot 5$ _____

8. $2\frac{3}{5} \cdot \frac{1}{4}$ _____

9. $2\frac{3}{5} \cdot \frac{7}{8}$ _____

10. $4\frac{1}{5} \cdot \frac{5}{7}$ _____

11. $\frac{1}{2} \cdot 2\frac{1}{8}$ _____

12. $3\frac{5}{6} \cdot 2\frac{1}{4}$ _____

13. $2\frac{5}{7} \cdot 1\frac{1}{3}$ _____

14. $7\frac{2}{3} \cdot 2\frac{1}{7}$ _____

15. $5\frac{1}{2} \cdot 2\frac{2}{3}$ _____

16. $\frac{5}{6} \cdot 3\frac{3}{5}$ _____

17. $7\frac{3}{4} \cdot 2$ _____

Enrichment 3-4

Multiplying Fractions and Mixed Numbers

Critical Thinking

Find the area of each shaded part.

1. _____

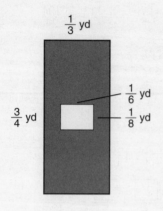

$\frac{1}{3}$ yd

$\frac{3}{4}$ yd

$\frac{1}{6}$ yd

$\frac{1}{8}$ yd

2. _____

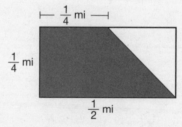

$\frac{5}{8}$ in.

$\frac{5}{8}$ in.

$\frac{7}{8}$ in.

$\frac{7}{8}$ in.

3. _____

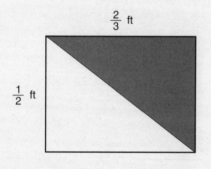

$\frac{2}{3}$ ft

$\frac{1}{2}$ ft

4. _____

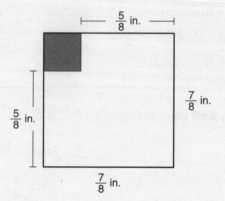

$\frac{1}{4}$ mi

$\frac{1}{4}$ mi

$\frac{1}{2}$ mi

5. _____

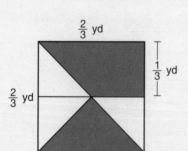

$\frac{2}{3}$ yd

$\frac{1}{3}$ yd

$\frac{2}{3}$ yd

6. _____

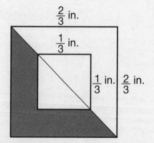

$\frac{2}{3}$ in.

$\frac{1}{3}$ in.

$\frac{1}{3}$ in. $\frac{2}{3}$ in.

Puzzle 3-4

Multiplying Fractions and Mixed Numbers

Write a fraction or mixed number in each blank square so that the equations across and down are correct. Study the example.

Example:

$1\frac{1}{4} \cdot 1\frac{1}{2}$

$1\frac{1}{4} \cdot \frac{3}{4}$

Use this square as a check.

1.

2.

3.

4.

5. Make a square of your own.

Practice 3-5

Dividing Fractions and Mixed Numbers

Find the reciprocal of each number.

1. $\frac{1}{2}$ _____

2. $\frac{9}{16}$ _____

3. $\frac{4}{5}$ _____

4. $1\frac{1}{4}$ _____

5. $2\frac{9}{10}$ _____

6. $3\frac{1}{6}$ _____

Find each quotient.

7. $\frac{3}{4} \div \frac{1}{4}$ _____

8. $\frac{5}{6} \div \frac{1}{12}$ _____

9. $\frac{1}{12} \div \frac{5}{6}$ _____

10. $6 \div \frac{3}{4}$ _____

11. $5 \div \frac{9}{10}$ _____

12. $\frac{4}{5} \div 2$ _____

13. $\frac{7}{8} \div 3$ _____

14. $\frac{4}{9} \div 8$ _____

15. $1\frac{1}{2} \div \frac{2}{3}$ _____

16. $\frac{3}{4} \div 1\frac{1}{3}$ _____

17. $2\frac{1}{2} \div 1\frac{1}{4}$ _____

18. $1\frac{3}{4} \div \frac{3}{4}$ _____

19. $1\frac{7}{10} \div \frac{1}{2}$ _____

20. $4\frac{1}{2} \div 2\frac{1}{2}$ _____

21. $6 \div 3\frac{4}{5}$ _____

22. $4\frac{3}{4} \div \frac{7}{8}$ _____

23. $5\frac{5}{6} \div 1\frac{1}{3}$ _____

24. $3\frac{3}{8} \div 1\frac{1}{4}$ _____

25. $6\frac{1}{2} \div 1\frac{1}{2}$ _____

26. $2\frac{9}{10} \div 1\frac{3}{4}$ _____

27. $3\frac{1}{4} \div 1\frac{1}{3}$ _____

Solve each problem.

28. Rosa makes $2\frac{1}{2}$ c of pudding. How many $\frac{1}{3}$ c servings can she get from the pudding?

_____

29. One type of lightning bug glows once every $1\frac{1}{2}$ s. How many times can it glow in 1 min?

_____

30. Bea can run $\frac{1}{6}$ mi in 2 min. How long should it take her to run 2 mi?

_____

31. Joe drives 20 mi in $\frac{1}{2}$ h. How long will it take him to drive 50 mi?

_____

3-5 • Guided Problem Solving

GPS **Student Page 145, Exercise 44:**

Biology A manatee can swim 5 mi in $1\frac{1}{4}$ h. If the manatee swims at the same average speed, how far can it swim in 1 h?

Understand

1. Circle the information you will need to solve.

2. What are you being asked to do?

   _____

   _____

Plan and Carry Out

3. Write a ratio comparing 5 miles to $1\frac{1}{4}$ hours.

   _____

4. Write a ratio comparing x miles to 1 hour.

   _____

5. Write a proportion comparing the ratios in Steps 3 and 4.

   _____

6. How far can the manatee swim in 1 hour?

   _____

Check

7. Will the manatee swim more or less than 5 miles in 1 hour? Is your answer reasonable? Explain.

   _____

   _____

Solve Another Problem

8. Glenda ran 8 miles in $2\frac{1}{2}$ hours. If she runs at the same average speed, how far can she run in 1 hour?

   _____

Practice 3-5

Dividing Fractions and Mixed Numbers

Find the reciprocal of each number.

1. $\frac{1}{2}$ _____

2. $\frac{9}{16}$ _____

3. $\frac{4}{5}$ _____

4. $1\frac{1}{4}$ _____

5. $2\frac{9}{10}$ _____

6. $3\frac{1}{6}$ _____

Find each quotient.

7. $\frac{3}{4} \div \frac{1}{4}$

8. $\frac{5}{6} \div \frac{1}{12}$

9. $\frac{1}{12} \div \frac{5}{6}$

10. $6 \div \frac{3}{4}$

11. $5 \div \frac{9}{10}$

12. $\frac{4}{5} \div 2$

13. $\frac{7}{8} \div 3$

14. $\frac{4}{9} \div 8$

15. $1\frac{1}{2} \div \frac{2}{3}$

16. $\frac{3}{4} \div 1\frac{1}{3}$

17. $2\frac{1}{2} \div 1\frac{1}{4}$

18. $1\frac{3}{4} \div \frac{3}{4}$

19. $1\frac{7}{10} \div \frac{1}{2}$

20. $4\frac{1}{2} \div 2\frac{1}{2}$

Solve each problem.

21. Rosa makes $2\frac{1}{2}$ c of pudding. How many $\frac{1}{3}$ c servings can she get from the pudding?

22. One type of lightning bug glows once every $1\frac{1}{2}$ s. How many times can it glow in 1 min?

23. Joe drives 20 mi in $\frac{1}{2}$ h. How long will it take him to drive 50 mi?

Activity Lab 3-5

Dividing Fractions and Mixed Numbers

Materials needed: calculator (optional), dominoes

Work in pairs.

1. Turn all the dominoes face down. Mix them up.

2. Copy the table below on a separate sheet of paper.

Dividend	Fraction	Division Problem	Solution	Reciprocal	Multiplication Problem	Solution
3						
6						
12						
15						
$\frac{2}{3}$						
$\frac{5}{6}$						

3. Your opponent chooses one domino randomly and turns it face up. Turn the domino so that the half with the fewest dots is on top. Write the fraction that the domino represents in the Fraction column of the table. For example, if there are 2 dots on the top half of the domino and 5 dots on the bottom half, the fraction is $\frac{2}{5}$.

4. **a.** In the Division Problem column, write a division problem using the number provided in the table above as the dividend, and the fraction you wrote in Step 3 as the divisor. For example, if you wrote the fraction $\frac{2}{5}$, your first problem is $3 \div \frac{2}{5}$.

   b. Use a calculator or a model to solve the problem. Write the solution in the Solution column next to the Division Problem column.

5. Now rotate the domino 180°. Write the fraction it represents in the Reciprocal column. For example, if your original fraction was $\frac{2}{5}$, the new fraction is $\frac{5}{2}$.

6. In the Multiplication Problem column, write a multiplication problem using the numbers in the Dividend column and the Reciprocal column. Write the solution in the Solution column next to the Multiplication Problem.

7. Your opponent will check your work. For each problem you solve correctly, you get one point. If you solve a problem incorrectly and your opponent fixes it, your opponent gets one point. Keep a tally of your points.

8. Switch roles and complete the next row in the table. The player with the most points, when the table is filled in, wins.

9. Compare the Solution columns in your table. What do you notice?

10. Based on your observations, how can you use a multiplication problem to solve a division problem involving fractions?

Reteaching 3-5   **Dividing Fractions and Mixed Numbers**

To find the **reciprocal** of a fraction, interchange the numerator and the denominator.

Examples: The reciprocal of $\frac{1}{4}$ is $\frac{4}{1}$.   The reciprocal of $\frac{7}{5}$ is $\frac{5}{7}$.

Follow these steps to divide fractions and mixed numbers.

		Divide: $\frac{2}{3} \div \frac{1}{4}$	Divide: $3\frac{3}{4} \div 1\frac{2}{5}$
①	Rewrite mixed numbers as improper fractions as needed.		$\frac{15}{4} \div \frac{7}{5}$
②	Multiply by the reciprocal of the divisor.	$\frac{2}{3} \cdot \frac{4}{1}$	$\frac{15}{4} \cdot \frac{5}{7}$
③	Multiply numerators. Multiply denominators.	$\frac{2 \cdot 4}{3 \cdot 1} = \frac{8}{3}$	$\frac{15 \cdot 5}{4 \cdot 7} = \frac{75}{28}$
④	Simplify.	$\frac{8}{3} = 2\frac{2}{3}$	$\frac{75}{28} = 2\frac{19}{28}$

Find the reciprocal of each number.

1. $\frac{7}{8}$ _____

2. $\frac{8}{3}$ _____

3. $\frac{9}{10}$ _____

Write each mixed number as an improper fraction. Then find the reciprocal.

4. $1\frac{1}{2}$ _____

5. $1\frac{4}{5}$ _____

6. $2\frac{3}{4}$ _____

Complete to find each quotient. Write the quotient in simplest form.

7. $\frac{2}{3} \div \frac{3}{8}$

$\frac{2}{3} \cdot \frac{\boxed{}}{3} = \frac{\boxed{}}{9}$

Quotient _____

8. $10 \div \frac{7}{8}$

$\frac{\boxed{}}{1} \div \frac{7}{8} = \frac{\boxed{}}{1} \cdot \frac{\boxed{}}{\boxed{}}$

$= \frac{\boxed{}}{7}$

Quotient _____

9. $3\frac{3}{5} \div 1\frac{1}{5}$

$\frac{\boxed{}}{5} \div \frac{\boxed{}}{5} = \frac{\boxed{}}{5} \cdot \frac{\boxed{}}{\boxed{}}$

$= \frac{\boxed{}}{30}$

Quotient _____

10. $\frac{1}{5} \div \frac{1}{2}$ _____

11. $\frac{3}{8} \div \frac{2}{3}$ _____

12. $8 \div \frac{4}{5}$ _____

13. $6 \div \frac{3}{4}$ _____

14. $1\frac{1}{8} \div 2\frac{2}{5}$ _____

15. $3\frac{1}{5} \div 2\frac{2}{3}$ _____

Enrichment 3-5

Dividing Fractions and Mixed Numbers

Eliminating Information

Given the list of numbers, determine which number is the dividend, which number is the divisor and which number is the quotient. Write the division problem. Mark an "X" over the number that does not belong in the problem.

1. $\frac{3}{8}, \frac{3}{7}, \frac{7}{8}, 2\frac{1}{3}$

dividend _____   divisor _____   quotient _____   problem _____

2. $26, \frac{1}{5}, \frac{1}{5}, 1$

dividend _____   divisor _____   quotient _____   problem _____

3. $\frac{5}{6}, 16\frac{2}{3}, 6, \frac{1}{20}$

dividend _____   divisor _____   quotient _____   problem _____

4. $\frac{6}{8}, 1\frac{1}{48}, \frac{6}{7}, \frac{7}{8}$

dividend _____   divisor _____   quotient _____   problem _____

5. $\frac{3}{4}, \frac{1}{8}, 6, 8$

dividend _____   divisor _____   quotient _____   problem _____

6. $4\frac{1}{9}, 2\frac{7}{15}, 1\frac{2}{3}, \frac{2}{3}$

dividend _____   divisor _____   quotient _____   problem _____

7. $\frac{2}{3}, \frac{9}{14}, \frac{3}{7}, \frac{1}{21}$

dividend _____   divisor _____   quotient _____   problem _____

3D: Visual Vocabulary Practice

For use after Lesson 3-5

High-Use Academic Words

Study Skill When learning a new concept, try to draw a picture to illustrate it.

Concept List

compare	table	estimate
equivalent	convert	define
order	figure	sum

1. 3 yd = 9 ft	**2.** $-5 + 20 + 13 + (-2) = 26$	**3.** Two numbers are *reciprocals* if their product is one.
4. 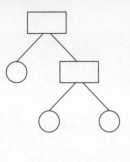	**5.** $5^2 < 2^5$	**6.** $\frac{2}{5}$ and $\frac{4}{10}$
7. $-28, 4, \frac{1}{2}, -2, 0.1$ $-28, -2, 0.1, \frac{1}{2}, 4$	**8.** $23.15 + 5.79 \approx 23 + 6$	**9.** **Average Lifespan**

For item 9:

Average Lifespan

Insect	Weeks
Ant	4
Butterfly	2
Cockroach	104
Mosquito	2

Puzzle 3-5

Dividing Fractions and Mixed Numbers

Here are some Egyptian fraction symbols.

$\Box = \dfrac{1}{2}$ $\bigcirc = \dfrac{1}{3}$ $\bigcirc = \dfrac{1}{4}$ $\bigcirc = \dfrac{1}{6}$ $\oplus = \dfrac{2}{3}$

Use the symbols to make each equation true.

1. $\bigcirc \div \Box =$ _____

2. $\bigcirc \div \Box =$ _____

3. $\bigcirc \div \bigcirc =$ _____

4. $\bigcirc \div \oplus =$ _____

5. _____ $\div \bigcirc = 2$

6. _____ $\div \bigcirc = 2$

7. $\oplus \div$ _____ $= 4$

8. $\bigcirc \div$ _____ $= \dfrac{3}{8}$

9. _____ $\div \oplus = \Box$

10. $\bigcirc \div$ _____ $= \oplus$

11. _____ $\div \Box = \bigcirc$

12. $2 \div$ _____ $= 3$

Practice 3-6

Changing Units in the Customary System

Tell whether you would multiply or divide to change from one unit of measure to the other.

1. tons to pounds

_____

2. pints to quarts

_____

3. feet to yards

_____

4. gallons to pints

_____

5. cups to quarts

_____

6. pounds to ounces

_____

Change each unit of length, capacity, or weight.

7. 9 qt = _____ gal

8. $2\frac{1}{4}$ t = _____ lb

9. $3\frac{1}{2}$ yd = _____ in.

10. 4 yd = _____ ft

11. 60 c = _____ qt

12. 246 in. = _____ ft

13. 1,750 oz = _____ lb

14. 84 ft = _____ yd

15. 198 in. = _____ yd

16. 480 fl oz = _____ pt

17. $\frac{1}{4}$ gal = _____ fl oz

18. $\frac{1}{2}$ mi = _____ ft

19. $\frac{1}{10}$ mi = _____ in.

20. 2 lb 6 oz = _____ lb

21. 2 qt 8 fl oz = _____ qt

Solve.

22. United States farms produced 2,460,000,000 bushels of soybeans in 1994. How many quarts is this? (A bushel is 32 quarts.)

_____

23. In 1994, Brian Berg built an 81-story "house" using playing cards. The house was $15\frac{2}{3}$ ft tall. How many inches is this?

_____

Choose an appropriate customary unit of measure.

24. capacity of a mug

_____

25. length of a family room

_____

26. distance between two capital cities

_____

27. capacity of a shampoo bottle

_____

3-6 • Guided Problem Solving

GPS **Student Page 151, Exercise 42:**

The length of the Amazon River in South America is about 4,000 mi.
How many feet is this?

Understand

1. Circle the information you will need to solve.

2. What are you being asked to do?

   _____

Plan and Carry Out

3. How many feet are there in 1 mile?

   _____

4. Do you multiply or divide to find the number of feet in 4,000 miles?

   _____

5. Write a multiplication expression to solve this problem.

   _____

6. How many feet are there in 4,000 mi?

   _____

Check

7. Should the number of feet in 4,000 miles be more or less than 4,000? Explain why.

   _____

Solve Another Problem

8. A fishing boat is working 90 miles from shore. How many feet from shore is this?

   _____

Practice 3-6

Changing Units in the Customary System

Tell whether you would multiply or divide to change from one unit of measure to the other.

1. tons to pounds

_____

2. pints to quarts

_____

3. feet to yards

_____

4. gallons to pints

_____

5. cups to quarts

_____

6. pounds to ounces

_____

Change each unit of length, capacity, or weight.

7. 9 qt = _____ gal

8. $2\frac{1}{4}$ t = _____ lb

9. $3\frac{1}{2}$ yd = _____ in.

10. 4 yd = _____ ft

11. 60 c = _____ qt

12. 246 in. = _____ ft

13. 1,750 oz = _____ lb

14. 84 ft = _____ yd

15. 198 in. = _____ yd

Solve.

16. United States farms produced 2,460,000,000 bushels of soybeans in 1994. How many quarts is this? (A bushel is 32 quarts.)

_____

17. In 1994, Brian Berg built an 81-story "house" using playing cards. The house was $15\frac{2}{3}$ ft tall. How many inches is this?

_____

Choose an appropriate customary unit of measure.

18. capacity of a mug

_____

19. distance between two capital cities

_____

20. capacity of a shampoo bottle

_____

Activity Lab 3-6

Changing Units in the Customary System

The ratio 1 ft : 12 in. is equal to 1. Notice that both the numbers and the units are different but you know that 1 foot is equal to 12 inches. Ratios such as 1 ft : 12 in. or 12 in. : 1 ft are called *conversion factors*. They are used to convert one unit of measurement to another related unit of measurement.

For example: Vicky hiked 4 miles in 1 hour. If you want to know how many feet she walked in 1 hour, you can use the conversion factor 5,280 ft : 1 mi.

$$\frac{4 \text{ mi}}{1 \text{ hr}} \times \frac{5{,}280 \text{ ft}}{1 \text{ mi}} = \frac{4 \text{ mi} \times 5{,}280 \text{ ft}}{1 \text{ hr} \times 1 \text{ mi}} = \frac{21{,}120 \text{ ft}}{1 \text{ hr}}$$

Vicky hiked 21,120 ft in 1 hour.

Complete the following conversion factors.

1. 1 min : 60 _____

2. 60 min : _____ hr

3. 1 day : _____ hr

4. 60 sec : 1 _____

5. 1 hr : 60 _____

6. 24 hr : 1 _____

7. 1 mi : _____ ft

8. 3 ft : 1 _____

9. 1 yd : 36 _____

10. 1 yr : _____ days

Use a conversion factor to convert each rate to an equivalent rate.

11. 100 ft : 1 sec = _____ ft : 1 min

12. 99 ft : 1 min = _____ yd : 1 min

13. 60 in. : 1 hr = _____ in. : 1 min

14. 12 mi : 1 hr = _____ ft : 1 hr

15. $1,825 : 1 yr = $_____ : 1 day

16. 72 in. : 1 day = _____ yd : 1 day

Use a conversion factor to help you solve each problem.

17. A newborn baby's heart beats 35 times in 15 sec. How many times will it beat in 1 minute? _____

18. An adult's heart beats 20 times in 15 sec. How many times will it beat in 1 hour? _____

19. A subcompact car travels 170 mi on 10 gal of gas. How many feet can it travel on 10 gal? _____

20. A snail travels 50 inches in 1 day. How many feet can it travel in 5 days? _____

Reteaching 3-6

Changing Units in the Customary System

Length	Weight	Capacity
12 inches (in.) = 1 foot (ft)	16 ounces (oz) = 1 pound (lb)	8 fluid ounces (fl oz) = 1 cup (c)
3 ft = 1 yard (yd)	2,000 lb = 1 ton (t)	2 c = 1 pint (pt)
5,280 ft = 1 mile (mi)		2 pt = 1 quart (qt)
		4 qt = 1 gallon (gal)

To change to a *larger* unit, divide.

66 in. = __?__

1 ft is larger than 1 in.
12 in. = 1 ft

$66 \div 12 = \frac{66}{12} = 5\frac{6}{12} = 5\frac{1}{2}$

66 in. = $5\frac{1}{2}$ ft

To change to a *smaller* unit, multiply.

$3\frac{1}{2}$ qt = __?__ pt

1 pt is smaller than 1 qt.
1 qt = 2 pt

$3\frac{1}{2} \cdot 2 = \frac{7}{2} \cdot \frac{2}{1} = \frac{14}{2} = 7$

$3\frac{1}{2}$ qt = 7 pt

Multiply to change to a smaller unit. Write the fact you used.

1. $3\frac{1}{2}$ ft = _____

2. $1\frac{1}{2}$ c = _____

3. 5 lb = _____

4. $5\frac{1}{2}$ qt = _____

5. $3\frac{1}{4}$ gal = _____

6. 4 pt = _____

7. 2 mi = _____

8. 6 qt = _____

9. $1\frac{1}{2}$ t = _____

Divide to change to a larger unit. Write the fact you used.

10. 24 fl oz = _____

11. 32 oz = _____

12. 3 c = _____

13. 4,000 lb = _____

14. 7 pt = _____

15. 27 ft = _____

16. The Missouri River is 4,470,400 yards long. Express this measurement in miles.

_____

Enrichment 3-6

Changing Units in the Customary System

Patterns in Measurement

On a far-off planet, the following four units are used for measuring length: lap, mut, pal, and word. Their relationships are shown in the table at the right.

1 lap = 6 muts	
1 mut = 9 pals	
1 pal = 3 words	

1. Use a conversion factor to convert 324 words to pals.

   _____

2. Use a conversion factor to convert 108 pals to muts.

   _____

3. Use a conversion factor to convert 12 muts to laps.

   _____

4. Which of the units is the smallest?

   _____

5. Which of the units is the largest?

   _____

6. What pattern do you notice about the quantity of units as you convert from the smallest unit to the largest unit?

   _____

   _____

7. Use a conversion factor to convert 8 laps to muts.

   _____

8. Use a conversion factor to convert 48 muts to pals.

   _____

9. Use a conversion factor to convert 432 pals to words.

   _____

10. What pattern do you notice about the quantity of units as you convert from the largest unit to the smallest unit?

    _____

    _____

11. What general statement can you make about the quantity of units relative to their size?

    _____

    _____

3B: Reading Comprehension

Study Skill Make a realistic study schedule. Set specific goals for yourself, rather than general ones. For example, read Chapter 2, do problems 1–20, or study for a math test before doing homework.

Read the paragraph below and answer the questions.

In ancient times, people measured things by comparing them to parts of the body. For example, a foot length or a finger width was considered an acceptable measurement. Later, other common objects were used to represent measurements. Below is a list of some common lengths and their early standards of measurement.

Inch: the width of a man's thumb, 3 grains of barley placed end to end

Foot: the length of an average man's foot, about $11\frac{1}{42}$ inches

Yard: the length of a man's belt, or the distance from a man's nose to the tip of his outstretched arm

Span: the length of a man's stretched out hand, about 9 inches

Hand: approximately 5 inches across, today a hand is 4 inches and is used to measure the height of a horse

1. What is the paragraph about? _____

2. Which measurement is given as a mixed number?

   _____

3. Order the numbers given in the paragraph from least to greatest.

   _____

4. How much shorter was a foot in ancient times than our modern measurement?

   _____

5. In ancient times, how many grains of barley would you need to make a foot?

   _____

6. In modern times, how many grains of barley would you need to make a foot?

   _____

7. **High-Use Academic Words** In question three, what does it mean to *order*?

   a. to arrange information in a sequence   b. to determine the value of

3C: Reading/Writing Math Symbols   **For use after Lesson 3-6**

Study Skill Read problems carefully. Pay special attention to units when working with measurements.

Match the abbreviation in Column A with its appropriate U.S. customary units in Column B.

Column A	Column B
1. lb	A. ounces
2. c	B. quarts
3. oz	C. pounds
4. yd	D. pints
5. pt	E. gallons
6. ft	F. yards
7. qt	G. feet
8. gal	H. cups

Write each of the following using appropriate mathematical symbols.

9. one hundred kilometers _____

10. forty-seven pounds _____

11. three and seven tenths ounces _____

12. two and five-tenths milliliters _____

13. five and thirty three hundredths grams _____

14. four and three-quarter inches _____

15. thirteen meters _____

16. five and one-third tons _____

Puzzle 3-6

Changing Units in the Customary System

Cut out the puzzle pieces. Arrange the pieces by matching the
equivalent units to find the customary unit that is equal to about
30.48 cm in the metric system.

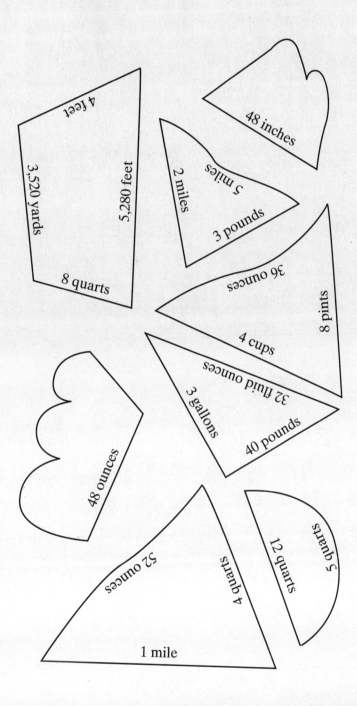

Practice 3-7

Precision

Underline the more precise measurement.

1. 23 oz, 20.7 oz

2. 1,830 g, 2.5 kg

3. 63.7 L, 63.70 L

4. 3.7 t, 5,610 lb

5. 58.3 cm, 4.6 m

6. 12 L, 1,735 mL

7. 3,008 pt, 0.95 pt

8. 7.3 min, 516 sec

9. 2.7 mL, 12 mL

10. 26.4 cm, 8.39 cm

11. 216 ft, 3,106 in.

12. 4.1 lb, 6.123 lb

Find each sum or difference. Round your answer to match the less precise measurement.

13. 6.35 oz + 4.2 oz

14. 83 g − 1.8 g

15. 4.20 yd + 8.64 yd

_____

_____

_____

16. 21 cm + 53.60 cm

17. 5.382 m + 8 m

18. 6.4 ft + 4300 ft

_____

_____

_____

19. 2.713 mL + 8.4 mL

20. 50 lb − 4.6 lb

21. 6.83 km + 10.3 km

_____

_____

_____

22. Boundary Peak in Nevada is 13,000 ft high. Guadalupe Peak in Texas is 8,749.75 ft high. How much higher than Guadalupe Peak is Boundary Peak? Round your answer to match the less precise measurement.

_____

23. You measure the area of your garden as 9 yd wide by 11 yd long. Your brother measures the garden as $27\frac{1}{2}$ ft wide by $32\frac{3}{4}$ ft long. Whose measurement is more precise? Why?

_____

_____

_____

3-7 • Guided Problem Solving

GPS Student Page 157, Exercise 35:

A climber ascends 2,458.75 ft up a 3,000-ft mountainside. How much farther does the climber have to go to reach the top? Round your answer appropriately.

Understand

1. Circle the information you will need to solve.

2. What are you being asked to do?

   _____

3. Which measurement is the least precise? Explain.

   _____

4. What will you round to?

   _____

Plan and Carry Out

5. How far has the climber climbed?   _____

6. How tall is the mountain?   _____

7. What is the difference between
   3,000 ft and 2,458.75 ft?   _____

8. Round the answer in Step 7
   to the least precise measurement.   _____

Check

9. Round 2,458.75 ft to the nearest whole number. Subtract this from 3,000 ft. Is your answer reasonable?

   _____

   _____

Solve Another Problem

10. Aaron used 3.25 oz of peanut butter and 0.5 oz of marshmallow cream for a fruit dip. How many ounces did he use in total? Round your answer appropriately.

    _____

Guided Problem Solving

Practice 3-7

Precision

Underline the more precise measurement.

1. 23 oz, 20.7 oz

2. 1,830 g, 2.5 kg

3. 63.7 L, 63.70 L

4. 3.7 t, 5,610 lb

5. 58.3 cm, 4.6 m

6. 12 L, 1,735 mL

7. 3,008 pt, 0.95 pt

8. 7.3 min, 516 sec

9. 2.7 mL, 12 mL

Find each sum or difference. Round your answer to match the less precise measurement.

10. 6.35 oz + 4.2 oz

11. 83 g − 1.8 g

_____

_____

12. 21 cm + 53.60 cm

13. 5.382 m + 8 m

_____

_____

14. 2.713 mL + 8.4 mL

15. 50 lb − 4.6 lb

16. Boundary Peak in Nevada is 13,000 ft high. Guadalupe Peak in Texas is 8,749.75 ft high. How much higher than Guadalupe Peak is Boundary Peak? Round your answer to match the less precise measurement.

_____

_____

17. You measure the area of your garden as 9 yd wide by 11 yd long. Your brother measures the garden as $27\frac{1}{2}$ ft wide by $32\frac{3}{4}$ ft long. Whose measurement is more precise? Why?

_____

_____

_____

Activity Lab 3-7

Precision

Materials needed: ruler or yardstick marked in inch, half-inch, quarter-inch, eighth-inch, and sixteenth-inch increments; pencil; eraser

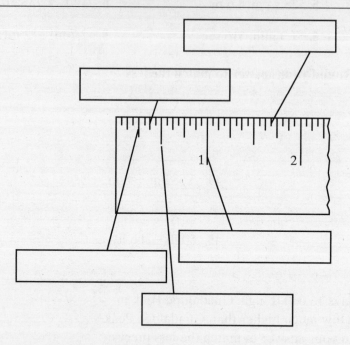

1. Examine the ruler shown above. Which marks show inches? Half inches? Quarter inches? Eighth inches? Sixteenth inches? Label each type of mark on the diagram.

2. Measure the length of your pencil to the nearest quarter inch, to the nearest eighth inch, and to the nearest sixteenth inch. Record your answers.

   a. Length of pencil to the nearest quarter inch: _____

   b. Length of pencil to the nearest eighth inch: _____

   c. Length of pencil to the nearest sixteenth inch: _____

3. Which measurement is most precise? Which is least precise? Explain.

   _____

4. If you were building a picture frame, which degree of precision would you use to measure your materials? Why?

   _____

   _____

Activity Lab

Reteaching 3-7

The precision of a measurement refers to its degree of exactness. The smaller the unit of measure, the more precise the measurement. If the same unit is used in two measurements, then the measurement to the smallest decimal place is more precise.

Determine which measurement in each set is more precise.

a. 3 yd, 110 in.

Since the units of measure are different, the measurement with the smaller unit of measure is more precise. An inch is smaller than a yard, so 110 in. is more precise than 3 yd.

b. 45.12 cm, 45.2 cm

Since the units of measure are the same, the measurement with the smaller decimal place is more precise. Since 45.12 has the smaller decimal place, 45.12 cm is more precise than 45.2 cm.

Write the more precise measurement.

1. 1.6 mi, 8,448 ft

2. 8.9 km, 8.87 km

3. 2 ft, 13 in.

4. 5.64 cm, 56.2 cm

5. 4.3 yd, 2 mi

6. 17.33 mm, 17 mm

Compute. Round your answer appropriately.

7. 2.3 in. + 6.31 in.

8. 17.2 cm × 5 cm

9. 4 cm × 7.70 cm

10. 19.65 ft − 4.3 ft

11. 24 mm − 16.1 mm

12. 2.25 yd × 6 yd

Enrichment 3-7

Critical Thinking

For any measurement the **greatest possible error (GPE)** is one half the unit of measure.

For example, if the length of any object measures 5 in. to the nearest inch, the unit of measure is 1 in. The greatest possible error is one half of one inch, or $\frac{1}{2}$ in. The measurement range is $5 \pm \frac{1}{2}$, which is between $4\frac{1}{2}$ in. and $5\frac{1}{2}$ in.

If the length of an object measures 6.1 cm to the nearest 0.1 cm, the unit of measure is 0.1 cm. The greatest possible error is one half of 0.1 cm, or 0.05 cm. The measurement range is 6.1 ± 0.05 cm, which is between 6.05 cm and 6.15 cm.

For each measurement below, name the unit of measure, the greatest possible error, and the range of measurement.

	Unit of Measure	GPE	Range of Measurement
1. 19 mm	_____	_____	_____
2. 20.8 m	_____	_____	_____
3. 54.75 m	_____	_____	_____
4. 25 in.	_____	_____	_____
5. 30 g	_____	_____	_____
6. 54.8 mg	_____	_____	_____

7. Carlos wanted a GPE of 40.05 m for the measurements of his bookcases. How many centimeters is equal to his GPE?

_____

8. Manuela is writing the specifications for a new product. The GPE was 40.005 g. The lowest measure is 10.565 g. What is the largest measure?

_____

9. Pate mixed two liquids in his chemistry class. He measured each liquid to the nearest milliliter. What was his GPE?

_____

3E: Vocabulary Check

Study Skill Strengthen your vocabulary. Use these pages and add cues and summaries by applying the Cornell Notetaking style.

Write the definition for each word or term at the right. To check your work, fold the paper back along the dotted line to see the correct answers.

benchmark

precision

reciprocals

mean

opposites

3E: Vocabulary Check (continued)

Write the definition for each word or term at the right. To check your
work, fold the paper forward along the dotted line to see the correct
answers.

a convenient number used to
replace fractions that are less than 1

_____

the exactness of a measurement,
determined by the unit of measure

_____

two numbers whose product is 1

_____

the sum of the data divided by the
number of data items

_____

two numbers that are the same
distance from 0 on the number line,
but in opposite directions

_____

Name _____ Class _____ Date _____

3F: Vocabulary Review Puzzle   For use with the Chapter Review

Study Skill Take short breaks between assignments. You will be able to concentrate on a new assignment more easily if you take a brief "time out" before starting.

Complete the crossword puzzle using the words below. For help, use the glossary in your textbook.

improper fraction   denominator   numerator   benchmark   mode

mixed number   precision   composite   median   prime

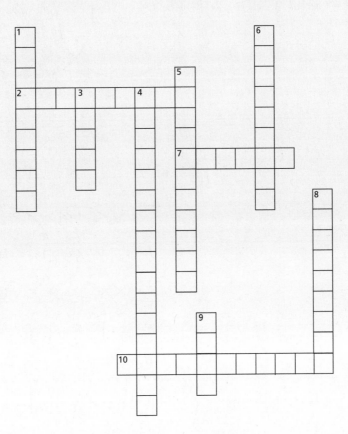

ACROSS

4. number with more than two factors
7. number that is in the middle of a data set when the values are ranked in order from least to greatest
10. sum of a whole number and a fraction

DOWN

1. refers to the degree of exactness
2. value that can be used as a reference point
3. bottom number in a fraction
5. number with exactly two factors
6. numerator is greater than or equal to the denominator
8. top number in a fraction
9. number that occurs most often in a data set

Puzzle 3-7

Precision

The letter in each circle represents a digit from 1 to 9. Where two
circles intersect and a number is given, the number is the sum of the
values of the letters in those two circles. Find the value of each letter.
Hint: There are two circles labeled A and two labeled E. The value of
a letter is the same each time it occurs in the puzzle.

Example

Possible values of x and y:
$x = 1, y = 4$; $x = 4, y = 1$;
$x = 2, y = 3$; $x = 3, y = 2$

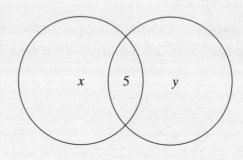

1. $A =$ _____

2. $B =$ _____

3. $C =$ _____

4. $D =$ _____

5. $E =$ _____

6. $F =$ _____

7. $G =$ _____

8. $H =$ _____

9. $I =$ _____

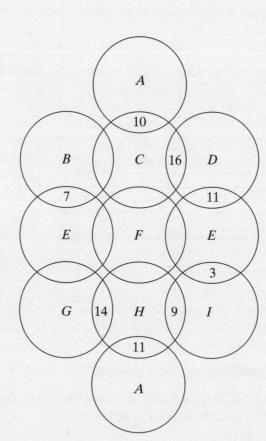

Chapter 3 Project: Toss and Turn

Write Your Own Recipe

Beginning the Chapter Project

Did you ever make pancakes? The recipe can be pretty simple—an egg, some pancake mix, milk, and maybe some oil. Or forget the mix and start from scratch! Either way, you can vary the ingredients to suit your tastes. Do you want to include some wheat germ? How about some pecans, or maybe some fruit? Bananas are always in season!

In this chapter project, you will write your own recipe for pancakes. Your final product will be a recipe that will feed everyone in your class.

Activities

Activity 1: Interviewing

Interview some people who know how to make pancakes or start with a new recipe in a cookbook. Use that information to write your own recipe. Most of the ingredients should involve fractions. Include things that you like, such as fruits or nuts.

Activity 2: Researching

With an adult present, test your recipe by making pancakes for your family. (You may ask some cooks to review your recipe if you do not have an opportunity to cook.) Revise it if necessary. Adjust quantities so you have the right amount to feed your family.

Activity 3: Calculating

Now that you have a good pancake recipe for feeding your family, adjust it to serve the number of people that are in your class. Remember to keep the number of eggs as a whole number, even though most of the other ingredients use fractions. Did you multiply fractions or divide fractions to get the class recipe? Explain.

Chapter 3 Project: Toss and Turn (continued)

Finishing the Project

Present your recipe to the class. Sell them on how tasty your pancakes are!

Be sure your work is neat and clear. Show all your calculations. Write any explanations you think are necessary.

Reflect and Revise

With an adult, make a batch of your pancakes for your family. Get their comments and change your recipe as needed.

Think about the math that you used to complete this project. What have you learned in this chapter that helped you? What advice did you get from others to create a great recipe?

Ask a classmate to review your project with you. Are your calculations correct? Did you make the correct adjustments?

Extending the Project

Find the recipe for your favorite food. Is it a casserole, a dessert, an appetizer, or soup, perhaps? Rewrite the recipe so that you will have enough to feed one serving to 50 people.

Next, select another recipe of an ethnic dish. With an adult, prepare the recipe. Serve it at a family dinner. Try to rewrite the recipe so that it serves only one person. Compare the methods you used to increase and decrease a recipe's serving size.

Go Online PHSchool.com

Visit PHSchool.com for information and links you might find helpful as you complete your project.

Chapter Project Manager

Getting Started

Read about the project. As you work on it, you will need several sheets of paper. If available, a spreadsheet program also can be used. Keep all your work for the project in a folder, along with this Project Manager.

Checklist	**Suggestions**
❑ Activity 1: interviewing	❑ Interview people who make pancakes that you like.
❑ Activity 2: researching	❑ Make pancakes for dinner so your family can enjoy them together.
❑ Activity 3: calculating	❑ Write all fractions in simplest form.
❑ Recommendations	❑ Bring in samples of your pancakes to prove how tasty they are.

Scoring Rubric

3 Your pancake recipe works. You provided step-by-step explanations of how you calculated the amount of ingredients required for your family and for your whole class. You provided evidence that either you tested your recipe by making it for your family or you interviewed someone with cooking experience to make sure your recipe made sense.

2 You wrote a pancake recipe and explained how you calculated the amounts of ingredients required for your family and the class, but either some of your calculations were inaccurate or you did not verify that your recipe made sense.

1 You wrote a pancake recipe but did not calculate the amounts of ingredients required for either your family or the whole class.

0 You did not write a pancake recipe.

Your Evaluation of Project   Evaluate your work, based on the Scoring Rubric.

Teacher's Evaluation of Project

Chapter Project Teacher Notes

About the Project

Students will have an opportunity to apply their knowledge of fractions to writing and using a recipe.

Introducing the Project

Talk about what types of pancakes people like the best. Determine what type of ingredients make sense. Ask students if they have ever prepared food from a recipe, and if so, ask them if they had to change anything in the recipe. Discuss with students how they would adapt recipes that make four servings to feed eight people. Determine how fractions are used in recipes.

Activity 1: Interviewing

Tell students that they can usually find a recipe for pancakes on a pancake-mix box. The boxes also list optional ingredients that they can add to the mix.

Activity 2: Researching

Have several cookbooks available for students to compare recipes. Urge students to have an adult present when making their pancakes.

Activity 3: Calculating

Ask students why the number of eggs must be a whole number.

Finishing the Project

You may wish to plan a project day on which students share their completed projects. Encourage students to explain their process as well as their products. Have students review their methods for conducting their interview, writing their recipes, and calculating a recipe to feed the entire class.

Name _____ Class _____ Date _____

✔ Checkpoint Quiz 1

Use with Lessons 3-1 through 3-3.

Estimate each answer.

1. $4\frac{4}{5} + 2\frac{7}{8}$

2. $8\frac{1}{8} - 2\frac{6}{7}$

3. $6\frac{3}{10} \div 1\frac{9}{10}$

4. $3\frac{1}{12} \times 1\frac{7}{9}$

_____ _____ _____ _____

5. Mr. Higgins's beard is $2\frac{5}{8}$ in. long. His barber trimmed $\frac{3}{4}$ of an inch off his beard. How long is his beard now?

_____

Find each sum or difference.

6. $\frac{2}{5} + \frac{3}{10}$

7. $\frac{2}{3} + 4\frac{2}{5}$

8. $\frac{1}{3} - \frac{2}{9}$

9. $8\frac{7}{10} - 3\frac{1}{3}$

_____ _____ _____ _____

- - - - ✂ -

Name _____ Class _____ Date _____

✔ Checkpoint Quiz 2

Use with Lessons 3-4 through 3-6.

Complete.

1. 24 in. = _____ ft   2. $4\frac{3}{4}$ lb = _____ oz   3. 5 pt = _____ qt

Find each product.

4. $\frac{2}{3} \cdot 12$

5. $4\frac{1}{6} \cdot 2\frac{3}{4}$

6. $\frac{2}{3} \cdot \frac{3}{8}$

7. $1\frac{1}{8} \cdot \frac{4}{5}$

_____ _____ _____ _____

8. Alejandro is hiking along a $6\frac{5}{8}$-mile trail. If he has walked $\frac{2}{3}$ of the trail, how many miles has he traveled?

_____

Find each quotient.

9. $\frac{3}{17} \div \frac{3}{4}$

10. $2\frac{1}{4} \div 6\frac{1}{2}$

11. $\frac{9}{24} \div \frac{1}{6}$

12. $10\frac{2}{3} \div 2\frac{1}{6}$

_____ _____ _____ _____

13. How many $4\frac{1}{2}$-inch square photographs can fit, side by side, on a $31\frac{1}{2}$-inch ledge?

_____

Chapter Test

Form A

Chapter 3

Estimate each answer to the nearest whole number.

1. $\frac{5}{9} + 2\frac{3}{4}$

2. $4\frac{2}{5} + 5\frac{5}{9}$

3. $\frac{2}{3} \cdot 119$

_____

4. $2\frac{7}{8} \cdot 4\frac{2}{3}$

5. $8\frac{1}{5} - 5\frac{6}{7}$

6. $23\frac{9}{10} \div 12\frac{1}{4}$

_____

Write each sum or difference as a fraction or mixed number in simplest form.

7. $\frac{2}{3} - \frac{5}{12}$

8. $\frac{3}{4} - \frac{1}{2}$

9. $2\frac{1}{3} + 4\frac{3}{5}$

_____

10. $7\frac{1}{4} + 5\frac{1}{2}$

11. $\frac{1}{17} + \frac{5}{17}$

12. $\frac{7}{8} - \frac{3}{5}$

_____

13. The price of a company's stock was $21\frac{3}{8}$ dollars a share. Then the price went up $4\frac{1}{2}$ dollars a share. What is the new price of the stock?

_____

Find each product or quotient.

14. $\frac{3}{8} \cdot \frac{4}{9}$

15. $\frac{3}{4} \div \frac{7}{12}$

16. $2\frac{3}{8} \cdot 4\frac{4}{5}$

_____

17. $2\frac{2}{7} \div 4$

18. $10\frac{5}{6} \div \frac{5}{9}$

19. $11\frac{9}{10} \cdot \frac{2}{17}$

_____

20. Tiles $\frac{3}{4}$ ft long are being placed alongside a vanity top that is $4\frac{1}{2}$ ft long. How many tiles are needed?

_____

21. A pattern for curtains requires $1\frac{3}{4}$ yd of fabric. How much fabric is needed to make 5 sets of these curtains?

_____

Chapter Test (continued)

Form A

Chapter 3

Complete.

22. 440 yd = _____ mi   **23.** $16\frac{1}{2}$ qt = _____ c

24. $1\frac{2}{3}$ mi = _____ ft   **25.** $3\frac{2}{5}$ t = _____ lb

Choose the more precise measurement.

26. 6 oz, 320 lb _____   **27.** 52 mi, 12 ft _____   **28.** 3 pt, 5 qt _____

29. A ride on a roller coaster takes $2\frac{1}{2}$ min. Antonio rode 6 times. For how many minutes did he ride?

_____

30. You need to use $\frac{2}{3}$ of a can of pizza sauce to make a pizza. The can contains 1 lb 2 oz of sauce. How many ounces do you need for the pizza?

_____

31. Four pumpkins weigh $7\frac{1}{8}$ lb, $11\frac{3}{4}$ lb, $6\frac{7}{8}$ lb, and $9\frac{1}{4}$ lb. What is the total weight of the pumpkins?

_____

32. To find $\frac{1}{2}$ of a circle, think of two equal parts. To find $\frac{1}{3}$ of a circle, think of three equal parts. Does thinking of five equal parts help you to find $\frac{1}{3}$ of $\frac{1}{2}$? Explain why or why not.

_____

_____

Chapter Test

Form B

Chapter 3

Estimate each answer to the nearest whole number.

1. $\frac{5}{9} + 2\frac{3}{4}$

2. $4\frac{2}{5} + 5\frac{5}{9}$

3. $2\frac{7}{8} \cdot 4\frac{2}{3}$

4. $8\frac{1}{5} - 5\frac{6}{7}$

Write each sum or difference as a fraction or mixed number in simplest form.

5. $\frac{2}{3} - \frac{5}{12}$

6. $\frac{3}{4} - \frac{1}{2}$

7. $7\frac{1}{4} + 5\frac{1}{2}$

8. $\frac{1}{17} + \frac{5}{17}$

Solve.

9. The price of a company's stock was $21\frac{3}{8}$ dollars a share. Then the price went up $4\frac{1}{2}$ dollars a share. What is the new price of the stock?

10. Tiles $\frac{3}{4}$ ft long are being placed alongside a vanity top that is $4\frac{1}{2}$ ft long. How many tiles are needed?

Find each product or quotient.

11. $\frac{3}{8} \cdot \frac{4}{9}$

12. $\frac{3}{4} \div \frac{7}{12}$

13. $2\frac{3}{8} \cdot 4\frac{4}{5}$

14. $2\frac{2}{7} \div 4$

15. $10\frac{5}{6} \div \frac{5}{9}$

16. $11\frac{9}{10} \cdot \frac{2}{17}$

Chapter Test (continued)

Form B

Chapter 3

Complete.

17. 440 yd = _____ mi

18. $16\frac{1}{2}$ qt = _____ c

19. $3\frac{2}{5}$ t = _____ lb

Choose the more precise measurement.

20. 6 oz, 320 lb

_____

21. 3 pt, 5 qt

_____

Solve.

22. A ride on a roller coaster takes $2\frac{1}{2}$ min. Antonio rode 6 times. For how many minutes did he ride?

_____

_____

23. You need to use $\frac{2}{3}$ of a can of pizza sauce to make a pizza. The can contains 1 lb 2 oz of sauce. How many ounces do you need for the pizza?

_____

_____

24. Four pumpkins weigh $7\frac{1}{8}$ lb, $11\frac{3}{4}$ lb, $6\frac{7}{8}$ lb, and $9\frac{1}{4}$ lb. What is the total weight of the pumpkins?

_____

_____

Alternative Assessment

Form C

Chapter 3

MARATHON TRAINING

To train for the Centerville Marathon, Keith drew a map of his
favorite practice routes.

Running Times

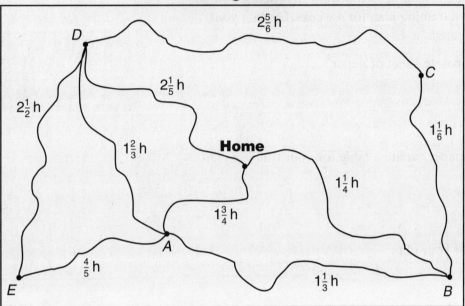

Show all your work on a separate sheet of paper.

1. Keith plans to run from Home to point *B*, then to point *A*, then
   back Home. How long will this route take? If he runs this route
   once each day from Monday to Friday, what is the total running
   time?

2. Yesterday Keith ran for nearly 6 hours. If he started at point *E*,
   name two possible routes he could have taken. Explain your
   thinking.

3. Keith's trainer suggested that he run from Home to point *D,* then
   to point *C,* then to point *B,* and then to Home. How long is the
   route in *hours?* How long is the route in *minutes?*

4. Design a route so that Keith runs each path once. How long will
   this route take?

5. If Keith runs a mile in $\frac{1}{6}$ hour, how far will he run from point *C* to
   point *D*? Explain your answer.

Alternative Assessment (continued)　　　Form C

Chapter 3

Excursion

Imagine you want to train for a marathon in your community. (A marathon usually covers about 26 miles.) Create a community map and design possible running routes. Estimate and record the time it will take to run each route. Then suppose you want to practice about 3 hours each day. Develop a training plan for 4 weeks. Explain your plan using the map you created.

a. Draw your map on a separate sheet of paper.

b. On a separate sheet of paper, create a table for your training plan.

c. Write an explanation for your plan.

Cumulative Review

Chapter 1–3

Multiple choice. Choose the letter of the best answer.

1. You buy a sandwich for $2.89, a drink for $.95, and an apple for $.75. Estimate to the nearest dollar how much change you will get back from a ten-dollar bill.

   A. about $4

   B. about $5

   C. about $6

   D. about $7

2. When multiplying 0.23×1.492, how many decimal places does the answer have?

   F. 2 places   **G.** 3 places

   H. 4 places   **J.** 5 places

3. Kate divided 0.54 by 0.9 and got 6 for the answer. This answer is not correct. Which answer below is correct?

   A. 60   **B.** 0.6

   C. 0.06   **D.** 0.006

4. Which of the following is equivalent to $5(52) + 27 \div 9$?

   F. $5(50 + 2) + 3$

   G. $5(50 - 2) + 3$

   H. $(260 + 27) \div 9$

   J. $260 \div 3$

5. Which is greatest, $4^3, 8^2, 3^4,$ or 2^6?

   A. 4^3 **B.** 8^2

   C. 3^4 **D.** 2^6

6. What is the units digit when you evaluate 37×49?

   F. 1   **G.** 3

   H. 7   **J.** 9

7. What is the value of $5 + 3 \times 4$?

   A. 12   **B.** 17

   C. 19   **D.** 32

8. This data represents the number of magazines sold at a newstand each day for the last five days.

   153   217   182   150   298

   What is the mean?

   F. 145   **G.** 153

   H. 182   **J.** 200

9. Harold entered the elevator on the tenth floor. He rode 26 floors up, 32 floors down, 28 floors up, then 17 floors down. On which floor is he now?

   A. floor 5   **B.** floor 15

   C. floor 40   **D.** floor 113

10. Which statement is true?

    F. $-27 > -20$

    G. $-15 > 15$

    H. $-6 > -9$

    J. $0 > 17$

11. Enise wants to be in school at 8:00 A.M. It takes her $\frac{1}{2}$ h to get dressed, $\frac{1}{3}$ h to fix and eat breakfast, and 20 min to bike to school. What time should she get up?

    A. 6:50 A.M.   **B.** 6:30 A.M.

    C. 6:00 A.M.   **D.** 7:30 A.M.

12. How many feet are in 12 yd 2 ft?

    A. $12\frac{2}{3}$ ft   **B.** 26 ft

    C. 36 ft   **D.** 38 ft

Cumulative Review (continued)

Chapter 1–3

13. Which is a pair of equivalent fractions?

F. $\frac{24}{36}, \frac{2}{3}$

G. $\frac{8}{9}, \frac{40}{50}$

H. $\frac{3}{4}, \frac{33}{34}$

J. $\frac{15}{18}, \frac{12}{15}$

14. Which is the greatest common factor, or GCF, of 36 and 24?

A. 3   B. 6

C. 9   D. 12

15. What is the prime factorization of 156?

F. $2 \times 3 \times 39$

G. $2 \times 2 \times 3 \times 13$

H. $3 \times 4 \times 13$

J. $2 \times 6 \times 13$

16. Which number is prime?

A. 67   B. 123

C. 456   D. 785

17. Which number is equivalent to $\frac{56}{9}$?

F. $\frac{18}{8}$ G. $6\frac{2}{3}$

H. $\frac{9}{56}$ J. $6\frac{2}{9}$

18. Which list is in order from greatest to least?

A. $\frac{3}{8}, \frac{1}{4}, \frac{4}{5}$

B. $2\frac{1}{2}, 2\frac{5}{6}, 2\frac{9}{10}$

C. $\frac{7}{6}, \frac{1}{2}, \frac{1}{3}$

D. $\frac{5}{8}, \frac{5}{6}, \frac{5}{9}$

19. Which decimal is closest to $\frac{7}{19}$?

F. 0.36   G. 0.372

H. 0.37   J. 0.368

20. Estimate the sum $7\frac{3}{4} + 3\frac{9}{10} + 1\frac{1}{5}$ by rounding to the nearest whole number.

A. 14   B. 13

C. 12   D. 11

21. This year, about $\frac{3}{4}$ of the seventh-grade students went on a field trip. If there are 242 students in the seventh grade, about how many students went on the field trip?

F. 312 students

G. 240 students

H. 200 students

J. 180 students

22. One serving of nuts is $\frac{3}{4}$ oz. How many servings are in a $13\frac{1}{2}$-oz can?

A. 20 servings

B. 19 servings

C. 18 servings

D. 16 servings

Short Response

23. Write 3 fractions that are equivalent to $\frac{3}{7}$.

_____

_____

_____

Practice 4-1

Evaluating and Writing Algebraic Expressions

Evaluate each expression using the values $m = 7$, $r = 8$, and $t = 2$.

1. $5m - 6$

2. $4m + t$

3. $r \div t$

4. $m \times t$

5. $5t + 2m$

6. $r \times m$

7. $3m - 5t$

8. $(m \times r) \div t$

9. mrt

10. Write an algebraic expression for the nth term of the table below.

A	0	1	2	3	4	5	n
B	3	5	7	9	11	13	?

Write a word phrase for each algebraic expression.

11. $n + 16$

12. $3.2n$

13. $25.6 - n$

14. $n \div 24$

15. $\frac{45}{n}$

16. $15.4 - n$

Write an algebraic expression for each word phrase.

17. 12 more than m machines

18. six times the daily amount of fiber f in your diet

19. your aunt's age a minus 25

20. the total number of seashells s divided by 10

21. You and four friends plan a surprise party. Each of you contributes the same amount of money m for food.

a. Write an algebraic expression for the total amount of money contributed for food.

b. Evaluate your expression for $m = \$5.25$.

4-1 • Guided Problem Solving

GPS **Student Page 172, Exercise 38:**

Estimation This section of a page from a telephone directory shows a column with 11 names in 1 inch. Each page has four 10-inch columns. Write an algebraic expression for the approximate number of names in p pages of the directory.

6-4462	**Daalling V** 8 Everett All...........
2-3302	.... K ... . y R..........
4-1775	**Dabady V** 94 Burns ...e All......
2-0014	**Dabagh L** 13 Lanca ter R.......
6-3356	**Dabagh W** Dr 521 W eston All..
4-7322	**Dabar G** 98 River A ....
6-1530	**Dabarera F** 34 Ros land All...
2-2279	**Dabas M** 17 Rivers e R..........
4-9978	**D'Abate D** 86 Moss ill Rd All..
2-6745	**D'Abate G** 111 Sou Central R ...
4-5456	**Dabbous H** 670 Wa ren Dr All..
6-3064	**Dabbraccio F** 151 entury All..
6-2257	**Dabby D** 542 Waln All..........
2-9987	.... Green R....
6-5643	**Dabcovich M** 72 Main All.........

Understand

1. What are you being asked to do?

   _____

2. What is an algebraic expression?

   _____

   _____

3. What does p represent?

   _____

   _____

Plan and Carry Out

4. How many names are in 1 in. of one column? _____

5. How many names are in one 10-in. column? _____

6. How many names are in four 10-in. columns? _____

7. How many names are listed on one page? _____

8. How many names are listed on p pages? _____

9. Write an algebraic expression for the approximate number of names in p pages of the directory. _____

Check

10. Substitute $p = 1, 2,$ and 3 in the expression and solve. Does your expression provide reasonable values?

   _____

Solve Another Problem

11. The yearbook committee can fit 1 student picture in one inch of a row. If there are eight 6-inch rows on each page, write an expression for the approximate number of pictures that can fit on p pages.

   _____

Practice 4-1

Evaluating and Writing Algebraic Expressions

Evaluate each expression using the values $m = 7$, $r = 8$, and $t = 2$.

1. $5m - 6$

2. $4m + t$

3. $r \div t$

_____

4. $m \times t$

5. $5t + 2m$

6. $r \times m$

_____

7. Write an algebraic expression for the nth term of the table below.

A	0	1	2	3	4	5	n
B	3	5	7	9	11	13	?

_____

Write a word phrase for each algebraic expression.

8. $n + 16$

9. $3.2n$

_____

10. $n \div 24$

11. $\frac{45}{n}$

_____

Write an algebraic expression for each word phrase.

12. 12 more than m machines

13. six times the daily amount of fiber f in your diet

_____

14. You and four friends plan a surprise party. Each of you contributes the same amount of money m for food.

a. Write an algebraic expression for the total amount of money contributed for food.

_____

b. Evaluate your expression for $m = \$5.25$.

_____

Activity Lab 4-1

Evaluating and Writing Algebraic Expressions

Circle the equation or equations that give the solution.

1. $y = 5$

$y - 6 = 11$ $\qquad\qquad$ $y + 15 = 20$ $\qquad\qquad$ $6 + y = 60$

2. $n = 12$

$4n = 48$ $\qquad\qquad$ $n - 12 = 1$ $\qquad\qquad$ $12 \div n = 1$

3. $t = 10$

$5 + t = 10$ $\qquad\qquad$ $t - 10 = 10$ $\qquad\qquad$ $t \times 6 = 60$

4. $p = \frac{5}{12}$

$p + \frac{7}{12} = 1$ $\qquad\qquad$ $p - \frac{3}{12} = \frac{8}{12}$ $\qquad\qquad$ $p - \frac{4}{12} = \frac{1}{12}$

5. $r = \frac{1}{8}$

$r + \frac{1}{8} = \frac{1}{4}$ $\qquad\qquad$ $r - \frac{3}{8} = \frac{1}{4}$ $\qquad\qquad$ $\frac{5}{8} + r = \frac{7}{8}$

Circle the equation or equations that are satisfied by the given value of s.

6. $s = 4$ $\qquad$ $s - 2 = 3$ $\qquad\qquad$ $10 - s = 6$ $\qquad\qquad$ $3s = 9$

7. $s = 10$ $\qquad$ $s - 2 = 8$ $\qquad\qquad$ $4 \times s = 36$ $\qquad\qquad$ $s + 10 = 22$

8. $s = \frac{7}{10}$ $\qquad$ $s + \frac{4}{10} = 1$ $\qquad\qquad$ $s - \frac{2}{10} = \frac{1}{2}$ $\qquad\qquad$ $2 - s = 1\frac{1}{10}$

Reteaching 4-1

Evaluating and Writing Algebraic Expressions

To evaluate an *expression*, substitute a value for the *variable* and compute.

Evaluate $5y - 8$ for $y = 7$.
$$5y - 8$$
$5 \times 7 - 8$ ← **Substitute y with 7.**
$35 - 8 = 27$ ← **Compute.**

You can use key words to write a word phrase for an algebraic expression.

$a + 5$	→	a plus 5
	or	a increased by 5
$2n$	→	the product of 2 and n
	or	2 times n

Evaluate each expression using the values $m = 3$ and $x = 8$.

1. $4m + 9$
Substitute m: $4 \times$ _____ $+ 9$

Compute: _____ $+ 9 =$ _____

2. $4x - 7$
Substitute x: $4 \times$ _____ $- 7$

Compute: _____ $- 7 =$ _____

3. $5x + x$
Substitute x: $5 \times$ _____ $+$ _____

Compute: _____ $+$ _____ $=$ _____

4. $x + 2m$
Substitute x and m: _____ $+ 2 \times$ _____

Compute: _____ $+$ _____ $=$ _____

Evaluate each expression using the values $y = 4$, $z = 8$, and $p = 10$.

5. $3y + 6 =$ _____

6. $4z - 2 =$ _____

7. $p + 2p =$ _____

8. $3z \times z =$ _____

Write a word phrase for each algebraic expression.

9. $9 + x$

_____

10. $6x$

_____

11. $x - 8$

_____

12. $\frac{x}{5}$

_____

Write an algebraic expression for each word phrase.

13. x newspapers plus 10

_____

14. 4 less than x teabags

_____

15. 3 more than x envelopes

_____

16. 6 times x school buses

_____

Course 2 Lesson 4-1

Enrichment 4-1

Evaluating and Writing Algebraic Expressions

Critical Thinking

This spring the 7th graders will be going on a class trip to Space Camp. In order to raise money for their trip, the 7th grade students are selling calendars for $5 each. The students will make a profit of $2 per calendar.

Rob sells twice as many calendars as Kayla. Michael sells 6 fewer than Rob. Sherrill sells half as many as Kayla. Troy sells eight more than Rob.

1. Let *c* represent the number of calendars that Kayla sells. Write an expression that shows how many calendars each student sells.

   a. Rob _____ **b.** Michael _____

   c. Sherrill _____ **d.** Troy _____

2. Write the expression for the total number of calendars sold.

   _____

Suppose Kayla sold 100 calendars.

3. How many calendars did each of these students sell?

   a. Rob _____ **b.** Michael _____

   c. Sherrill _____ **d.** Troy _____

4. How many calendars were sold in all?

   _____

5. How much money did the students earn?

   _____

Suppose Rob sold 40 calendars.

6. How many calendars did each of these students sell?

   a. Kayla _____ **b.** Michael _____

   c. Sherrill _____ **d.** Troy _____

7. How many calendars were sold in all?

   _____

8. How much money did the students earn?

   _____

4A Graphic Organizer

Study Skill Take notes when your teacher presents new material in class and when you read the lesson yourself. Organize these notes as a way to study, reviewing them as you go.

Write your answers.

1. What is the chapter title? _____

2. How many lessons are there in this chapter? _____

3. What is the topic of the Test-Taking Strategies page? _____

4. Complete the graphic organizer below as you work through the chapter.
   - In the center, write the title of the chapter.
   - When you begin a lesson, write the lesson name in a rectangle.
   - When you complete a lesson, write a skill or key concept in a circle linked to that lesson block.
   - When you complete the chapter, use this graphic organizer to help you review.

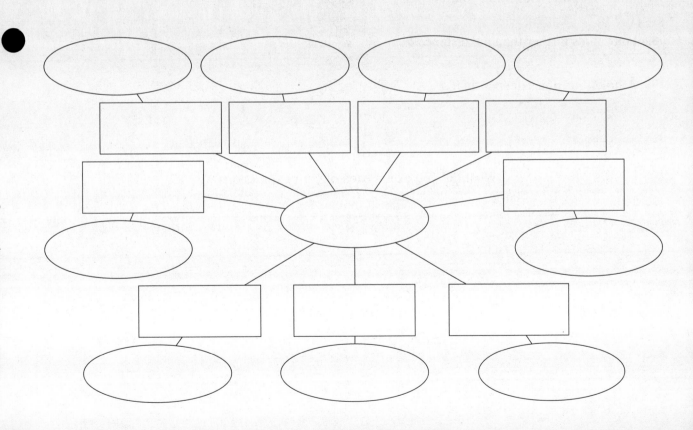

Puzzle 4-1

Evaluating and Writing Algebraic Expressions

Write an algebraic expression to reflect each description. Write the
letter of the correct answer above the exercise number at the bottom
of the page.

1. Seven more than b bananas   **r.** $q - 5$

2. Four times c cookies   **a.** $2a - 3$

3. Five less than your quiz score q **a.** $c - 4$

4. Two more than three times your age a **l.** $4d$

5. Four less than c cups   **a.** $b + 7$

6. Five times the number of questions q **i.** $d + 4$

7. Three less than two times your age a **b.** $3a + 2$

8. Four miles farther than the distance d **v.** $4c$

9. A hole four times deeper than d **e.** $5q$

What did you use in each of your expressions?

___ ___ ___ ___ ___ ___ ___ ___ ___
5   2   1   3   8   7   4   9   6

Practice 4-2

Using Number Sense to Solve Equations

Identify a solution for each equation from the given set of numbers.

1. $30p = 900$; 3, 20, 30, or 60

2. $\frac{h}{9} = 11$; 3, 30, 72, or 99

_____

_____

3. $t + 32.4 = 62$; 29.6, 31.4, or 18.6

4. $r - 17 = 40$; 23, 57 or 63

_____

_____

Solve each equation using mental math.

5. $5t = 25$

6. $8w = 64$

7. $p + 5 = 12$

_____

_____

_____

8. $a + 2 = 15$

9. $\frac{h}{6} = 4$

10. $\frac{g}{8} = 16$

_____

_____

_____

11. $y - 11 = 28$

12. $d - 4 = 12$

13. $w - 10 = 15$

_____

_____

_____

14. $18 - t = 14$

15. $21 + y = 31.64$

16. $18.43 + x = 123.4$

_____

_____

_____

17. The seventh-grade class has been collecting aluminum cans for recycling. The class has collected 210 cans. Their goal is to collect 520 cans. Write an equation and estimate the number of aluminum cans needed to reach their goal.

_____

18. A seamstress bought some bolts of fabric at $25.30 each. She spent a total of $227.70. Write an equation and estimate the number of bolts of fabric that she purchased.

_____

19. For your party you purchased balloons for $.79 each. You spent a total of $11.85. Write an equation and estimate the number of balloons purchased.

_____

4-2 • Guided Problem Solving

GPS Student Page 176, Exercise 25:

An elevator has a maximum lift of 2,000 lb. You are moving
55-lb boxes of books. Write an equation and estimate how many boxes
you can safely place on the elevator.

Understand

1. Circle the information you will need to solve.

2. What are you being asked to do?

   _____

   _____

3. What will your variable represent?

   _____

   _____

Plan and Carry Out

4. How much weight does the elevator hold? _____

5. How much does each box weigh? _____

6. Write an equation to find how many boxes the elevator can hold.

   _____

7. Estimate how many boxes the elevator
   can safely hold at one time.   _____

Check

8. Determine if your answer to Step 7 times 55 lb each is less than
   2,000.

   _____

   _____

Solve Another Problem

9. Laurie can type 65 words per minute. She has to write a 5,000-word
   paper for her Shakespeare class. Write an equation to calculate how
   long it will take Laurie to type her paper. Estimate the answer.

   _____

   _____

Name _____ Class _____ Date _____

Practice 4-2

Using Number Sense to Solve Equations

Identify a solution for each equation from the given set of numbers.

1. $30p = 900$; 3, 30, or 60

_____

2. $\frac{h}{9} = 11$; 3, 72, or 99

_____

Solve each equation using mental math.

3. $5t = 25$

_____

4. $8w = 64$

_____

5. $p + 5 = 12$

_____

6. $a + 2 = 15$

_____

7. $\frac{h}{6} = 4$

_____

8. $\frac{g}{8} = 16$

_____

9. $y - 11 = 28$

_____

10. $d - 4 = 12$

_____

11. $w - 10 = 15$

_____

12. The seventh-grade class has been collecting aluminum cans for recycling. The class has collected 210 cans. Their goal is to collect 520 cans. Write an equation and estimate the number of aluminum cans needed to reach their goal.

_____

_____

13. A seamstress bought some bolts of fabric at $25.30 each. She spent a total of $227.70. Write an equation and estimate the number of bolts of fabric that she purchased.

_____

_____

14. For your party you purchased balloons for $.79 each. You spent a total of $11.85. Write an equation and estimate the number of balloons purchased.

_____

_____

Activity Lab 4-2

Using Number Sense to Solve Equations

> **Materials needed:** index cards

Work in pairs. Copy the equations below onto index cards, one equation per card. Pass out the cards so that each partner gets the same number of cards. You must solve for your card's variable each time. The winner of each round has the card with the highest-value variable and wins the cards involved in that round. The winner of each game is the player who wins the entire deck or who has the most cards when time is called.

$n + 4 = 8$	$5n = 20$
$7 + n = 12$	$3n = 15$
$n + 12 = 18$	$6n = 36$
$n + 7 = 14$	$7n = 42$
$4 + n = 12$	$4n = 28$
$7 - n = 3$	$7n = 56$
$14 - n = 9$	$n \div 4 = 8$
$16 - 9 = n$	$n \div 8 = 9$
$19 - n = 11$	$n \div 9 = 7$

Name _____ Class _____ Date _____

Reteaching 4-2

Using Number Sense to Solve Equations

One way to solve some equations is to use mental math.

Solve $t + 9 = 13$.	Solve $y - 7 = 15$.
Ask yourself, what number added to 9 is 13?	Ask yourself, what number minus 7 is 15?
$4 + 9 = 13$ So $t = 4$.	$22 - 7 = 15$ So $y = 22$.
Solve $\frac{a}{3} = 9$	Solve $3y = 15$.
Ask yourself, what number divided by 3 equals 9?	Ask yourself, what number multiplied by 3 is 15?
$\frac{27}{9} = 3$ So $a = 27$.	$3 \cdot 5 = 15$ So $y = 5$.

Solve each equation using mental math.

1. $4t = 24$

_____

2. $p + 8 = 16$

_____

3. $\frac{h}{3} = 7$

_____

4. $\frac{g}{4} = 7$

_____

5. $y - 7 = 15$

_____

6. $d - 6 = 14$

_____

Solve each equation using mental math or estimation.

7. $d + 7 = 21$

_____

8. $c - 21 = 4$

_____

9. $a + 9 = 50$

_____

10. $q - 43.94 = 400.12$

_____

11. $3 + b = -6$

_____

12. $91 + r = 100$

_____

Course 2 Lesson 4-2

Enrichment 4-2

Using Number Sense to Solve Equations

Critical Thinking

Use number sense—estimation, mental math, rounding—to complete each puzzle.

1. Solve each equation. Then write your answers in the circles so that the differences between any two circles connected by a straight line are the same.

   a. $w + 5 = 7.4$ _____

   b. $e - 2 = 2.5$ _____

   c. $12 + r = 22.5$ _____

   d. $m + 5 = 15$ _____

   e. $14 - y = 5.6$ _____

   f. $t - 6 = 4.2$ _____

   g. $13 - q = 0.9$ _____

   h. $7 + c = 15.1$ _____

2. Solve each equation. Then write your answers in the circles so that the sums of any two circles connected by a straight line are the same.

   a. $\frac{s}{2} = 2$ _____

   b. $6d = 36$ _____

   c. $6a = 3$ _____

   d. $\frac{30}{z} = 10$ _____

   e. $\frac{25}{v} = 5$ _____

   f. $2n = 13$ _____

   g. $\frac{76}{g} = 38$ _____

   h. $4u = 4$ _____

Name _____ Class _____ Date _____

4B: Reading Comprehension

Study Skill As you learn more vocabulary, more concepts are within your reach.

Read the paragraph below and answer the questions that follow.

> November is American Indian and Alaska Native Heritage Month. According to the U.S. Census Bureau, more than 4 million people in the United States identified themselves as American Indian or Alaska native in 2004. That is 1.5% of the total U.S. population. About 687,000 people with this heritage live in California, giving it the largest American Indian and Alaska native population of any state. However, $\frac{1}{5}$ of the Alaska population is American Indian or Alaska native. This is a much greater fraction than in California.

1. What is the subject of this paragraph?

   _____

2. What is the largest number in the paragraph?

   _____

3. What is the smallest number?

   _____

4. Which state has the greatest number of people with American Indian and Alaska native ancestry?

   _____

5. The population of Alaska is about 665,000. How many Alaskans have American Indian or Alaska native heritage?

   _____

6. Explain how California can have the greatest population but not the largest fraction of people with this ancestry.

   _____

7. **High-Use Academic Words** In Exercise 6, what does the word *explain* mean?

   a. to put or use in place of   b. to give facts and details that
      something else   make an idea easier
                                        to understand

Puzzle 4-2

Using Number Sense to Solve Equations

Each of the equations listed on the left can be solved using one of the operations listed on the right. For each exercise, choose the appropriate operation, then solve using mental math.

Equations	**Operations**
1. $x - 3 = 12$	Subtract 3 from each side
2. $5 + m = 8$	Add 52 to each side
3. $k + 12 = 2$	Subtract 5 from each side
4. $t + 7 = 0$	Add 3 to each side
5. $3 + d = -5$	Subtract 12 from each side
6. $y - 52 = 73$	Subtract 7 from each side
7. $w - 17 = 8$	Subtract 14 from each side
8. $q + 14 = 117$	Add 17 to each side

Practice 4-3

Solving Equations by Adding or Subtracting

Solve each equation. Check your answer.

1. $n + 2 = 5$

2. $x - 1 = -3$

3. $7 = a + 2$

4. $p + 2 = -6$

_____

_____

_____

_____

5. $-9 = -4 + a$

6. $-2 = c + 2$

7. $x - (-3) = 7$

8. $a + (-6) = 5$

_____

_____

_____

_____

9. $16 + s = 6$

10. $p + (-2) = 19$

11. $r - 7 = -13$

12. $25 = a - (-3)$

_____

_____

_____

_____

Use a calculator, paper and pencil, or mental math. Solve each equation.

13. $t + 43 = 28$

14. $-19 = r + 6$

15. $25 = r + 7$

16. $13 = 24 + c$

_____

_____

_____

_____

17. $d - 19 = -46$

18. $b + 27 = -18$

19. $46 = f - 19$

20. $z - 74 = -19$

_____

_____

_____

_____

21. The odometer on your family car reads 20,186.7 after going 62.3 miles. Write and solve an equation to determine how many miles were on the odometer before going 62.3 miles.

_____

22. Michael bought a $25.00 gift for a friend. After he bought the gift, Michael had $176.89. Write and solve an equation to calculate how much money Michael had before he bought the gift.

_____

23. This spring it rained a total of 11.5 inches. This was 3 inches less than last spring. Write and solve an equation to find the amount of rain last season.

_____

4-3 • Guided Problem Solving

GPS **Student Page 183, Exercise 24:**

Biology A student collects 12 ladybugs for a science project. This is 9 fewer than the number of ladybugs the student collected yesterday. Write and solve an equation to find the number of ladybugs the student collected yesterday.

Understand

1. Circle the information you will need to solve.

2. What are you being asked to do?

   _____

   _____

3. What will your variable represent?

   _____

   _____

Plan and Carry Out

4. How many ladybugs did the student
   collect today?   _____

5. Determine a variable for the number
   of ladybugs the student collected yesterday. _____

6. Write an expression for the phrase;
   *9 fewer than the number of ladybugs
   the student collected yesterday.*   _____

7. Write an equation that compares the answer
   to step 4 with the answer to Step 6.   _____

8. Solve the equation written in Step 7. _____

9. How many ladybugs did the student
   collect yesterday?   _____

Check

10. Substitute the answer to Step 9 into the equation for the variable
    and solve.

    _____

    _____

Solve Another Problem

11. Jason is 72 in. tall. If Kenny is 15 in. shorter than Jason, write and
    solve an equation for the height of Kenny.

    _____

    _____

Practice 4-3

Solving Equations by Adding or Subtracting

Solve each equation. Check your answer.

1. $n + 2 = 5$

2. $x - 1 = -3$

3. $7 = a + 2$

4. $-9 = -4 + a$

5. $-2 = c + 2$

6. $x - (-3) = 7$

7. $16 + s = 6$

8. $p + (-2) = 19$

9. $r - 7 = -13$

Use a calculator, paper and pencil, or mental math. Solve each equation.

10. $t + 43 = 28$

11. $-19 = r + 6$

12. $25 = r + 7$

13. $d - 19 = -46$

14. $b + 27 = -18$

15. $46 = f - 19$

16. The odometer on your family car reads 20,186.7 after going 62.3 miles. Write and solve an equation to determine how many miles were on the odometer before going 62.3 miles.

_____

17. Michael bought a $25.00 gift for a friend. After he bought the gift, Michael had $176.89. Write and solve an equation to calculate how much money Michael had before he bought the gift.

_____

18. This spring it rained a total of 11.5 inches. This was 3 inches less than last spring. Write and solve an equation to find the amount of rain last season.

_____

Activity Lab 4-3
••• **Solving Equations by Adding or Subtracting**

Each problem below is followed by two equations. Circle the equation that fits the situation. Then solve it.

1. Claudia had $300 left in her savings account after she withdrew $48 to buy running shoes. How much did Claudia have in her savings account before she purchased the shoes?

   $x - 48 = 300$ $x + 48 = 300$

   _____

   _____

2. Casey's language arts teacher requires 6 book reports the first semester. Casey has 4 more reports to complete. How many book reports has Casey already finished?

   $x - 4 = 6$ $x + 4 = 6$

   _____

   _____

3. Terri had a total of 12 tennis balls after she bought a can of 3 balls. How many tennis balls did she have before buying the new ones?

   $x - 3 = 12$ $x + 3 = 12$

   _____

   _____

4. Tait finds lost golf balls and sells them. After selling 13, she had 22 balls left. How many golf balls did Tait have before selling the 13?

   $x - 13 = 22$ $x + 13 = 22$

   _____

   _____

5. When Corry successfully launched his model rocket twice on Saturday, he reached his goal of 5 successful launches with one rocket. How many times had Corry launched that rocket successfully before Saturday?

   $x - 2 = 5$ $x + 2 = 5$

   _____

   _____

6. Mr. Young displayed 16 of the science fair projects in the library. He put the rest of the projects in the auditorium. Altogether there were 36 projects. How many were in the auditiorium?

   $x - 16 = 36$ $x + 16 = 36$

   _____

   _____

Name _____ Class _____ Date _____

Reteaching 4-3

Solving Equations by Adding or Subtracting

Follow these steps to solve equations.

Solve: $n + (-2) = 11$ Solve: $n - 6 = -36$

① Use the inverse
operation on both sides $n + (-2) - (-2) = 11 - (-2)$ $n - 6 + 6 = -36 + 6$
of the equation.

② Simplify. $n = 13$ $n = -30$

③ Check. $n + (-2) = 11$ $n - 6 = -36$
$13 + (-2) \stackrel{?}{=} 11$ $-30 - 6 \stackrel{?}{=} -36$
$11 = 11$ ✔ $-36 = -36$ ✔

Solve each equation. Check each answer.

1. $n + 6 = 8$

$n + 6 - 6 = 8 - $ _____

$n = $ _____

2. $n - 3 = 20$

$n - 3 + $ _____ $ = 20 + 3$

$n = $ _____

3. $n - (-3) = -1$

$n - (-3) + $ _____ $ = -1 + $ _____

$n = $ _____

4. $-2 = n + 5$

$-2 - $ _____ $ = n + 5 - $ _____

_____ $ = n$

5. $n - (-4) = -2$

$n - (-4) + $ _____ $ = -2 + $ _____

$n = $ _____

6. $n - 16 = -23$

$n - 16 + $ _____ $ = -23 + $ _____

$n = $ _____

Use a calculator, pencil and paper, or mental math. Solve each equation.

7. $n + 1 = 17$

_____

8. $n - (-6) = 7$

_____

9. $n - 8 = -12$

_____

10. $61 = n + 29$

_____

11. $n + 84 = 131$

_____

12. $-13 = n + 9$

_____

13. In track practice, Jesse ran a mile in 7 minutes. His mile time was
$2\frac{1}{2}$ minutes faster than Michael's time. Write and solve an
equation to calculate Michael's mile time.

_____

Enrichment 4-3

Solving Equations by Adding or Subtracting

Decision Making

Carlos decided to join a hockey league. The annual fee is $500 and can be paid in 4 installments. He chooses to take beginner hockey lessons which cost $10 per week.

He has these choices of equipment that he can buy from each of the following stores. The more expensive equipment is usually chosen by the more experienced skaters.

Sam's Pro Shop: skates, $395; stick, $65; helmet, $105; pads, $214; gloves, $135
Don's Sports: skates, $120; stick, $60; helmet, $85; pads, $85: gloves, $80
Economy Sports: skates, $65; stick, $10; helmet, $70; pads, $60; gloves, $20
Hockey Shop: skates, $100; stick, $65; helmet, $90; pads, $80; gloves, $45

He has saved $500 and can save an additional $20 each week.

1. From which shops can Carlos buy a complete package of equipment with the money he now has?

   _____

2. From which shops can Carlos buy a complete package of equipment and have enough money left to pay the first installment for the league fee and the first week of hockey lessons? Explain.

   _____

   _____

   _____

3. Hockey season begins in 7 months. If Carlos chooses to buy all his equipment at Sam's Pro Shop, will he be able to afford the first installment for the league fee and the first installment for lessons? Explain.

   _____

   _____

4. From which shop would you advise Carlos to purchase his equipment? Explain.

   _____

   _____

   _____

4C: Reading/Writing Math Symbols   **For use after Lesson 4-3**

Study Skill Mathematics builds on itself, so build a strong foundation.

Match each expression with its word form.

1. $x - 3$

2. $4m$

3. $\frac{7}{x}$

4. $m + 6$

5. $m \div 5$

   A. six more than a number

   B. the quotient of a number and five

   C. a number decreased by three

   D. seven divided by a number

   E. four multiplied by a number

Write a mathematical expression or equation for each word description.

6. nine less than the product of eleven and x

_____

7. a number plus four equals thirteen

_____

8. the quotient of x and 4

_____

9. the absolute value of a number

_____

Write two different word phrases for each of the following expressions.

10. $x - 10$

_____

_____

11. $5m$

_____

_____

12. $3^2 + m$

_____

_____

Puzzle 4-3   Solving Equations by Adding or Subtracting

Solve each equation in the diagram below, and then draw straight
lines between equations with the same solution. When you are done,
you should see a mathematical expression. What is it?

$x + 3 = 5$ $20 + x = 17$

         $27 - x = 25$

$x + 13 = 7$ $56 + x = 44$

$-20 + x = -15$ $35 - x = 24$

            $x + 4 = 15$

$x + (-2) = 16$

$x + 7 = 12$

$-7 + x = -10$ $17 + x = 35$

$6 + x = 0$ $-x + 3 = 15$

Practice 4-4

Solving Equations by Multiplying or Dividing

Use a calculator, paper and pencil, or mental math. Solve each equation.

1. $9n = 126$

2. $\frac{d}{3} = -81$

3. $-2t = 56$

4. $\frac{k}{-3} = 6$

_____ _____ _____ _____

5. $-18 = \frac{y}{-2}$

6. $\frac{y}{16} = 3$

7. $-56 = 8r$

8. $9w = -63$

_____ _____ _____ _____

9. $-3v = -48$

10. $13 = \frac{x}{-4}$

11. $28 = -4a$

12. $\frac{t}{-42} = 3$

_____ _____ _____ _____

13. $24 = \frac{f}{-4}$

14. $15 = -3j$

15. $102k = 408$

16. $\frac{b}{-96} = -3$

_____ _____ _____ _____

Solve and check each equation.

17. $\frac{x}{19} = -21$

18. $\frac{x}{-22} = -63$

19. $-41x = 164$

_____ _____ _____

20. $\frac{x}{91} = -98$

21. $452 = -4x$

22. $50x = -2,500$

_____ _____ _____

Write and solve an equation to represent each situation.

23. One of the largest flowers, the Rafflesia, weighs about 15 lb. How many Rafflesia flowers can be placed in a container that can hold a maximum of 240 lb?

_____

24. "Heavy water" is a name given to a compound used in some nuclear reactors. Heavy water costs about $1,500 per gallon. If a nuclear plant spent $10,500 on heavy water, how many gallons of heavy water were bought?

_____

4-4 • Guided Problem Solving

GPS **Student Page 190, Exercise 45:**

Trees A growing tree absorbs about 26 lb of carbon dioxide each year. How many years will the tree take to absorb 390 lb of carbon dioxide?

Understand

1. Circle the information you will need to solve.

2. What are you being asked to do?

   _____

   _____

3. If 390 lb is on one side of the equation, what operation will be performed with the other two values? Explain.

   _____

   _____

   _____

Plan and Carry Out

4. How much carbon dioxide does a tree absorb each year? _____

5. How much carbon dioxide does a tree absorb in y years? _____

6. Write an equation that can be used to solve for y. _____

7. Solve the equation. _____

8. How many years will the tree take to absorb 390 lb of carbon dioxide? _____

Check

9. Substitute the answer in Step 8 into the equation for the variable and solve.

   _____

Solve Another Problem

10. Delila runs 8 mi every day at her health club. She earns a free month membership after she's run 1,000 mi. Write and solve an equation to determine how many days she has to run before she earns the free month.

    _____

Guided Problem Solving

Practice 4-4

Solving Equations by Multiplying or Dividing

Use a calculator, paper and pencil, or mental math. Solve each equation.

1. $9n = 126$

2. $\frac{d}{3} = -81$

3. $-2t = 56$

_____ _____ _____

4. $-18 = \frac{y}{-2}$

5. $\frac{y}{16} = 3$

6. $-56 = 8r$

_____ _____ _____

7. $-3v = -48$

8. $13 = \frac{x}{-4}$

9. $28 = -4a$

_____ _____ _____

Solve and check each equation.

10. $\frac{x}{19} = -21$

11. $\frac{x}{-22} = -63$

_____ _____

12. $-41x = 164$

13. $\frac{x}{91} = -98$

_____ _____

14. $452 = -4x$

15. $50x = -2{,}500$

_____ _____

Write and solve an equation to represent the situation.

16. One of the largest flowers, the Rafflesia, weighs about 15 lb. How many Rafflesia flowers can be placed in a container that can hold a maximum of 240 lb?

_____

_____

Activity Lab 4-4

Solving Equations by Multiplying or Dividing

A car manufacturer has developed new models for the coming year. The cars were put through trials to determine their gas mileage. Use the information in the chart below to write an equation for finding the gas mileage of each vehicle model. Then solve each equation and record the gas mileage on the chart.

1.

Model	Distance (miles)	Fuel Used (gallons)	Distance ÷ Fuel Used	Gas Mileage = miles/gallon
A	598	13		
B	608	19		
C	406	14		
D	660	20		
E	690	23		
F	504	18		
G	459	17		

2. Which model vehicle gets the best gas mileage?

_____

3. Do you think gas mileage of a vehicle is something a consumer considers when purchasing? Explain.

_____

_____

_____

Reteaching 4-4

Solving Equations by Multiplying or Dividing

Follow these steps to solve equations.

	Solve: $\frac{t}{5} = -7$	Solve: $-2x = 8$
① Use the inverse operation on both sides of the equation.	$(5)\frac{t}{5} = (5)(-7)$	$\frac{-2x}{-2} = \frac{8}{-2}$
② Simplify.	$t = -35$	$x = -4$
③ Check.	$\frac{t}{5} = -7$	$-2x = 8$
	$\frac{-35}{5} \overset{?}{=} -7$	$-2(-4) \overset{?}{=} 8$
	$-7 = -7$ ✔	$8 = 8$ ✔

Solve and check each equation.

1. $-5n = 30$

$\dfrac{-5n}{\boxed{}} = \dfrac{30}{\boxed{}}$

$n = $ _____

2. $\frac{a}{2} = -16$

$(\boxed{})\frac{a}{2} = (\boxed{})(-16)$

$a = $ _____

3. $-2w = -4$

$\dfrac{-2w}{\boxed{}} = \dfrac{-4}{\boxed{}}$

$w = $ _____

4. $8t = 32$

$\dfrac{8t}{\boxed{}} = \dfrac{32}{\boxed{}}$

$t = $ _____

5. $5 = \frac{g}{6}$

$(\boxed{})(5) = (\boxed{})\frac{g}{6}$

_____ $= g$

6. $\frac{n}{-3} = -5$

$(\boxed{})\frac{n}{-3} = (\boxed{})(-5)$

$n = $ _____

Use a calculator, pencil and paper, or mental math. Solve each equation.

7. $\frac{x}{4} = -1$

_____

8. $-5w = 125$

_____

9. $\frac{m}{-8} = 10$

_____

10. $-2 = \frac{x}{-4}$

_____

11. $\frac{a}{-4} = 12$

_____

12. $-6b = 42$

_____

13. $-3 = \frac{c}{-8}$

_____

14. $5 = \frac{d}{7}$

_____

15. $2t = 38$

_____

16. $-9 = 9q$

_____

17. $n \div 6 = -3$

_____

18. $-8k = -40$

_____

Enrichment 4-4   **Solving Equations by Multiplying or Dividing**

Critical Thinking

The equation $d = r \times t$ relates rate (r), time (t) and distance (d).

1. If you are traveling at 55 miles per hour, what formula would you use to find the distance you will travel over various time intervals?

   _____

2. Sometimes you are given distances and need to know how long it would take to travel at various rates. Complete the table to find the time it would take to travel 500 miles at speeds of 40, 55, 60, 65, and 70 miles per hour. Round your times to the nearest quarter hour, if necessary.

Rate (in mi/h)					
Time (in hours)					
Distance (in miles)					

3. What operation did you use to find the time? Rewrite the equation so that t stands alone on one side of the equal sign.

   _____

4. Rewrite the equation so that r stands alone on one side of the equal sign. Explain your reasoning.

   _____

   _____

5. How is rewriting an equation like solving an equation?

   _____

6. Why would you want to rewrite an equation?

   _____

   _____

   _____

7. The equation for the perimeter of a regular polygon can be written as $P = n \times s$ where P is the perimeter, n is the number of sides and s is the length of each side. How could you rewrite the equation to find the length of a side?

   _____

Puzzle 4-4

Solving Equations by Multiplying or Dividing

Help each lost number find its home. Be sure that each number listed
in the Answer Box below is accounted for.

1. Double the lost number is −44.

Equation: _____

Lost Number: _____

2. The sum of the lost number and 87 is −98.

Equation: _____

Lost Number: _____

3. 7 subtracted from the lost number is 15.

Equation: _____

Lost Number: _____

4. The product of −6 and the lost number
is 102.

Equation: _____

Lost Number: _____

5. 10 more than the lost number is −66.

Equation: _____

Lost Number: _____

6. 17 less than the lost number is −80.

Equation: _____

Lost Number: _____

7. The lost number divided by −9 is 54.

Equation: _____

Lost Number: _____

8. Triple the lost number is −204.

Equation: _____

Lost Number: _____

9. −29 subtracted from the lost number is 128.

Equation: _____

Lost Number: _____

10. The product of the lost number and
−19 is −152.

Equation: _____

Lost Number: _____

11. The sum of the lost number and 43 is −2.

Equation: _____

Lost Number: _____

12. The lost number multiplied by −4 is 344.

Equation: _____

Lost Number: _____

Answer Box

−22	−17	−68	
8			−63
22		−486	99
−76	−185	−45	−86

Practice 4-5 **Exploring Two-Step Problems**

Define a variable and write an algebraic expression for each phrase.

1. six times the price of gas minus 20

   _____

2. one-half the distance from Boston to New York minus 25

   _____

3. two fewer than five times the number of eggs needed in the recipe

   _____

4. 10 megabytes less than the number of megabytes in a computer, divided by 6

   _____

Solve each equation using number sense.

5. $10 + 5h = 25$ 6. $8s - 8 = 64$ 7. $3y + 78 = 81$

   _____   _____   _____

8. $2g + 4 = 12$ 9. $5j + 5 = 15$ 10. $3w + 8 = 20$

   _____   _____   _____

11. $\frac{h}{2} + 1 = 4$ 12. $\frac{g}{8} + 12 = 16$ 13. $2 + \frac{b}{7} = 3$

   _____   _____   _____

14. For a walk-a-thon a sponsor committed to give you a flat fee of $5 plus $2 for every mile you walk. Write an expression for the total amount you will collect from your sponsor at the end of the walk-a-thon. Then evaluate your expression for 20 miles walked.

   _____

4-5 • Guided Problem Solving

GPS Student Page 198, Exercise 39:

Food You are helping to prepare food for a large family gathering. You can slice 2 zucchinis per minute. You need 30 sliced zucchinis. How long will it take you to finish, if you have already sliced 12 zucchinis?

Understand

1. Circle the information you will need to solve.

2. What are you being asked to do?

   _____

   _____

3. What will your variable represent?

   _____

Plan and Carry Out

4. How many sliced zucchinis do you need? _____

5. How many sliced zucchinis do you already have? _____

6. Write and simplify an expression for the number of zucchinis you still need to slice. _____

7. To calculate the number of minutes it will take to slice the remaining zucchinis, what number will you divide your answer to Step 7 by? _____

8. Write an equation to solve the problem. _____

9. How long will it take you to finish slicing the remaining zucchinis? _____

Check

10. Multiply your answer to Step 9 by your answer to Step 7. Does your answer match your result from Step 6?

    _____

Solve Another Problem

11. Jordan skates 6 mi/h. Today she has already skated 8 miles. Her goal is to skate a total of 20 miles. How much longer does she have to skate to reach her goal?

    _____

Practice 4-5

Exploring Two-Step Problems

Define a variable and write an algebraic expression for each phrase.

1. six times the price of gas minus 20

   _____

2. one-half the distance from Boston to New York minus 25

   _____

Solve each equation using number sense.

3. $10 + 5h = 25$

   _____

4. $8s - 8 = 64$

   _____

5. $3y + 78 = 81$

   _____

6. $2g + 4 = 12$

   _____

7. $5j + 5 = 15$

   _____

8. $3w + 8 = 20$

   _____

9. $\frac{h}{2} + 1 = 4$

   _____

10. $\frac{g}{8} + 12 = 16$

   _____

Solve.

11. For a walk-a-thon a sponsor committed to give you a flat fee of
    $5 plus $2 for every mile you walk. Write an expression for the
    total amount you will collect from your sponsor at the end of the
    walk-a-thon. Then evaluate your expression for 20 miles walked.

    _____

    _____

Activity Lab 4-5

Exploring Two-Step Problems

Temperatures can be measured as degrees Celsius (°C) or degrees Fahrenheit (°F). Sometimes you need to convert from one scale to the other.

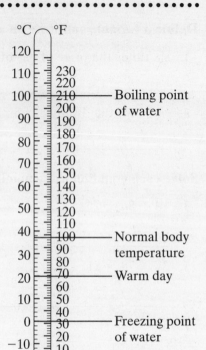

You can use this formula to convert Celsius to Fahrenheit. Substitute any Celsius temperature into the formula for C and solve to find the comparable Fahrenheit temperature, F.

You can use this formula to convert Fahrenheit to Celsius. Substitute any Fahrenheit temperature into the formula for F and solve to find the comparable Celsius temperature, C.

$$F = \tfrac{9}{5}C + 32 \qquad\qquad C = \tfrac{5}{9}(F - 32)$$

Convert each temperature to degrees Fahrenheit.

1. $0°C =$ _____°F
2. $-1°C =$ _____°F
3. $-2°C =$ _____°F
4. $-5°C =$ _____°F
5. $-10°C =$ _____°F
6. $-15°C =$ _____°F
7. $-20°C =$ _____°F
8. $-25°C =$ _____°F

9. Look at the negative Celsius temperatures. What pattern do you notice in the signs of their corresponding Fahrenheit temperatures?

_____

Convert each temperature to degrees Celsius. Round to the nearest tenth if necessary.

10. $40°F =$ _____°C 11. $34°F =$ _____°C 12. $33°F =$ _____°C

13. $32°F =$ _____°C 14. $31°F =$ _____°C 15. $30°F =$ _____°C

16. $0°F =$ _____°C 17. $-5°F =$ _____°C 18. $-10°F =$ _____°C

19. Look at the Fahrenheit temperatures less than 32°F. What pattern do you notice in the signs of their corresponding Celsius temperatures?

_____

20. Why do you think these patterns occur?

_____

_____

_____

Reteaching 4-5

Exploring Two-Step Problems

You can change a word expression into an algebraic expression by converting the words to variables, numbers, and operation symbols.

To write a two-step algebraic expression for *seven more than three times a number,* follow these steps.

① Define the variable.   Let n represent the number.

② Ask yourself are there any key words?   "More than" means add and "times" means multiply.

③ Write an algebraic expression. $7 + 3 \cdot n$

④ Simplify. $7 + 3n$

Define a variable and write an algebraic expression for each phrase.

1. 3 inches more than 4 times your height   _____

2. 4 less than 6 times the weight of a turkey   _____

3. 8 more than one-half the number of miles run last week   _____

Solve.

4. Three friends pay $4 per hour to rent a paddleboat plus $5 for snacks. Write an expression for the total cost of rental and snacks. Then evaluate the expression for 2 hours.

   _____

5. A lawn care service charges $10 plus $15 per hour to mow and fertilize lawns. Write an expression for the total cost of having your lawn mowed and fertilized. Then evaluate the expression for 4 hours.

   _____

Solve each equation using number sense.

6. $4x - 10 = 30$ 7. $2n - 7 = 13$ 8. $\frac{s}{3} + 2 = 4$

   _____   _____   _____

Enrichment 4-5

Exploring Two-Step Problems

Patterns in Numbers

You can write expressions for consecutive integers as follows.

Let n represent any integer.

Then $n + 1$ is equal to the next consecutive integer.

Suppose you only knew that the sum of three consecutive numbers was -51. Here's a way you can find the numbers.

Let n represent the first number.

Then $(n + 1)$ and $(n + 2)$ would be the second and the third consecutive numbers.

Write an equation.

1st 2nd   3rd   Sum
$$n + (n + 1) + (n + 2) = -51$$

$$n + n + 1 + n + 2 = -51$$ To simplify, write three n's as $3n$ and $1 + 2$ as 3.

$$3n + 3 = -51$$ Add -3 to both sides.

$$3n + 3 + (-3) = -51 + (-3)$$ Divide both sides by 3.

$$\frac{3n}{3} = \frac{-54}{3}$$

$$n = -18$$

So, the three consecutive numbers are -18, -17, and -16.

Solve each problem.

1. Find two consecutive integers with a sum of 23. _____

2. Find two consecutive integers with a sum of -109. _____

3. Find three consecutive integers with a sum of -24. _____

4. Find three consecutive integers with a sum of 195. _____

5. Find four consecutive integers with a sum of 90. _____

6. Find four consecutive integers with a sum of -430. _____

7. Find the middle integer if the sum of the greatest and the least of three consecutive integers is 82. _____

Puzzle 4-5

Exploring Two-Step Problems

In the diagram below are hidden 9 equations with $x = 2$ as a solution. Equations may be written vertically or horizontally. Find and circle the remaining 8 equations.

$$
\begin{array}{ccccccccc}
1 & 2 & x & + & 3 & = & 7 & 5 & 2 & 1 \\
x & + & 2 & = & x & 5 & + & x & = & 2 \\
5 & = & 3 & x & - & 2 & x & + & x & x \\
1 & 0 & x & + & 1 & 0 & = & 3 & 0 & - \\
2 & x & + & 6 & = & 1 & 1 & = & + & 1 \\
x & + & 3 & = & 5 & x & 0 & 1 & 7 & 0 \\
4 & x & = & 9 & + & 8 & x & 3 & 1 & = \\
= & + & 9 & x & + & 2 & = & 2 & 4 & 1 \\
6 & x & - & 6 & = & 6 & 3 & + & x & 4 \\
\end{array}
$$

1. $5x + 3 = 13; x = 2$

2.

3.

4.

5.

6.

7.

8.

9.

Practice 4-6

Solving Two-Step Equations

Solve each equation. Then check your answer.

1. $7m + 8 = 71$

2. $\frac{y}{7} + 6 = 11$

3. $12y + 2 = 146$

4. $\frac{m}{9} - 17 = 21$

_____ _____ _____ _____

5. $\frac{y}{-12} + 1 = 6$

6. $2a - 1 = 19$

7. $\frac{c}{9} - 8 = 17$

8. $-4t + 16 = 24$

_____ _____ _____ _____

9. $\frac{b}{-2} - 8 = -6$

10. $3d + 14 = 11$

11. $\frac{z}{17} - 1 = 8$

12. $\frac{e}{5} - 14 = 21$

_____ _____ _____ _____

13. $\frac{f}{-9} + 4 = 2$

14. $-2y + 16 = 10$

15. $4w - 26 = 82$

16. $\frac{j}{19} - 2 = -5$

_____ _____ _____ _____

Solve each equation.

17. $3n - 8 = 4$

18. $\frac{n}{5} - 4 = 11$

_____ _____

19. $2n - 3 = 9$

20. $1 + \frac{n}{4} = 9$

_____ _____

Match each sentence with a two-step equation.

21. Half of the height of a tree minus five equals fifteen.

_____

22. Two less than three times the number of feet of fencing required equals twelve feet.

_____

23. Eight less than the quotient of Dave's golf score and four equals negative five.

_____

24. Three times Gail's age increased by two years equals twelve years.

_____

A. $3n - 2 = 12$

B. $3n + 2 = 12$

C. $\frac{n}{2} - 5 = 15$

D. $\frac{n}{4} - 8 = -5$

4-6 • Guided Problem Solving

GPS Student Page 203, Exercise 32:

Jobs You earn $20 per hour landscaping a yard. You pay $1.50 in bus fare each way. How many hours must you work to earn $117?

Understand

1. Circle the information you will need to solve.

2. What are you being asked to do?

   _____

   _____

3. How much do you spend in bus fare
   to go to and from work? _____

Plan and Carry Out

4. Write an expression for the amount of money you make after
   h hours.

   _____

5. Write an expression for the amount of money you have after you
   pay for bus fare.

   _____

6. How much money do you need to earn? _____

7. Write an equation that can be solved for h. _____

8. Solve the equation. _____

9. How many hours must you work to earn $117? _____

Check

10. Substitute the answer in Step 9 into the equation for the variable
    and solve.

    _____

Solve Another Problem

11. You charge $6 per hour to babysit one child. You charge an
    additional $2 per hour for each additional child. The Taylors have
    4 children. How many hours would you have to babysit the
    Taylors' children to earn $84?

    _____

Practice 4-6

Solving Two-Step Equations

Solve each equation. Then check your answer.

1. $7m + 8 = 71$

2. $\frac{y}{7} + 6 = 11$

3. $12y + 2 = 146$

_____

_____

_____

4. $\frac{y}{-12} + 1 = 6$

5. $2a - 1 = 19$

6. $\frac{c}{9} - 8 = 17$

_____

_____

_____

7. $\frac{b}{-2} - 8 = -6$

8. $3d + 14 = 11$

9. $\frac{z}{17} - 1 = 8$

_____

_____

_____

Solve each equation.

10. $3n - 8 = 4$

_____

11. $\frac{n}{5} - 4 = 11$

_____

12. $2n - 3 = 9$

_____

Match each sentence with a two-step equation.

13. Half of the height of a tree minus five equals fifteen.

_____

14. Two less than three times the number of feet of fencing required equals twelve feet.

A. $3n - 2 = 12$

B. $3n + 2 = 12$

C. $\frac{n}{2} - 5 = 15$

_____

15. Three times Gail's age increased by two years equals twelve years.

_____

Activity Lab 4-6

Solving Two-Step Equations

Solve each equation. There are three different solutions for _y_.

1. $3y - 9 = 30$

2. $-8.4 = 8y + 1.2$

3. $\frac{1}{2}(4y) = -12$

4. $6.4 = 4 - 2y$

5. $-12 = 6 + 3y$

6. $2y - 14 = 12$

7. Which pairs of equations have equivalent solutions?

___ and ___

___ and ___

___ and ___

8. Which equations have addition or subtraction as the first step

in solving? _____

9. Which equations have multiplication or division as the first step

in solving? _____

10. How do you determine which operation to perform first?

_____

_____

Reteaching 4-6

Solving Two-Step Equations

The marbles and boxes represent this equation.

$$2x + 3 = 7$$

The variable x stands for the number of marbles (unseen) in each box.

To solve the equation, follow these steps.

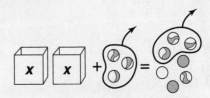

There are the same number of marbles on each side and the same number of marbles in each box.

Step 1

Subtract the extra marbles from both sides.

$$2x + 3 - 3 = 7 - 3$$
$$2x = 4$$

Step 2

Divide the number of marbles by 2, the number of boxes.

$$\frac{2x}{2} = \frac{4}{2}$$
$$x = 2$$

Write and solve an equation for each situation.

1.

_____ + _____ = _____

$x = $ _____

2.

_____ + _____ = _____

$x = $ _____

Complete to solve each equation.

3. $5x + 7 = 2$

$5x + 7 -$ _____ $= 2 -$ _____

$\dfrac{5x}{\square} = \dfrac{-5}{\square}$

$x = $ _____

4. $2x - 1 = 9$

$2x - 1 +$ _____ $= 9 +$ _____

$\dfrac{2x}{\square} = \dfrac{10}{\square}$

$x = $ _____

Solve each equation.

5. $4x + 7 = 15$ _____

6. $3b - 5 = 13$ _____

7. $5t - 2 = -17$ _____

Enrichment 4-6

Solving Two-Step Equations

Critical Thinking

Solve the equation $4x - 3 = 7$.

Jane solved the equation by reversing the normal order of operations.

John solved the equation by first dividing all terms by 4, the coefficient of x.

$4x - 3 = 7$

$4x - 3 + 3 = 7 + 3$

$4x = 10$

$\frac{4x}{4} = \frac{10}{4}$

$x = \frac{10}{4} = \frac{5}{2} = 2\frac{1}{2}$

$4x - 3 = 7$

$\frac{4x}{4} - \frac{3}{4} = \frac{7}{4}$

$x - \frac{3}{4} = \frac{7}{4}$

$x - \frac{3}{4} + \frac{3}{4} = \frac{7}{4} + \frac{3}{4}$

$x = \frac{10}{4} = \frac{5}{2} = 2\frac{1}{2}$

1. Did both students arrive at the same solution?

    _____

2. Compare the two approaches. Which one was easier? Explain.

    _____

    _____

Solve the following equation using both methods.

3. Jane's method
    $3x - 9 = 24$

    John's method
    $3x - 9 = 24$

4. When does dividing first work best?

    _____

    _____

Name _____ Class _____ Date _____

Puzzle 4-6

Solving Two-Step Equations

Solve the two-step equations below. Shade in your answers in the puzzle at the bottom of the page. The correct solutions will reveal the identity of the state that is the largest gold-producing state in the nation—second in the world behind South Africa.

1. $3y - 6 = 9$

$y =$ _____

2. $4x - 9 = 3$

$x =$ _____

3. $7 + 2y = 21$

$y =$ _____

4. $\frac{a}{5} + 7 = 10$

$a =$ _____

5. $3n - 6 = 12$

$n =$ _____

6. $-6 + 2x = 4$

$x =$ _____

7. $\frac{x}{4} - 2 = 3$

$x =$ _____

8. $6d - 4 = 8$

$d =$ _____

9. $4 + \frac{y}{2} = 8$

$y =$ _____

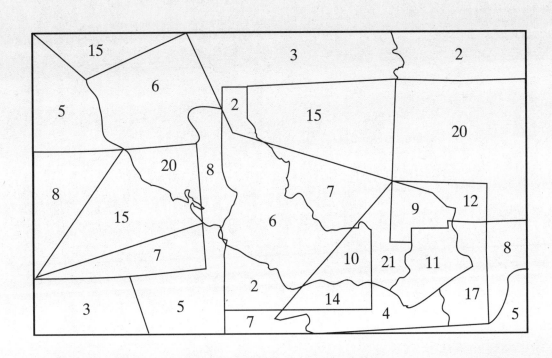

Course 2 Lesson 4-6

Practice 4-7

Graphing and Writing Inequalities

Graph the solution of each inequality on a number line.

1. $x \leq 3$ ⟵—+—+—+—+—+—+—+—+—⟶ x
                    -4 -3 -2 -1 0 1 2 3 4

2. $t > 1$ ⟵—+—+—+—+—+—+—+—+—⟶ t
                    -4 -3 -2 -1 0 1 2 3 4

3. $q \geq -10$ ⟵—+—+—+—+—+—+—+—+—⟶ q
                -20 -10 0 10 20

4. $m < 50$ ⟵—+—+—+—+—+—+—+—+—+—⟶ m
            -10 0 10 20 30 40 50 60 70

For each inequality, tell whether the number in bold is a solution.

5. $x < 7; \mathbf{7}$ _____

6. $p > -3; \mathbf{3}$ _____

7. $k \geq 5; \mathbf{0}$ _____

8. $3z \leq 12; \mathbf{4}$ _____

9. $n - 5 > 3; \mathbf{6}$ _____

10. $2g + 8 \geq 3; \mathbf{-1}$ _____

Write an inequality for each graph.

11. _____

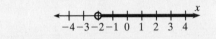

12. _____

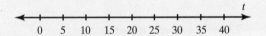

Write an inequality for each statement. Graph each solution on the number line shown.

13. You can walk there in 20 minutes or less.

    ⟵—+—+—+—+—+—+—+—+—+—⟶ t
      0 5 10 15 20 25 30 35 40

_____

14. Each prize is worth over $150.

    ⟵—+—+—+—+—+—+—+—+—⟶ v
      0 100 200 300 400

_____

15. A species of catfish, *malapterurus electricus*, can generate up to 350 volts of electricity.

    a. Write an inequality to represent the amount of electricity generated by the catfish.

    _____

    b. Draw a graph of the inequality you wrote in **a.**

        ⟵—+—+—+—+—+—+—+—⟶ e
          0 100 200 300 400

                                                            **

4-7 • Guided Problem Solving

GPS Student Page 208, Exercise 30:

Reasoning Explain why $-17 > -22$.

Understand

1. What are you being asked to do?

   _____

   _____

2. What visual representation can you use to help your explanation?

   _____

Plan and Carry Out

3. Graph -17 on a number line.

4. Graph -22 on the same number line.

5. Which number is farther to the right on the number line?

   _____

6. Why is $-17 > -22$?

   _____

   _____

Check

7. Which mathematical definition did you use to explain that $-17 > -22$?

   _____

   _____

Solve Another Problem

8. Explain why $-8 < -5$.

   _____

   _____

Practice 4-7

Graphing and Writing Inequalities

Graph the solution of each inequality on a number line.

1. $x \leq 3$

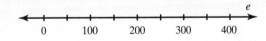

2. $t > 1$

3. $q \geq -10$

For each inequality, tell whether the number in bold is a solution.

4. $x < 7$; **7** _____

5. $p > -3$; **3** _____

6. $k \geq 5$; **0** _____

7. $3z \leq 12$; **4** _____

Write an inequality for each graph.

8. _____

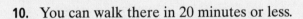

9. _____

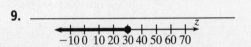

Write an inequality for each statement. Graph each solution on the number line shown.

10. You can walk there in 20 minutes or less.

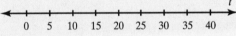

_____

11. Each prize is worth over $150.

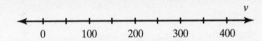

_____

12. A species of catfish, *malapterurus electricus,* can generate up to 350 volts of electricity.

a. Write an inequality to represent the amount of electricity generated by the catfish.

_____

b. Draw a graph of the inequality you wrote in **a.**

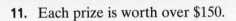

Activity Lab 4-7

Graphing and Writing Inequalities

To graph $x \geq 3$, you need to find all the points on the number line
that are 3 or more units to the right of 0 on the number line.

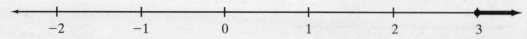

Graph each inequality.

1. $x < 2$ ←——+——+——+——+——+——+——+——+——+——+——+——+——→

2. $x > 3$ ←——+——+——+——+——+——+——+——+——+——+——+——+——→

3. $x < 5$ ←——+——+——+——+——+——+——+——+——+——+——+——+——→

4. $x \geq 2$ ←——+——+——+——+——+——+——+——+——+——+——+——+——→

5. $x \geq 3$ ←——+——+——+——+——+——+——+——+——+——+——+——+——→

6. $x \leq 2$ ←——+——+——+——+——+——+——+——+——+——+——+——+——→

7. What marks on a graph indicate that the graph is describing an inequality?

_____

Name _____ Class _____ Date _____

Reteaching 4-7

Graphing and Writing Inequalities

Two expressions separated by an inequality sign form an **inequality.**
An inequality shows that the two expressions *are not* equal. Unlike
the equations you have worked with, an inequality has many
solutions.

The **solutions of an inequality** are the values that make the inequality
true. They can be graphed on a number line. Use a closed circle (●)
for ≤ and ≥ and an open circle (O) for > and <. For example:

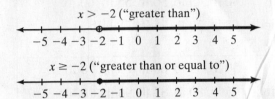

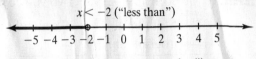

Graph the inequality $x > 4$.

The inequality is read as "x is greater than 4." Since all numbers to
the right of 4 are greater than 4, you can draw an arrow from 4 to the
right. Since 4 is not greater than itself, use an open circle on 4.

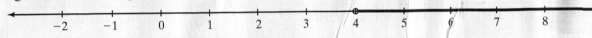

1. **Graph the inequality $x \leq -3$.**

   a. Write the inequality in words. _____

   b. Will the circle at -3 be open or closed? _____

   c. Graph the solution.
   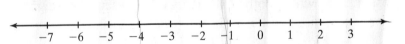

2. **Graph the inequality $x < 3$.**

   a. Write the inequality in words. _____

   b. Will the circle at 3 be open or closed? _____

   c. Graph the solution.
   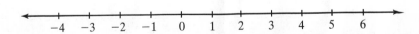

Enrichment 4-7

Exploring Inequalities

In order to create a sense of fairness in the sport, wrestling is divided into weight and age classes. The table below was used by the state of Florida for a 2001 junior wrestling tournament.

Division	Birthdate	Match Time Limit	Weight Classes
Bantam	Born 1997–1998 (State level program only)	Two 90-second periods 30-second rest between periods	40 lb, 45 lb, 50 lb, 55 lb, 60 lb 65 lb, 70 lb, 75 lb, 75+ lb
Midget	Born 1995–1996	Two 90-second periods 30-second rest between periods	50 lb, 55 lb, 60 lb, 65 lb, 70 lb 75 lb, 80 lb, 87 lb, 95 lb, 103 lb 112 lb, 120 lb, 120+ lb
Novice	Born 1993–1994	Two 2-minute periods 30-second rest between periods	60 lb, 65 lb, 70 lb, 75 lb, 80 lb 85 lb, 90 lb, 95 lb, 100 lb, 105 lb 112 lb, 120 lb, 130 lb, 140 lb, 140+ lb
Schoolboy/ girl	Born 1991–1992	Two 2-minute periods 30-second rest between periods	70 lb, 75 lb, 80 lb, 85 lb, 90 lb 95 lb, 100 lb, 105 lb, 110 lb 115 lb, 120 lb, 125 lb, 130 lb 140 lb, 150 lb, 160 lb, 160+ lb

For the following questions, assume the year is 2007.

1. Write an inequality to represent the age limit of a Novice wrestler. Then write another inequality to represent the weight limit for a Novice wrestler in the 90-lb weight class.

_____

2. A wrestler is 11 years old and weighs 68 pounds. What division is the wrestler in? What is the wrestler's match time limit?

_____

3. Write and graph an inequality to show the range of a wrestler's age in the Schoolboy/girl division.

_____

4. You attend a wrestling meet to watch your friend wrestle. Let $x =$ your friend's age and $y =$ your friend's weight. Use the following inequalities to determine what division your friend belongs. 9 years old $\leq x \leq$ 10 years old; 55 lb $\leq y <$ 60 lb

Puzzle 4-7

Graphing and Writing Inequalities

Match each description to the appropriate graph at the right. Write
the letter of each answer above the exercise number in the spaces at
the bottom of the page to complete the sentence.

1. You must be at least seven years old and
   over 50 in. tall to ride The Squealer.

2. Free Fall is reserved for visitors who are at
   least 58 in. tall and over the age of 16.

3. To ride The Splinter, you must be over
   ten years old and have a minimum height
   of 48 in.

4. You must be at least six years old and more
   than 45 in. tall to ride The Twist.

5. To enter the haunted house, you must be
   more than twelve years old and at least
   57 in. tall.

6. To ride the Snake, you must be at least nine
   years old. The minimum height requirement
   for the ride is 50 in.

A.

T.

M.

S.

O.

L.

Your younger cousin Abby spent the day at the carnival, but could
not go on many of the rides. She went home feeling a little

___ ___ ___   ___ ___ ___ ___ ___.
 1   2   2   3   4   5   6   6

Name _____ Class _____ Date _____

Practice 4-8

Solving Inequalities by Adding or Subtracting

Solve each inequality. Graph each solution.

1. $w + 4 < -2$

2. $a - 4 \geq 0$

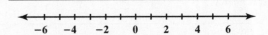

3. $a + 19 > 13$

4. $x + 7 \leq 12$

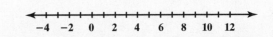

5. $a + 2 > -3$

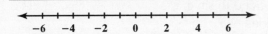

6. $t - 6 < 3$

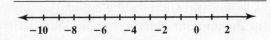

7. $r - 3.4 \leq 2.6$

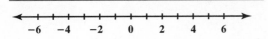

8. $a + 5.7 \geq -2.3$

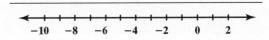

9. $h - 4.9 > -0.9$

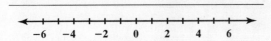

10. $y + 3.4 < -4.6$

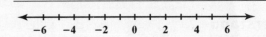

Write an inequality for each problem. Solve the inequality.

11. The school record for the most points scored in a football season is 85. Lawrence has 44 points so far this season. How many more points does he need to break the record?

_____

_____

12. The maximum weight limit for a fully loaded truck is 16,000 pounds. The truck you are loading currently weighs 12,500 pounds. How much more weight can be added and not exceed the weight limit?

_____

_____

_____

4-8 • Guided Problem Solving

GPS **Student Page 212, Exercise 25:**

Consumer Issues Your parents give you $35 for a scooter that costs at least $100. How much money do you have to save to buy the scooter?

Understand

1. Circle the information you will need to solve.

2. What are you being asked to do?

   _____

   _____

3. What expression would you use to represent the phrase "*at least* $100?"

   _____

Plan and Carry Out

Suppose the scooter costs *at least* $100.

4. Write an expression for the amount of money you need to save, *s*, plus the amount of money your parents will give you.

   _____

5. How much money do you need to buy the scooter?

   _____

6. Write an inequality to solve for *s*. _____

7. Solve the inequality. _____

8. How much money do you have to save for the scooter?

   _____

Check

9. If you save $65, how much money will you have?

   _____

Solve Another Problem

10. You have to be at least 42 in. tall to ride the big roller coasters at the amusement park. You are 36 in. tall right now. How much more do you have to grow? Write and solve an inequality.

    _____

Name _____ Class _____ Date _____

Practice 4-8

Solving Inequalities by Adding or Subtracting

Solve each inequality. Graph each solution.

1. $w + 4 < -2$

_____

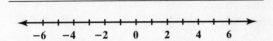

2. $a - 4 \geq 0$

_____

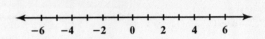

3. $a + 19 > 13$

_____

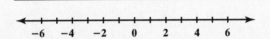

4. $x + 7 \leq 12$

_____

5. $a + 2 > -3$

_____

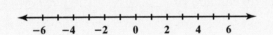

6. $t - 6 < 3$

_____

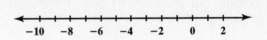

7. $r - 3.4 \leq 2.6$

_____

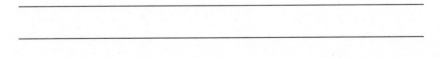

8. $a + 5.7 \geq -2.3$

_____

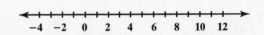

Write an inequality for the problem. Solve the inequality.

9. The school record for the most points scored in a football season is 85. Lawrence has 44 points so far this season. How many more points does he need to break the record?

_____

_____

_____

Activity Lab 4-8   Solving Inequalities by Adding or Subtracting

Solve the following inequalities by adding or subtracting. Graph your solutions.

1. $x + 6 \geq 8$

           ◄———————————————————►

2. $x - 5 \geq -3$

           ◄———————————————————►

3. $x + 3 \geq 4$

           ◄———————————————————►

4. $x - 7 \leq -12$

           ◄———————————————————►

5. $x + 0 \geq -3$

           ◄———————————————————►

6. $x - 4 \leq -9$

           ◄———————————————————►

7. Look at your graphs. Why does it make sense that you can add or subtract and still have a true inequality?

_____

_____

Reteaching 4-8   Solving Inequalities by Adding or Subtracting

To solve an inequality you can add the same number to or subtract it
from each side of the inequality.

Solve $x + 5 \geq 9$.   Graph the solution.   Solve $y - 3 < 2$.   Graph the solution.

$x + 5 \geq 9$ $y - 3 < 2$
$x + 5 - 5 \geq 9 - 5$ Subtract 5 from each side. $y - 3 + 3 < 2 + 3$ Add 3 to each side.
$\qquad x \geq 4$ Simplify. $\qquad y < 5$ Simplify.

Graph: Graph:

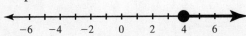

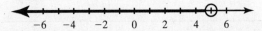

Solve each inequality. Graph the solution.

1. $2 + a > 6$ _____

2. $-4 + w \leq 0$ _____

3. $3 + a \geq 8$ _____

4. $w + 1 \leq 4$ _____

5. $y + 3 < 5$ _____

6. $6 + g \geq 12$ _____

7. $2 + x > 7$ _____

8. $2 + r < 8$ _____

Enrichment 4-8

Solving Inequalities by Adding or Subtracting

Each symbol below represents a number in an inequality. Use what you know about operations and properties to decide what number each symbol represents.

☺ means +		⚡ means >	
✚ means −		🚫 means ≤	
▢ means <		♡ means ≥	

1.

2. _____ _____ _____ _____ _____

3. _____ _____ _____ _____ _____

4. _____ _____ _____ _____ _____

5. _____ _____ _____ _____ _____

Complete the key with the correct symbol.

_____ means 12 _____ means 6 _____ means −2

_____ means 4 _____ means 3

4D: Visual Vocabulary Practice

For use after Lesson 4-8

Study Skill Making sense of mathematical symbols is like reading a foreign language that uses different letters.

Concept List

Addition Property of Equality   Subtraction Property of Inequality

Division Property of Equality   Multiplication Property of Inequality

variable   solution of an equation

open sentence   solution of an inequality

inequality

Write the concept that best describes each exercise. Choose from the concept list above.

1. If $5 - y = 2 - 3y$, then $5 - y + 3y = 2 - 3y + 3y$.	2. $8 + x \geq 2x$	3. $-2(3x + 5) = 14$ $3x + 5 = -7$ $3x = -12$ $x = -4$ -4 represents this for $-2(3x + 5) = 14$.
_____	_____	_____
4. z in the equation $\frac{2z}{5} = 12$	5. If $7m < 1 + 2m$, then $7m - 2m < 1 + 2m - 2m$.	6. $3z + \frac{1}{4} = 21$
_____	_____	_____
7. If $5b = 3$, then $\frac{5b}{5} = \frac{3}{5}$.	8. $-2x + 1 < 4$ $-2x < 3$ $x > -\frac{3}{2}$ 0 represents this for $-2x + 1 < 4$.	9. If $\frac{1}{9}z < 8$, then $9 \times \left(\frac{1}{9}z\right) < 9 \times 8$.
_____	_____	_____

Puzzle 4-8

Solving Inequalities by Adding or Subtracting

Choose the appropriate inequality for each problem. Find your way through the maze by navigating with correct answers. You may move up or down, left or right, or diagonally. Shade each answer square as you go.

1. The weight capacity of an elevator is 500 pounds. A 160-pound man is the only passenger on the elevator. How much more weight can it carry?

2. Your soccer team scored one point during the first half of a game, and your opponents scored three. Assuming you can prevent your opponents from scoring again, how many points must you score in the second half to win the game?

3. Each class at McKinney High School can have at most 25 students. A total of 14 students are currently enrolled in your biology class. How many more students will be able to enroll in the class?

4. An airliner has a total of 160 seats. 57 passengers have purchased tickets for a flight from Denver to Chicago. How many people will be able to purchase tickets for this flight?

5. The public radio station needs to raise more than $15,000 to meet its current goal. They have already raised $9,400. How much money must they raise to meet the goal?

6. A freight ship is scheduled to carry 273 tons of equipment. However, the ship's weight capacity is 250 tons. How much cargo will have to be left off of the ship?

Start Here ↓

$160 + x \leq 500$	$x + 14 \geq 25$	$127 + x \leq 399$	$x + 2 < 78$
$x + 1 < 3$	$x + 1 > 3$	$x + 58 > 163$	$x + 9 \leq 25$
$160 + x \geq 500$	$x + 14 \leq 25$	$x + 57 > 160$	$273 - x > 250$
$273 - x > 250$	$x + 12 \leq 26$	$x + 57 \leq 160$	$9{,}400 + x > 15{,}000$
$23x + 58 > 133$	$3{,}675 + x > 15{,}000$	$9{,}400 + x < 15{,}000$	$273 - x \leq 250$

Finish Here ↑

Name _____ Class _____ Date _____

Practice 4-9

Solving Inequalities by Multiplying or Dividing

Solve each inequality. Graph each solution.

1. $6w \leq 36$

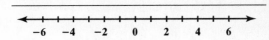

2. $10a \geq 40$

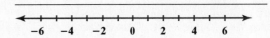

3. $\frac{f}{3} \leq -2$

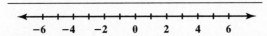

4. $\frac{v}{4} > 2$

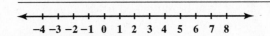

5. $7a > -28$

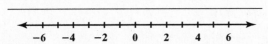

6. $\frac{c}{-3} \geq 3$

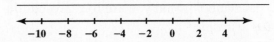

7. $\frac{f}{2} > -1$

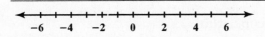

8. $9a \leq 63$

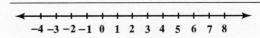

9. $4w \geq -12$

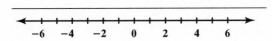

10. $\frac{h}{-2} \geq -5$

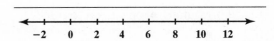

Write an inequality to solve each problem. Then solve the inequality.

11. Marcus wants to buy 5 baseballs. He has $35. What is the most each baseball can cost?

_____

_____

12. Melinda charges $4 per hour for babysitting. Mrs. Garden does not want to spend more than $25 for babysitting. What is the maximum number of hours that she can have Melinda babysit?

_____

_____

_____

4-9 • Guided Problem Solving

GPS Student Page 217, Exercise 32:

Rides A roller coaster can carry 36 people per run. At least how many times does the roller coaster have to run to allow 10,000 people to ride?

Understand

1. Circle the information you will need to solve.

2. What are you being asked to do?

   _____

   _____

3. What symbol would you use to represent the phrase *at least 10,000 people*?

   _____

Plan and Carry Out

4. Write an expression for the maximum number of people who could ride the roller coaster in *r* runs.

   _____

5. At least how many people need to ride? _____

6. Write an inequality to solve for *r*. _____

7. Solve the inequality. _____

8 How many times does the roller coaster
   need to run?   _____

Check

9. If the roller coaster runs 278 times, how many people will it have carried? Use a calculator to check your answer.

   _____

Solve Another Problem

10. Chicken is on sale for $1.99 per pound. You can only spend up to $20, and you must buy a whole number of pounds. How many pounds of chicken can you buy?

   _____

Practice 4-9

Solving Inequalities by Multiplying or Dividing

Solve each inequality. Graph each solution.

1. $6w \le 36$

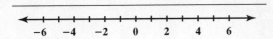

2. $10a \ge 40$

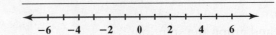

3. $\frac{f}{3} \le -2$

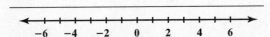

4. $\frac{v}{4} > 2$

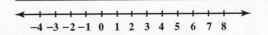

5. $7a > -28$

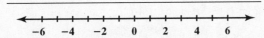

6. $\frac{c}{-3} \ge 3$

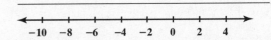

7. $\frac{f}{2} > -1$

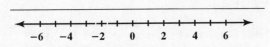

8. $9a \le 63$

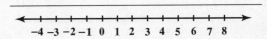

Write an inequality to solve the problem. Then solve the inequality.

9. Melinda charges $4 per hour for babysitting. Mrs. Garden does not want to spend more than $25 for babysitting. What is the maximum number of hours that she can have Melinda babysit?

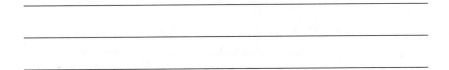

_____

_____

_____

Activity Lab 4-9

Solving Inequalities by Multiplying or Dividing

Find the error, if any, in each exercise. Identify the step(s) in which the error(s) occur, then correct the errors. If the exercise is correct, write, "No errors."

Solve and graph the solution.

1. $x + 13 < 2$

① $x + 13 - 13 < 2 - 13$

② $x < -11$

③

2. $x - 7 \geq 16$

① $x - 7 + 7 \geq 16 + 7$

② $x \geq 23$

③

3. $2y + 4 - y > 6$

① $y + 4 > 6$

② $y + 4 - 4 > 6 + 4$

③ $y > 10$

④

4. $2 + 6 \leq 5n + 8 - 4n$

① $8 \leq n + 8$

② $8 - 8 \leq n + 8 - 8$

③ $0 \leq n$

④

Solve.

5. $-5y \leq 25$

① $\left(-\frac{1}{5}\right)(-5y) \leq \left(-\frac{1}{5}\right)(25)$

② $y \leq -5$

6. $16x > -64$

① $\left(\frac{1}{16}\right)16x > \left(\frac{1}{16}\right)(-64)$

② $x < -4$

7. $-55 \geq -11x$

① $\left(-\frac{1}{11}\right)(-55) \leq \left(-\frac{1}{11}\right)(-11x)$

② $-5 \leq x$

8. $6m < -54$

① $\frac{1}{6}(6m) < \frac{1}{6}(-54)$

② $m < -9$

Translate to an inequality.

9. Twice a number is at most 40.

① $2x < 40$

10. Thirty times a number is less than 30.

① $30n > 30$

11. Seven times a number is under 30.

① $30 > 7y$

12. A number is at most 14.

① $x \leq 14$

13. Three times a number is less than 9.

① $3 < 9y$

14. Sixteen is less than twice a number.

① $2x > 16$

Activity Lab

Reteaching 4-9

Solving Inequalities by Multiplying and Dividing

To solve an inequality you can multiply or divide each side by the same number. However, if the number is negative, you must also reverse the direction of the inequality sign.

Solve $-4y \geq 16$. Graph the solution.

$$-4y \geq 16$$

$$\frac{-4y}{-4} \leq \frac{16}{-4}$$ Divide each side by -4.
Reverse the direction
of the inequality symbol.

$$y \leq -4$$ Simplify.

Graph:

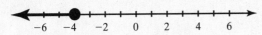

Solve $\frac{w}{3} > 2$. Graph the solution.

$$\frac{w}{3} > 2$$

$$(3)\frac{w}{3} > 2(3)$$ Multiply each side by 3.
$$w > 6$$ Simplify.

Graph:

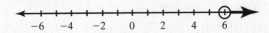

Solve each inequality. Graph the solution.

1. $2a > 10$ _____

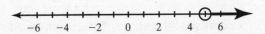

2. $-4w < 16$ _____

3. $\frac{r}{2} \geq -2$ _____

4. $\frac{a}{3} < 1$ _____

5. $6g < 6$ _____

6. $-3x \geq -6$ _____

7. $\frac{m}{-2} > 0$ _____

Enrichment 4-9

Solving Inequalities by Multiplying or Dividing

Critical Thinking

Many companies throughout the United States and Europe have been rating their customer management performance through a benchmark program. This program measures the average performance of customer satisfaction in various different categories.

The table to the right shows the average scores a computer company has received so far this year in their Information and Technology department. How does the company need to score in *managing customer information* to achieve an overall average score greater than 40?

Information and Technology	Average Score
Acquiring customer information	49
Managing customer information	?
Current system functions	32
Developing new systems	52

Source: http://www.qci.co.uk/Home_page.asp

1. Write an inequality to represent the overall score that the company wants to achieve.

   _____

2. What operations do you use to find an average?

   _____

3. Let x represent the score of managing customer information. Write an inequality that represents the desired average of the Information and Technology department.

   _____

4. Solve the inequality in Step 3. _____

5. Based on the other scores in the table, do you think the company can achieve their goal? Explain why or why not.

   _____

   _____

6. To be awarded a national certificate of achievement, the computer company must have an overall average in their Information and Technology Department of no less than 51.

   a. Write and solve an inequality to find what the company must score in managing customer information to achieve the certificate.

   _____

   b. Based on the other scores in the table, do you think the company can achieve the certificate? Explain why or why not.

   _____

   _____

4E: Vocabulary Check

For use after Lesson 4-9

Study Skill Strengthen your vocabulary. Use these pages and add cues and summaries by applying the Cornell Notetaking style.

Write the definition for each word or term at the right. To check your work, fold the paper back along the dotted line to see the correct answers.

_____   variable

_____

_____

_____   algebraic expression

_____

_____   equation

_____

_____

_____   open sentence

_____

_____

_____   inverse operations

_____

_____

4E: Vocabulary Check (continued)   **For use after Lesson 4-9**

Write the vocabulary word or term for each definition. To check your
work, fold the paper forward along the dotted line to see the correct
answers.

a symbol that represents one or
more numbers

_____

a mathematical expression with at
least one variable

_____

a mathematical sentence with an
equal sign

_____

an equation with one or more
variables

_____

operations that undo each other

_____

4F: Vocabulary Review

Study Skill Review notes that you have taken in class as soon as possible to clarify any points you missed and to refresh your memory.

Circle the word that best completes the sentence.

1. A (*variable, expression*) is a letter that stands for a number.

2. An (*expression, equation*) is a mathematical statement with an equal sign.

3. A (*solution, sentence*) is a value for a variable that makes an equation true.

4. To solve an equation, use (*inverse, variable*) operations.

5. A mathematical statement that contains $<$ or $>$ is called an (*equation, inequality*).

6. The statement $4 + (9 + 3) = (4 + 9) + 3$ is an example of the (*Commutative Property of Addition, Associative Property of Addition*).

7. The (*opposite, absolute value*) of 15 is -15.

8. The (*mean, median*) is the middle number in a data set when the data is arranged from least to greatest.

9. You can use the (*commutative, identity*) property to change the order in an expression.

10. The statement $a + 0 = a$ is an example of the (*Identity Property of Zero, Identity Property of Multiplication*).

11. The (*absolute value, opposite*) of a number is its distance from 0 on a number line.

12. (*Rational numbers, Integers*) are the set of whole numbers, their opposites, and zero.

13. Two numbers whose sum is 0 are (*additive, opposite*) inverses.

14. A(n) (*outlier, range*) is a data value that is much greater or less than the other values in the data set.

15. Using the (*distributive property, order of operations*), you can calculate that $12 + 5 \cdot 2$ equals 22.

Puzzle 4-9

Solving Inequalities by Multiplying or Dividing

Each solution is missing a symbol. Solve each inequality and select the correct symbol, and then write the letter of the symbol you selected above the exercise number at the bottom of the page.

1. $3y \geq 15$

$y \;\boxed{}\; 5$

   A. $\geq$ B. $\leq$

2. $-5k < -35$

$k \;\boxed{}\; 7$

   C. $>$ D. $<$

3. $x + (-7) \geq 14$

$x \;\boxed{}\; 21$

   E. $\geq$ F. $\leq$

4. $\dfrac{-y}{6} < 2$

$y \;\boxed{}\; 12$

   N. $<$ O. $>$

5. $\dfrac{m}{-2} \geq -16$

$m \;\boxed{}\; 32$

   K. $\geq$ L. $\leq$

6. $4t > -16$

$t \;\boxed{}\; -4$

   B. $>$ C. $<$

7. $-3s \leq 21$

$s \;\boxed{}\; -7$

   Q. $\leq$ R. $\geq$

8. $x - 1 > -5$

$x \;\boxed{}\; -4$

   U. $>$ V. $<$

9. $\dfrac{x}{-4} \leq \dfrac{1}{-4}$

$x \;\boxed{}\; 1$

   M. $\leq$ N. $\geq$

10. $-15m < 5$

$m \;\boxed{}\; -\dfrac{5}{15}$

   Y. $>$ Z. $<$

To solve the inequalities, make sure you do not lose:

$\overline{}\;\;\overline{}\;\;\overline{}\;\;\overline{}\qquad\overline{}\;\;\overline{}\;\;\overline{}\;\;\overline{}\;\;\overline{}\;\;\overline{}\;\;\overline{}$

 10   4   8   7   6   1   5   1   9   2   3

Chapter 4 Project: Read All About It!

Make a Savings Plan

Beginning the Chapter Project

Flexible hours! Great pay! Work before or after school! Newspaper deliverers needed! Suppose to earn extra money you get a job delivering newspapers in your neighborhood. You plan to save the money you make so that you can buy yourself brand new snow skiing gear.

In this chapter project, you will figure out how much time you can commit to your job, how much money you can earn per week, and how much money you need to make per week in order to reach your savings goal.

As part of your final project you will write a letter to your boss at the newspaper office describing your level of commitment as a newspaper deliverer.

Activities

Activity 1: Planning

As a newspaper deliverer you will be paid $0.10 for every daily paper that you deliver and $0.30 for every weekend paper that you deliver. Write this payment plan as an algebraic expression.

Activity 2: Evaluating

There are 220 houses in your neighborhood. You will be delivering the daily paper to 95 homes and the weekend paper to 167 homes. Use your expression from Activity 1 to find how much money you can earn in one day delivering the daily paper. Then find how much money you can earn in one day delivering the weekend paper.

Write and solve an equation showing how much money you can make delivering the paper over a one-week period. Show your work. Did you remember to follow the order of operations?

Chapter 4 Project: Read All About It! (continued)

Activity 3: Analyzing

Do you think you have enough time in the day to handle a job? Take a look at your daily schedule and compare it to your weekend schedule. You will need to plan at least 2 hours per day to deliver the daily paper and 5 hours per day to deliver the weekend paper.

Do you have at least two hours before or after school available every day? Do you have at least 5 hours on each weekend day available? Make a schedule that you can give to your boss showing the hours you will work each day. As a motive for you to work, figure out your hourly rate of pay. Use the weekly pay from Activity 2, and the minimum number of hours required per week, to write and solve an equation.

Activity 4: Calculating

Use the Internet or newspaper advertisements to determine the cost of new snow skiing equipment. Find the total cost of boots, skis, pants, jacket, goggles, and gloves. Use this total as the minimum amount of money you need to save from your earnings as a newspaper deliverer. Write and solve an inequality to calculate the minimum number of weeks, to the nearest whole number, that you will need to work in order to save enough money to buy the new equipment.

Finishing the Project

Your final product will be to write a letter to your boss at the newspaper office detailing the hours each day that you can work, the amount of money you plan to earn each week and the minimum number of weeks you need to work. Be sure your work is neat and clear. Write any explanations you think are necessary.

Reflect and Revise

Ask a classmate to review your project with you. Is your work schedule realistic? Is the cost of the snow skiing equipment reasonable? Are your calculations complete and accurate? Is the information in the letter presented in a clear and appropriate manner? If necessary, make changes to improve your project.

Visit PHSchool.com for information and links you might find helpful as you complete your project.

Chapter Project Manager

Getting Started

Read about the project. As you work on it, you will need several sheets of paper. If available, a spreadsheet program can be used. Keep all your work for the project in a folder, along with this Project Manager.

Checklist	**Suggestions**
❑ Activity 1: planning	❑ Be sure to define a variable for each unknown.
❑ Activity 2: evaluating	❑ Remember there are 5 days during the week and 2 weekend days. Review the order of operations before solving the equation.
❑ Activity 3: analyzing	❑ Make a timeline of each day to give yourself a visual display of your schedule.
❑ Activity 4: calculating	❑ Review the inequality symbols. Define a variable for the number of weeks.
❑ Recommendations	❑ When writing the letter to your boss, use proper letter writing format. Be sure to check your spelling, grammar, and punctuation.

Scoring Rubric

3 Your expressions and equations are complete and accurate. Your letter includes a detailed weekly schedule, a weekly pay rate, and the minimum number of whole weeks that you need to work. Your findings are accurate and the letter is written neatly in proper letter format with no spelling or grammatical errors.

2 Your letter is written neatly and is in proper form, but does not include all key elements. Almost all of your calculations are accurate.

1 Many of your calculations are inaccurate. Your letter is written in proper form but does not provide accurate information and is missing some key elements.

0 Major elements of the project are incomplete or missing. Your calculations of the weekly pay and the minimum weeks required are either inaccurate or disorganized. Your letter is not written at all or is not in proper form.

Your Evaluation of Project   Evaluate your work, based on the Scoring Rubric.

Teacher's Evaluation of Project

Chapter Project Teacher Notes

About the Project

Students will have an opportunity to use their knowledge of equations and inequalities to evaluate a job as a newspaper deliverer.

Introducing the Project

Ask students:

- *Have you ever considered getting a job?*

- *Are there items you wish you could buy but do not have the money for?*

- *Do you think you are too busy to work? What amount of pay might entice you to get up early in the morning or to work weekends?*

Activity 1: Planning

Explain the meaning of "daily paper" and "weekend paper." Tell students the price of the local newspaper and see if they think the delivery pay rate seems fair. Ask why they think a newspaper deliverer gets paid more for a weekend paper than for a daily paper.

Activity 2: Evaluating

Point out to students that not everyone in the neighborhood receives a newspaper. This is typical of many neighborhoods. Have students build on the expression that they wrote in Activity 1 to help them write the equation. Review the order of operations with students so that when they solve the equation, they multiply first before they add.

Activity 3: Analyzing

Encourage students to organize their schedule into a table or a timeline. Encourage students to figure out a way to make time to work 2 hours every morning or after school, and 5 hours each weekend day.

Activity 4: Calculating

Encourage students to use the Internet to search for equipment prices. They can search for example using the words, *skiing equipment*.

Finishing the Project

You may wish to plan a project day on which students share their completed projects. Encourage students to read aloud their letters.

Visit PHSchool.com for information and links you might find helpful as you complete your project.

Name _____ Class _____ Date _____

✔ Checkpoint Quiz 1

Use with Lessons 4-1 through 4-4.

Write an algebraic expression for each word phrase.

1. five less than a number

_____

2. 7 times a number

_____

3. the quotient of 2 and a number

_____

4. the sum of a number and 8

_____

Solve each equation.

5. $h - 4 = -8$

_____

6. $y + 5 = 12$

_____

7. $-6x = 36$

_____

8. $\frac{y}{4} = 3$

_____

9. Janet was born in 1973. She is 12 years older than Marta. Write and solve an equation to find the year that Marta was born.

_____

10. Ben can make 3 pizzas in an hour. How long will it take him to make 27 pizzas?

_____

- - - - ✂ -

Name _____ Class _____ Date _____

✔ Checkpoint Quiz 2

Use with Lessons 4-5 through 4-7.

Solve each equation

1. $2h - 4 = 8$

_____

2. $\frac{y}{3} - 4 = 9$

_____

3. $-3x - 4 = -7$

_____

Write an equation. Then solve.

4. Four more than three times a number is 19. _____

5. A new scooter costs $15 less than twice the cost of a skateboard. The scooter costs $78.00. Find the cost of the skateboard. _____

Graph eac h inequality.

6. $x > 4$

7. $y \le -3$

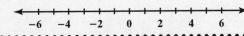

8. $w < 5$

9. $t \ge -2$

Chapter Test   Form A

Chapter 4

Evaluate each expression using the values *w* = 4, *a* = 2, and *h* = 5.

1. $w + a$

2. $h + 2w$

3. $w \div a$

4. $6w + 2a$

5. $3(h + w)$

6. $5w + 2a$

Solve each equation.

7. $x + 8 = 13$

8. $m - 9 = 21$

9. $5a = 55$

10. $9y = 81$

11. $6 + n = 20$

12. $\frac{y}{4} = 8$

13. $\frac{y}{-3} + 2 = -13$

14. $16 + 2n = 10$

Write an equation for each problem. Solve the equation.

15. The math club made a total of $1,155 from selling 210 T-shirts. How much did they sell each T-shirt for?

16. A youth baseball league recently completed registration. The league was able to form 15 teams of 11 players each. How many players registered?

Chapter Test (continued)

Form A

Chapter 4

Write an inequality for each verbal statement.

17. The maximum storage temperature on a particular medicine is 85°.

_____

18. To ride an amusement park ride you must be at least 48 inches tall.

_____

19. There are less than 200 tickets remaining for the baseball game.

_____

Solve each inequality. Graph your solution.

20. $n + 15 \geq 21$

_____

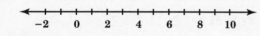

21. $y - 16 > 12$

_____

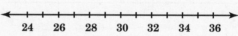

22. $13x < -65$

_____

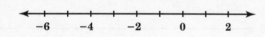

23. $\frac{p}{-4} \leq -2$

_____

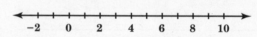

24. $-3x < -6$

_____

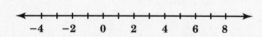

25. $\frac{y}{7} \geq -2$

_____

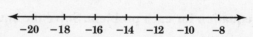

Write an inequality for each problem. Solve the inequality.

26. While shopping for school clothes Janice and Patty spent more than $175. Janice spent $34. How much did Patty spend?

_____

27. A transfer bus can carry 50 people per run At least how many times does the bus have to run in order to transfer 25,000 people?

_____

Chapter Test

Form B

Chapter 4

Evaluate each expression using the values $w = 4$ and $h = 5$.

1. $2h - 4$

_____

2. $h + 2w$

_____

3. $w \div 2$

_____

4. $6w + 4$

_____

5. $3(h + w)$

_____

6. $5w + h - 1$

_____

Solve each equation.

7. $x + 8 = 13$

_____

8. $m - 9 = 21$

_____

9. $5a = 55$

_____

10. $6 + n = 20$

_____

11. $\frac{y}{4} = 8$

_____

12. $16 + 2n = 10$

_____

Write an equation for each problem. Solve the equation.

13. The math club made a total of $1,155 from selling 210 T-shirts. How much did they sell each T-shirt for?

_____

14. A youth baseball league recently completed registration. The league was able to form 15 teams of 11 players each. How many players registered?

_____

Chapter Test (continued) · Form B

Chapter 4

Write an inequality for each verbal statement.

15. The maximum storage temperature on a particular medicine is 85°.

_____

16. There are less than 200 tickets remaining for the baseball game.

_____

Solve each inequality. Graph your solution.

17. $n + 15 \geq 21$

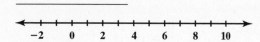

18. $y - 16 > 12$

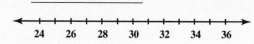

19. $13x < -65$

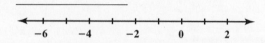

20. $\frac{p}{-4} \leq -2$

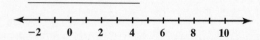

Write an inequality for each problem. Solve the inequality.

21. While shopping for school clothes Janice and Patty spent more than $175. Janice spent $34. How much did Patty spend?

_____

22. A transfer bus can carry 50 people per run. At least how many times does the bus have to run in order to transfer 25,000 people?

_____

Alternative Assessment

Form C

Chapter 4

ALGEBRA AT THE AMUSEMENT PARK

You just walked into the Amazing Amusement Park and are ready to buy tickets for the rides and games. The park sells tickets based on the "class" of a ride or a game. The chart below lists the names of the rides and games in the park in three classes: A, B, and C. One Class A ticket costs $1.50, one Class B ticket costs $2.00, and one Class C ticket costs $3.00.

Class A	Class B	Class C
Spider Swing	Bump Cars	Roller Coaster
Wiggly Worm	MicroCoaster	Ferris Wheel
Creepy Crawler	Water Roller	Wacky Wheel
Bongo Bears	Balloon Pop	Haunted House
Dancing Does	Basket Throw	Magic Mouse
Hoppity Hip	Jungle Gym	On the Wet Side

Show all of your work on a separate sheet of paper.

1. You asked your friend Marina how much she was going to spend on tickets. She decided to play a game with you. On a piece of paper, she wrote this algebraic expression:

$$2A + 3B + 2C$$

   She said, "*A* is the cost of a Class A ticket, *B* is the cost of a Class B ticket, and *C* is the cost of a Class C ticket." How much was Marina going to spend altogether? Show your work.

2. You may buy a total of six tickets. Which six activities would you choose? List each activity and the class of ticket it requires. (Although there may be some rides or games listed that you have never heard of, you should be able to imagine what each is like based on its name.)

3. **a.** Marina asked you how much you were going to spend. Playing Marina's game, write the algebraic expression that shows how much you would have to spend on the six rides and games you chose in Question 2 above.

   b. How much will all these activities cost you?

4. Max asked how much both you and Marina were going to spend on tickets. Marina continued to play her game. She wrote an expression with three terms that represented the amount the two of you were going to spend together. What expression might she have written? Be sure to write the expression in simplest terms.

Alternative Assessment (continued)   Form C

Chapter 4

5. Maggie and Millie wanted to play the game, too. They said they each wanted 20 tickets, and they wrote their total cost like this:

$$8A + 9B + 23C$$

They asked you to guess how many of each class of ticket each of them wanted. Write an expression that *could* represent the cost of the tickets Maggie wanted and another expression that *could* represent the cost of the tickets Millie wanted. (There is no *correct* amount for each.)

6. The amusement park also sells packets of tickets. There are three different sizes of packets, which are described by the following expressions:

Cost	Tickets in Packet
$15 Mini Pack	$2A + 3B + 4C$
$25 Regular Pack	$2A + 4B + 8C$
$65 Giant Pack	$5A + 10B + 20C$

Calculate how much you would save by buying each size packet instead of individual tickets. Show your work.

7. Assume that you buy a Mini Pack. Name the rides or games on which you would use each of your tickets. Write the class of ticket next to each ride or game.

Excursion

Maggie and Millie want to put their money together to buy their tickets for the least amount of money possible. (Remember that they want 8 A tickets, 9 B tickets, and 23 C tickets.) Find the least expensive way for them to buy their tickets, using any combination of ticket packets and individual tickets. The purchase should include *at least* the number of each class of ticket they want. It is acceptable for them to buy more tickets than they want if they save money by doing so.

How much would they save using your procedure instead of buying all individual tickets?

Cumulative Review

Chapters 1–4

Multiple Choice. Circle the letter of the best answer.

1. Find the mean and median of these bowling scores.

   123 138 142 133

   A. 134 and 19   **B.** 123 and 142

   C. 135 and 135.5   **D.** 134 and 135.5

2. Use $C = 35h + p$ to find the cost (C) of having a car tuned up if the charges are $35 per hour ($h$) for labor plus the cost of parts (p). The mechanic estimates it will require 2 hours of labor and $75 for parts.

   F. $220   **G.** $110

   H. $145   **J.** $35

3. Order from least to greatest.

   0.586 0.865 0.658 0.568

   A. 0.865, 0.658, 0.568, 0.586

   B. 0.658, 0.568, 0.865, 0.586

   C. 0.586, 0.568, 0.658, 0.865

   D. 0.568, 0.586, 0.658, 0.865

4. Pierre drove 305.8 miles on one tank of gas. Then he filled the tank with 11 gallons of gas. What was the average number of miles per gallon?

   F. 27.8   **G.** 28

   H. 30   **J.** 40

5. Which multiplication property is shown?
   $8(6.3) = 8(6) + 8(0.3)$

   A. Identity Property

   B. Commutative Property

   C. Associative Property

   D. Distributive Property

6. Use mental math to find the sum.

   $5.3 + 6.2 + 4.7 + 4.8$

   F. 20.0   **G.** 21.0

   H. 22.0   **J.** 23.0

7. Mark bought a salad special for $4.95. His brother bought a chicken special for $5.50. If the tax was $.55, how much change did they get back from a $20 bill?

   A. $10   **B.** $9

   C. $9.50   **D.** $8

8. When multiplying two factors, each with one decimal place, how many decimal places should the answer have?

   F. 0   **G.** 1

   H. 2   **J.** 3

9. Which of the following is true?

   A. $5 + (5 \div 5) - 5 = 1$

   B. $5 \times (5 + 5) - 5 = 25$

   C. $5 - 5 \times (5 - 5) = 0$

   D. $5 \div 5 + 5 + 5 = 75$

10. Solve the equation. $4y - 6 = -18$

    F. 3   **G.** 6

    H. -3 **J.** -6

11. Evaluate $8n - 3m$ for $n = 4$ and $m = 3$.

    A. 23   **B.** 50

    C. 41   **D.** 10

Cumulative Review (continued)

Chapter 1–4

12. The German Club members had a bake sale. They sold small cookies for $.35 and large cookies for $1.00. The ingredients cost $4.95. Which expression shows how much money they made from the sale of the cookies?

    F. $(0.35 + 1) - 4.95n$

    G. $0.35n + m - 4.95$

    H. $1.35n - 4.95$

    J. $1.35n + 4.95$

13. Which statement is *not* true about variables?

    A. A variable is used to represent a quantity whose values may change or vary.

    B. Letters are often used as variables.

    C. A variable is a rule showing relationships among quantities.

    D. Known values can be substitutes for variables in a formula.

14. Which of the expressions below is not equivalent to $-8 - (-8)$?

    F. $-8 + 8$

    G. 0

    H. $8 - 8$

    J. $-8 + (-8)$

15. Use mental math to simplify $-4 + (-6) - (-4) - (-7)$.

    A. -21

    B. 21

    C. 1

    D. 0

16. Jason opened his savings account with $100. In one week he withdrew $45 to buy presents and $20 to buy a new shirt. He deposited $125 the next week. Which expression could Jason use to show how much money he had after the second deposit?

    F. $100 - 65$

    G. $(100 + 125) - (45 + 20)$

    H. $(100 - 45 + 20) + 125$

    J. $100 + 125 - 45 + 20$

17. Shayna opened a new bank account. She deposited $75.50 on Monday, withdrew $15.75 on Tuesday, withdrew $35.48 on Wednesday, deposited $50.36 on Thursday, and withdrew $60.91 on Friday. What was her balance on Friday?

    A. $15.46   B. $74.63

    C. $13.72   D. $238.00

18. Solve $\frac{3n}{5} - 9 = 0$.

    F. -15 G. 5.4

    H. 15 J. 135

19. If everything to the left of -9 on a graph is shaded, which inequality is represented?

    A. $x \geq -9$ B. $x \leq -9$

    C. $x > -9$ D. $x < -9$

Short Response

20. Tara mows lawns as a summer job. She charges $9.50 for each lawn plus $2.50 for every hour she works. The gasoline she needs to mow an average lawn costs $1.85. Write an expression for the profit Tara makes from cutting a single lawn.

Name _____ Class _____ Date _____

Chapters 1–4 Answers

Chapter 1

Practice (regular) 1-1

1. $6.50 **2.** $3.00 **3.** $19.50 **4.** $4.50 **5.** 11 **6.** 5 **7.** 9 **8.** 6
9. 12 **10.** 13 **11.** 3 **12.** 10 **13.** 5 **14–19.** Sample answers are
given. **14.** $346; rounding **15.** 20; rounding **16.** 4,500; rounding
17. 1,100; rounding **18.** 12; compatible numbers **19.** 42;
front-end estimation **20.** 13; compatible numbers **21.** about $480
22. about 33,600 slices

Guided Problem Solving 1-1

1. eight postcards; $.59 each; $2 total **2.** Estimate the total cost
of eight postcards and stamps. **3.** the product of 8 and $.59
4. $.60 **5.** $4.80 **6.** $2 **7.** $4.80 1 $2 5 $6.80 **8.** yes, 8 3 0.59 1 2
5 6.72, which is close to 6.80 **9.** about $4.80

Practice (adapted) 1-1

1. $6.50 **2.** $3.00 **3.** $19.50 **4.** 11 **5.** 5 **6.** 6 **7.** 12 **8.** 3
9. 10 **10–15.** Sample answers are given. **10.** 20; rounding
11. 4,500; rounding **12.** 1,100; rounding **13.** 12; compatible
numbers **14.** 42; front-end estimation **15.** 13; compatible
numbers **16.** about $480 **17.** about 33,600 slices

Activity Lab 1-1

1–4. Check students' work.

Reteaching 1-1

1.	$\begin{array}{r}9\\+7\\\hline16\end{array}$	**2.**	$\begin{array}{r}13\\-8\\\hline5\end{array}$	**3.**	$\begin{array}{r}\$16\\-5\\\hline\$11\end{array}$
4.	$\begin{array}{r}2\\+1\\\hline3\end{array}$	**5.**	$\begin{array}{r}2\\\times5\\\hline10\end{array}$	**6.**	$\begin{array}{r}7\\\times1\\\hline7\end{array}$
7.	$\begin{array}{r}12\\-11\\\hline1\end{array}$	**8.**	$\begin{array}{r}6\\+1\\\hline7\end{array}$	**9.**	$\begin{array}{r}65\\-22\\\hline43\end{array}$
10.	$\begin{array}{r}27\\\times3\\\hline81\end{array}$	**11.**	$\begin{array}{r}9\\\div4\\\hline2.25\end{array}$	**12.**	$\begin{array}{r}110\\\div11\\\hline10\end{array}$

Enrichment 1-1

1. front-end: $900 \div 10 = 90$; rounding: $1,000 \div 20 = 50$;
compatible numbers: $1,000 \div 20 = 50$. **2.** Sample answer: No;
there would be too many batches made if they use front-end
estimation. **3.** They will need to make about 10 more batches
than originally planned. **4.** Sample answers: Too much; Donate
leftovers to homeless shelters. Not enough; Give coupons to
redeem at next supper.

Puzzle 1-1

1. 6 **2.** 5 **3.** 12 **4.** 2 **5.** 8 **6.** 3 **7.** 10 **8.** 12 **9.** 1 **10.** 12

11. 9 **12.** 2

Practice (regular) 1-2

1. Associative Property **2.** Identity Property **3.** Commutative
Property **4.** Commutative Property **5.** 13.39 **6.** 43.87 **7.** 35.863
8. 41.913 **9.** 18.14 **10.** 17.8 **11.** 113.5 **12.** 67.51 **13.** 100.152
14. 6.67 **15.** 49.84 **16.** 6.29 **17.** 16.39 **18.** 37.39 **19.** 7.98
20. 1.763 **21.** 0.632 **22.** 0.702 **23.** $.55 **24.** $.40 **25.** $.75
26. $.50 **27.** $1.05 **28.** $1.30

Guided Problem Solving 1-2

1. 8.91 in.; 4.24 in. **2.** Find how much more rain there was in
Tallahassee than in St. Augustine. **3.** *how much more*
4. Align the decimal points $\begin{array}{r}8.91\\-4.24\end{array}$ **5.** regroup **6.** 4.67 in.
7. Add 4.67 in. and 4.24 in. to get 8.91 in. **8.** $14.50

Practice (adapted) 1-2

1. Associative Property **2.** Identity Property **3.** Commutative
Property **4.** Commutative Property **5.** 13.39 **6.** 43.87
7. 41.913 **8.** 18.14 **9.** 113.5 **10.** 67.51 **11.** 6.67 **12.** 49.84
13. 16.39 **14.** 37.39 **15.** 1.763 **16.** 0.632 **17.** $.55 **18.** $.40
19. $.75 **20.** $.50 **21.** $1.05 **22.** $1.30

Activity Lab 1-2

1. Bedford to Clermont: 12.4, 6.3, 11.4; Clermont to Sparksville:
13, 11, 21.6; Bedford to Sparksville: 16, 17.3, 31.4 **2.** Check
students' answers. **3.** Check students' answers.

Reteaching 1-2

1. 12.11 **2.** 12.385 **3.** 1.86 **4.** 91.26 **5.** 9.937 **6.** 6.01
7. 11.802 **8.** 3.8 **9.** 31.49 **10.** 0.132 **11.** 7.14 **12.** 11.909

Enrichment 1-2

1.
$$\begin{array}{r}9\;9\;.\;9\;9\;9\\+\;\boxed{8}\;\boxed{7}\;.\;\boxed{6}\;\boxed{5}\;\boxed{5}\\\hline1\;8\;7\;.\;6\;5\;4\end{array}$$

2.
$$\begin{array}{r}2\;3\;\boxed{5}\;.\;0\;\boxed{0}\;9\\+\;\boxed{9}\;7\;.\;8\;9\;\boxed{2}\\\hline\boxed{3}\;3\;2\;.\;9\;0\;1\end{array}$$

3.
$$\begin{array}{r}7\;\boxed{0}\;8\;.\;6\;\boxed{2}\;9\\+\;\boxed{4}\;3\;0\;.\;\boxed{9}\;8\;\boxed{6}\\\hline1\;1\;3\;\boxed{9}\;.\;6\;1\;5\end{array}$$

4.
$$\begin{array}{r}\boxed{8}\;2\;7\;.\;3\;\boxed{4}\;0\\-\;6\;\boxed{3}\;\boxed{6}\;.\;0\;5\;\boxed{9}\\\hline1\;9\;1\;.\;\boxed{2}\;8\;1\end{array}$$

Chapters 1–4 Answers (continued)

Puzzle 1-2

1. 8; 7; 6; 5; 5 **2.** 5; 0; 9; 8; 2; 3 **3.** 0; 2; 4; 9; 8; 9 **4.** 8; 4; 3; 6; 9; 2
5. 8; 6; 5; 9; 0 Sum = 150

Practice (regular) 1-3

1. 168 **2.** 6.57 **3.** 121.8 **4.** 2,805 **5.** 165 **6.** 1.26 **7.** 2.457
8. 17.94 **9.** 263.479 **10.** 8.2948 **11.** 230.85 **12.** 300,182.9642
13. $5.6 \times 1.2 = 6.72$ **14.** $3.7 \times 2.4 = 8.88$ **15.** $6.5 \times 2.5 = 16.25$
16. $1.02 \times 6.9 = 7.038$ **17.** $4.4 \times 6.51 = 28.644$ **18.** 0.6×9.312
$= 5.5872$ **19.** Commutative Property **20.** Associative Property
21. Zero Property **22.** Identity Property **23.** $5.00 **24.** $18.50

Guided Problem Solving 1-3

1. 2.6 times; 5.2 million **2.** Find how many head of cattle Texas
had. **3.** 5.2 **4.** 2.6 times more **5.** 2.6×5.2 **6.** 2 decimal
places **7.** 1,352 **8.** 13.52 million **9.** 15; yes **10.** $51.68

Practice (adapted) 1-3

1. 168 **2.** 6.57 **3.** 121.8 **4.** 2,805 **5.** 165 **6.** 1.26 **7.** 2.457
8. 17.94 **9.** 263.479 **10.** $5.6 \times 1.2 = 6.72$ **11.** $3.7 \times 2.4 = 8.88$
12. $1.02 \times 6.9 = 7.038$ **13.** $4.4 \times 6.51 = 28.644$ **14.** Commutative
Property **15.** Associative Property **16.** Zero Property **17.** Identity
Property **18.** $5.00 **19.** $18.50

Activity Lab 1-3

$1.89; $2.17; $1.46; $2.33; $1.73; $1.95; $1.06; $1.24; $1.84

Reteaching 1-3

1. 10.224 **2.** 9.02 **3.** 1.533 **4.** 21.344 **5.** 0.14 **6.** 1.015
7. 10.143 **8.** 5.208 **9.** 0.0225 **10.** 3,465.6 **11.** 19.2×12.3
$= 236.16$ **12.** $4.35(2.44) = 10.6140$ **13.** $14 \times 8.66 = 121.24$
14. $10.821 \times 62.4 = 675.2304$ **15.** $1.321 \times 2.23 = 2.94583$
16. $0.233 \times 19.22 = 4.47826$

Enrichment 1-3

1. 78; 7.8; 0.78; 0.078 **2.** 78; 7.8; 0.78; 0.078 **3–13.** Sample
answers are given. **3.** Corresponding products are the same
because the factors of each problem have the same number of
decimal places. **4.** (3)0.0000026; (0.3)0.000026; (0.03)0.00026
5. $16 \times 11.75 = 188$ **6.** $16 \times 1.175 = 18.8$ **7.** $16 \times 0.1175 = 1.88$
8. $16 \times 0.01175 = 0.188$ **9.** $16 \times 0.001175 = 0.0188$
10. $16 \times 0.0001175 = 0.00188$ **11.** $16 \times 0.00001175 = 0.000188$
12. $16 \times 0.000001175 = 0.0000188$
13. $0.000000016 \times 1175 = 0.0000188$

Puzzle 1-3

1. $0.52 **2.** $2.55 **3.** $24.36 **4.** $25.06/hr **5.** 50.2 ft **6.** 4.23 ft

Practice (regular) 1-4

1. 0.007 **2.** 48.5 **3.** 0.708 **4.** 35 **5.** 84,700 **6.** 3 **7.** 3,260

8. 50.2 **9.** 6 **10.** 42.5 **11.** 185 **12.** 79 **13.** 1.01 **14.** 0.213
15. 0.028 **16.** 0.062 **17.** 1.625 **18.** 2.25 **19.** 8.32
20. 15.325 **21.** 5.625 **22.** 32.25 **23.** 2.4 lbs **24.** $4.46

Guided Problem Solving 1-4

1. $2.25/yd; $31.50 **2.** Find how much sod the landscape architect
buys. **3.** division **4.** $31.50 **5.** $2.25 **6.** 14 **7.** 31.5; yes
8. 12 boards

Practice (adapted) 1-4

1. 0.007 **2.** 48.5 **3.** 0.708 **4.** 35 **5.** 84,700 **6.** 3 **7.** 3,260
8. 50.2 **9.** 6 **10.** 42.5 **11.** 185 **12.** 79 **13.** 1.625 **14.** 2.25
15. 15.325 **16.** 5.625 **17.** 2.4 lbs **18.** $4.46

Activity Lab 1-4

1. 78; 7.8; 0.78 **2.** 78; 7.8; 0.78 **3.** Sample answer: Products with
the same number of decimal places are equivalent.
4. Sample answer: 3×0.0000026; 0.3×0.000026; $0.003 \times$
0.00026 **5.** 34; 340; 3,400; 34,000 **6.** 34; 3.4; 0.34; 0.034
7. Sample answer: Decreasing the divisor by a power of 10
increases the quotient by the same; decreasing the dividend by
a power of 10 decreases the quotient by the same. **8.** Sample
answer: $0.000408 \div 12$; $0.00408 \div 120$; $0.0408 \div 1,200$

Reteaching 1-4

1. $51)\overline{3519}$ **2.** $18)\overline{149}$ **3.** $32)\overline{396,800}$ **4.** $6)\overline{94.8}$ **5.** $8)\overline{21,120}$
6. $49)\overline{945.7}$ **7.** 7.9 **8.** 55 **9.** 1,100 **10.** 4.5 **11.** 20,100
12. 8 **13.** $18.6 \div 2.4 = 7.75$ **14.** $44.66 \div 11.2 = 3.9875$
15. $48.15 \div 16.05 = 3.0$ **16.** $10.8 \div 0.9 = 12.0$ **17.** 111.6018
$\div 16.2 = 6.889$ **18.** $41.35456 \div 3.2 = 12.9233$

Enrichment 1-4

1. 34; 340; 3,400; 34,000 **2.** 34; 3.4; 0.34; 0.034 **3.** Sample
answer: Decreasing divisor by power of ten increases quotient
by same; decreasing dividend by power of ten decreases
quotient by same. **4.** Sample answer: $0.000408 \div 12$;
$0.00408 \div 120$; $0.0408 \div 1,200$

5.

34.83	÷	0.0000215	=	**1,620,000**
34.83	÷	**0.000215**	=	162,000
34.83	÷	0.00215	=	**16,200**
34.83	÷	0.0215	=	**1,620**
34.83	÷	**0.215**	=	162
34.83	÷	**2.15**	=	16.2
34.83	÷	21.5	=	**1.62**
34.83	÷	**215**	=	0.162

Chapters 1–4 Answers (continued)

Puzzle 1-4

39.06; 26.04; 12.6; 2; 3; 1; 2; 5; 4; Code: 31254

Practice (regular) 1-5

1. 18 cm **2.** 100 m **3.** 25 mm **4.** 250 mL **5.** 700 **6.** 0.04
7. 83,000 **8.** 9.5 **9.** 0.008 **10.** 800,000 **11.** 43.014 km
12. 8,415 cm **13.** 9.421 kg **14.** 14.007 L **15.** g **16.** cm **17.** L
18. cm **19.** km **20.** mm **21.** 26 **22.** 2 **23.** 3,300 mL or 3.3 L
24. 2 grams

Guided Problem Solving 1-5

1. 350 mL; 2 L **2.** Find how many coffee mugs you can fill
from a 2 L container. **3.** 1,000 mL **4.** 2 L **5.** multiply
6. 2,000 mL **7.** divide **8.** 5 mugs **9.** less than 2,000 mL; yes
10. Yes; 0.5 L is 500 mL, which is greater than 300 mL.

Practice (adapted) 1-5

1. 18 cm **2.** 100 m **3.** 25 mm **4.** 250 mL **5.** 700 **6.** 0.04
7. 9.5 **8.** 0.008 **9.** 43.014 km **10.** 8,415 cm **11.** 9.421 kg
12. g **13.** cm **14.** L **15.** cm **16.** 26 **17.** 2 **18.** 2 grams

Activity Lab 1-5

1. c; 2 cm = 20 mm **2.** e; 6 cm = 60 mm **3.** a; 0.7 cm = 7 mm
4. b; 1.6 cm = 16 mm
5. d; 3.2 cm = 32 mm

Reteaching 1-5

1. larger to smaller unit; multiply; 1,000; 16,000 **2.** smaller to larger
unit; divide; 1,000; 1.6 **3.** 600 **4.** 162,000 **5.** 1 mm **6.** 50 m

Enrichment 1-5

1. 472.44 in. **2.** 0.35 ft **3.** one centimeter **4.** one meter
5. There are fewer of the larger unit. **6.** There are more of the
smaller unit. **7.** 4,389.17 cm **8.** The larger the unit, the smaller
the quantity and vice versa.

Puzzle 1-5

1. C **2.** D **3.** B **4.** E **5.** F **6.** A **7.** G **8.** H

Practice (regular) 1-6

1. −8 **2.** 3 **3.** −4 **4.** 9 **5.** 7 **6.** −2 **7.** < **8.** > **9.** =
10. < **11.** < **12.** > **13.** > **14.** >
15.
16.
17.
18.
19. 2 **20.** 3 **21.** 38 **22.** 3 **23.** 44 **24.** 7 **25.** 16 **26.** 4 **27.** 5

28. −5 **29.** 100 **30.** −135

Guided Problem Solving 1-6

1. the person with the lowest score **2.** Compare the numbers
on a number line.
3. ; −12
4. −12, −5, −4, −3, +10 **5.** T. Woods, R. Goosen, V. Singh, P.
Mickelson, E. Els **6.** yes; yes **7.** best: −11; worst: +13

Practice (adapted) 1-6

1. −8 **2.** 3 **3.** −4 **4.** 9 **5.** 7 **6.** −2 **7.** < **8.** > **9.** =
10. < **11.** > **12.** >
13.
14.
15.
16.
17. 2 **18.** 3 **19.** 38 **20.** 44 **21.** 7 **22.** 16 **23.** 5 **24.** −5
25. 100 **26.** −135

Activity Lab 1-6

Check students' work.

Reteaching 1-6

1. > **2.** < **3.** > **4.** > **5.** < **6.** > **7.** < **8.** < **9.** >
10. > **11.** < **12.** > **13.** 6 **14.** 3 **15.** 8 **16.** 9 **17.** 5
18. 0 **19.** 6 **20.** 10 **21.** 20 **22.** −4, −2, 0, 1, 5 **23.** −6,
−5, −3, 4, 6 **24.** −7, −5, −4, 0, 3, 4 **25.** −7, −6, −2, 1, 3, 5

Enrichment 1-6

1. All, because all depths are *below* sea level. **2.** California:
−11,357; Russia: −31,911; South Africa: −15,005; China: −2000
3.
4.
Use a number line to compare. **5.** −31,911, −15,005,
−11,357, −2,000 **6.** Order absolute values from greatest to
least. **7.** −1,312, −512, −282, −131 **8.** Valdes Peninsula

Puzzle 1-6

Francis: −406; Thuy: 299; Eduardo: 509; Vanita: −354;
Henrietta: 201

Chapters 1–4 Answers (continued)

Practice (regular) 1-7

1. −5 **2.** 5 **3.** 3 **4.** 12 **5.** −8 **6.** −3 **7.** −14 **8.** 2 **9.** −17
10. −19 **11.** 28 **12.** 43 **13.** 27 **14.** 28 **15.** −254 **16.** −239
17. 51 **18.** −152 **19.** 9 **20.** 108 **21.** 7 **22.** 2 **23.** 10 **24.** −6
25. −9 **26.** −15 **27.** > **28.** > **29.** > **30.** > **31.** < **32.** =
33. 147°F **34.** 147°F

Guided Problem Solving 1-7

1. 134°F; −80°F; difference **2.** Find the difference between
134°F and −80°F. **3.** *difference* **4.** 134 − (−80) **5.** a positive
number **6.** 134 + 80 **7.** 214°F **8.** −80°F **9.** 38°F

Practice (adapted) 1-7

1. −5 **2.** 5 **3.** 3 **4.** −8 **5.** −3 **6.** −14 **7.** −17 **8.** −19
9. 28 **10.** 27 **11.** 28 **12.** −254 **13.** 51 **14.** −152 **15.** 9
16. 7 **17.** 2 **18.** −6 **19.** −9 **20.** > **21.** > **22.** > **23.** <
24. 147°F

Activity Lab 1-7

Check students' work.

Reteaching 1-7

1. 6 **2.** −5 **3.** 1 **4.** 10 **5.** 25 **6.** −4 **7.** 9 **8.** −8 **9.** −3
10. −2 **11.** 11 **12.** 5 **13.** (−4); −7 **14.** (−2); 3 **15.** 10; 4
16. −1 **17.** −9 **18.** −1 **19.** 25 **20.** −22 **21.** −22 **22.** 1
23. 1 **24.** 16 **25.** −3 **26.** −2 **27.** 10

Enrichment 1-7

1. $53 **2.** $73 **3.** $20 **4.** $39

Puzzle 1-7

The numbers in the triangles are equal.
1. 1; 1; −1; 3; 2; 2 **2.** −4; 5; 2; −1; 1; 1 **3.** 0; 0; 2; −2; 0; 0
4. −6; 9; 5; −2; 3; 3 **5.** −3; −7; −4; −6; −10; −10
Mystery number = 12

Practice (regular) 1-8

1. positive; check students' answers **2.** negative; check students'
answers **3.** positive; check students' answers **4.** positive; check
students' answers **5.** negative; check students' answers **6.** positive;
check students' answers **7.** negative; check students' answers
8. positive; check students' answers **9.** −4,200 **10.** 3,600 **11.** −5
12. −4,000 **13.** −9 **14.** 80,000 **15.** 3,000 **16.** −8 **17.** −4
18. 13 **19.** 100 **20.** 7 **21.** −30 **22.** −11 **23.** −78 **24.** 20
25. 180 **26.** −8 **27.** −344 **28.** 13

Guided Problem Solving 1-8

1. 180 ft; 30 ft/min **2.** Find the time it takes for the diver to
reach the surface. **3.** divide **4.** 180 ft **5.** 30 ft/min **6.** 6 min
7. 180 ft; yes **8.** 25 min

Practice (adapted) 1-8

1. positive; check students' answers **2.** negative; check students'
answers **3.** positive; check students' answers **4.** positive; check
students' answers **5.** negative; check students' answers **6.** positive;
check students' answers **7.** negative; check students' answers
8. positive; check students' answers **9.** −4,200 **10.** 3,600 **11.** −5
12. −9 **13.** 80,000 **14.** 3,000 **15.** −4 **16.** 13 **17.** 100
18. 7 **19.** −30 **20.** −11 **21.** −78 **22.** 20 **23.** 180

Activity Lab 1-8

1. −108 **2.** −30 **3.** −168 **4.** −144 **5.** one **6.** negative **7.** 51
8. 240 **9.** 54 **10.** 112 **11.** two **12.** positive **13.** −140
15. −192 **16.** −70 **17.** three **18.** negative **19.** 60 **20.** 108
21. 264 **22.** 1,800 **23.** four **24.** positive **25.** A product
containing an even number of negative factors is positive; a
product containing an odd number of negative factors is
negative.

Reteaching 1-8

1. positive **2.** negative **3.** positive **4.** positive **5.** positive
6. negative **7.** positive **8.** negative **9.** positive **10.** negative
11. negative **12.** negative **13.** positive **14.** positive

Enrichment 1-8

1. The numbers decrease by 3 when going from top to bottom
and from right to left.
2.

Column −3										Column 3	
−25	−20	−15	−10	−5	**5**	0	5	10	15	20	25
−20	−16	−12	−8	−4	**4**	0	4	8	12	16	20
−15	−12	−9	−6	−3	**3**	0	3	6	9	12	15	Row 3
−10	−8	−6	−4	−2	**2**	0	2	4	6	8	10
−5	−4	−3	−2	−1	**1**	0	1	2	3	4	5
0	0	0	0	0	**0**	0	0	0	0	0	0
−5	**−4**	**−3**	**−2**	**−1**	×	0	1	2	3	4	5
5	4	3	2	1	−1	0	−1	−2	−3	−4	−5
10	8	6	4	2	−2	0	−2	−4	−6	−8	−10
15	12	9	6	3	−3	0	−3	−6	−9	−12	−15	Row −3
20	16	12	8	4	−4	0	−4	−8	−12	−16	−20
25	20	15	10	5	−5	0	−5	−10	−15	−20	−25

3. Quadrant I shows positive × positive; Quadrants II and IV
show positive × negative; Quadrant III shows negative × negative.

Puzzle 1-8

1a. 3 + 2 = 5 **1b.** 2 + 2 = 4 **1c.** 3 × 1 = 3 **1d.** 2 + 1 = 3
1e. 2 + 0 = 2 WINTER **2a.** 2 + 1 = 3 **2b.** 3 × 1 = 3
2c. 3 + 0 = 3 **2d.** 2 + 2 = 4 **3.** Check students' work.

Chapters 1–4 Answers (continued)

Practice (regular) 1-9

1. 90 **2.** 4.75 **3.** 0.5 **4.** 38 **5.** 27 **6.** 36 **7.** 5 **8.** 9 **9.** 9; 6; 75
10. 4; 4; 6.4 **11.** 9; 0.2; 34.2 **12.** 6; 178.2 **13.** 19.2 **14.** 35.5 **15.** 44.5
16. 36.8 **17.** 99.9 **18.** 62.3 **19.** $(6 + 6) \div 6 \times (6 + 6) = 24$
20. $6 \times (6 + 6) \times 6 - 6 = 426$ **21.** $(6 + 6) \div 6 \times (6 - 6) = 0$
22. $(6 - 6) \times 6 + 6 \div 6 = 1$ **23.** 9,670 ft^2

Guided Problem Solving 1-9

1. Determine the cost of the lilies. **2.** mental math **3.** 30
4. $3 \times \$.98$ **5.** $30(\$1.00 - \$.02)$ **6.** $\$30 - \$.60 = \$29.40$
7. \$29.40 **8.** \$29.40; yes **9.** \$44.65

Practice (adapted) 1-9

1. 90 **2.** 4.75 **3.** 0.5 **4.** 38 **5.** 27 **6.** 36 **7.** 5 **8.** 9 **9.** 3
10. 9; 6; 75 **11.** 4; 4; 6.4 **12.** 35.5 **13.** 44.5 **14.** 99.9 **15.** 62.3
16. $(6 + 6) \div 6 \times (6 + 6) = 24$ **17.** $6 \times (6 + 6) \times 6 - 6 = 426$
18. 9,670 ft^2

Activity Lab 1-9

1. Sample answers: $4 \times 4 \div (4 + 4) =$; $4 \div 4 + 4 \div 4 =$ **2.** 256;
$4 \times 4 \times 4 \times 4 =$ **3.** Sample answer: $(5 + 5) \div 5 - 5 \div 5 =$
4. 35; sample answer: $(3 + 5) \times 6 + 12 \div 6$; sample answer:
$(3 + 5) \times (6 + 12) \div 6$; sample answer: $3 + (5 \times 6) + (12 \div 6)$
5. Check students' work.

Reteaching 1-9

1. 8; 11 **2.** 20 + 6; 26 **3.** 20 + 3 − 2; 21 **4.** 14; 19 **5.** 48;
16; 64 **6.** 12; 6; 18 **7.** 40 **8.** 18 **9.** 25 **10.** 4 **11.** 38 **12.** 5
13. 8; 8; 56 **14.** 4; 0.4; 22.4 **15.** 5; 52 **16.** 14; 70

Enrichment 1-9

1. 62; 0.05 **2.** multiplication **3.** addition **4.** \$65.10 **5.** \$65.10
6. If you use the Distributive Property of multiplication on the
second formula, you get the first. **7.** Sample answer:
$C = p + ip$. You can use mental math to solve the problem.

Puzzle 1-9

A–G. Sample answers are given. **A.** $1 - 4(3 + 2)$
B. $2 - 3(1 + 4)$ **C.** $3 + 1(4 - 2)$ **D.** $2(4 + 3) - 1$
E. $2(4 - 3) + 1$ **F.** $4(2 - 1) + 3$ **G.** $4(3) - 2 + 1$

Practice (regular) 1-10

1. 23 students **2a.** 12 students **2b.** 11 students **3.** mean: 287.5;
median: 300, mode: 200, range: 450 **4.** 50 **5.** lower **6.** 8 points
7. 23 points **8.** 18.4; 18; no mode; 7 **9.** 1.4; 2; 2 and 0; 3

Guided Problem Solving 1-10

1. the number of hours of practice before a concert **2.** Find the
mean, median, and mode of the data. **3.** 12 **4.** 24 **5.** 2 **6.** 0 0
1 1 1 2 2 2 3 3 4 5 **7.** 2 and 2 **8.** 2 **9.** 1 and 2 **10.** 2 **11.** 2
is the mean, median, and mode of the data. **12.** 3 siblings

Practice (adapted) 1-10

1. 23 students **2.** 12 students **3.** mean: 287.5, median: 300,
mode: 200, range: 450 **4.** 50 **5.** 8 points **6.** 23 points
7. 18.4; 18; no mode; 7 **8.** 1.4; 2; 2 and 0; 3

Activity Lab 1-10

1a. \$38,500 **1b.** \$26,000 **1c.** \$25,000 **1d.** \$85,000 **2.** Sample
answer: The advertisement should use the mean because it is
highest. **3.** Sample answer: It is accurate; however, it could be
misleading because many of the salaries are much higher or
much lower than \$38,500. **4.** Sample answer: Using the mode
would give the impression that salaries are lower. **5.** Check
students' answers.

Reteaching 1-10

1. 9 **2.** 12.3 points **3.** 9, 10, 10, 10, 11, 12, 15, 16, 18; 11 points
4. 10 points **5.** 9 points **6.** 28; 30; 23; 25

Enrichment 1-10

1a. \$38,500 **1b.** \$26,000 **1c.** \$25,000 **1d.** \$85,000 **2.** Sample
answer: Mean, because it is the highest salary and will appear
more attractive to prospective employees. **3.** It is accurate.
However, it could be misleading because it implies that most
employees make about \$38,500 **4.** Sample answer: Mode,
because it is the lowest salary and it would appear that workers
are not overpaid. **5.** Sample answers: Mode, because more
employees earn \$25,000 than any other salary; median, because
half the salaries are greater and half are lower.

Puzzle 1-10

1–8. Sample answers are given.
1. 6, 4, 5 **2.** 1, 1, 3, 5, 6 **3.** 1, 3, 5, 5, 6 **4.** 4, 6 **5.** 4, 4, 5, 3 **6.** 1,
1, 1, 1, 3, 2, 5 **7.** 1, 1, 2, 4 **8.** 1, 3, 5

Chapter 1A Graphic Organizer

1. Decimals and Integers **2.** 10 **3.** Writing Gridded Responses
4. Check students' diagrams.

Chapter 1B Reading Comprehension

1. Kareem Abdul-Jabbar **2.** Bill Russell **3.** Bill Russell
4. Shaquille O'Neal **5.** Kareem Abdul-Jabbar **6.** Wilt
Chamberlain and Bill Russell **7.** points per game **8.** Wilt
Chamberlain **9.** b

Chapters 1–4 Answers (continued)

Chapter 1C Reading/Writing Math Symbols

1. E **2.** C **3.** A **4.** G **5.** B **6.** F **7.** D **8.** C **9.** F **10.** B
11. D **12.** G **13.** A **14.** E

Chapter 1D Visual Vocabulary Practice

1. order of operations **2.** Associative Property of Addition
3. mode **4.** range **5.** mean **6.** Distributive Property
7. Commutative Property of Multiplication **8.** Associative
Property of Multiplication **9.** median

Chapter 1E Vocabulary Check

Check students' answers.

Chapter 1F Vocabulary Review Puzzle

C	Q	E	D	E	T	A	J	P	K	A	Z	L	H	N
F	K	E	E	R	E	D	R	O	N	D	A	H	U	N
M	Z	D	W	I	T	E	P	I	E	B	B	I	P	O
R	N	O	U	R	O	L	C	C	V	E	S	E	F	I
A	O	M	B	A	P	B	M	E	I	T	O	V	X	T
N	P	R	J	N	P	I	E	P	T	I	L	A	S	A
G	F	I	R	L	O	T	T	E	U	F	U	T	E	C
E	I	N	P	M	S	A	R	T	B	E	T	K	T	I
Y	O	T	H	G	I	P	A	A	I	I	E	O	R	L
I	D	E	O	O	T	M	N	R	R	N	V	U	O	P
W	A	G	R	F	E	O	V	O	T	K	A	T	I	T
P	D	E	F	N	S	C	O	O	S	E	L	L	J	T
G	K	R	N	N	A	W	S	O	I	G	U	I	R	L
N	M	S	D	K	A	E	V	N	D	S	E	E	U	U
M	E	D	I	A	N	F	M	A	R	O	M	R	L	M

Chapter 1 Checkpoint Quiz 1

1. 40.00 **2.** $9.00 **3.** 2 **4.** 28.34 **5.** 41.56 **6.** 4.446 **7.** 22.5
8. 0.54 **9.** 35.5

Chapter 1 Checkpoint Quiz 2

1. < **2.** > **3.** > **4.** = **5.** 7 **6.** 1.56 **7.** 8 **8.** 240 **9.** 2.78
10. 0.017 **11.** 5,000 cm **12.** 40 mL

Chapter 1 Test (regular)

1. about 1,100 **2.** about 9 **3.** 20.17 **4.** 6.265 **5.** 12.36 **6.** 6.361
7. 1.04 **8.** 91.8 **9.** 20.7 **10.** 51.06 **11.** 1.888 **12.** 0.2692 **13.** 25
14. 0.052 **15.** 2,405 cm **16.** 5.24 kg **17.** 11.017 L **18.** L **19.** mm
20. 25 tricycles **21.** $-10, -6, -4, -3, 0, 7$ **22.** $-1,000, -100,$
$-10, -1, 0, 100$ **23.** > **24.** = **25.** < **26.** 10°C **27.** 0 **28.** 29
29. -5 **30.** -23 **31.** -8 **32.** -16 **33.** 88 **34.** -250
35. Divide 30 by 2. **36.** range: 70; mean: 164.8 **37.** none

Chapter 1 Test (below level)

1. about 1,100 **2.** about 9 **3.** 20.17 **4.** 6.265 **5.** 12.36 **6.** 6.361
7. 20.7 **8.** 0.2692 **9.** 25 **10.** 0.052 **11.** 2,405 cm **12.** 5.24 kg
13. L **14.** mm **15.** 25 tricycles **16.** $-10, -6, -4, -3, 0, 7$
17. $-1,000, -100, -10, -1, 0, 100$ **18.** > **19.** = **20.** < **21.** 0
22. 29 **23.** -5 **24.** -8 **25.** -16 **26.** 88 **27.** Divide 30 by 2.
28. range: 70; mean: 164.8 **29.** none

Chapter 1: Alternative Assessment

Exercise	Points	Explanation
1.	3	The summer movie pass would be cheaper if a person saw more than 20 movies before 5:00 P.M., or more than 12 movies at or after 5:00 P.M. OR other similar argument.
	2	Similar argument, but with computational error
	1	Other argument OR partial argument
	0	No response
2.	1	Any justified response
	0	No justified response
3.	3	Between $165 and $220; one admission per week equals $4.50. The weekly minimum for snacks would be $3.75 per person. The weekly maximum would be $6.50 per person. Therefore, $(2 \times \$4.50 \times 10) + (2 \times \$3.75 \times 10) = \$90.00 + \$75.00 = \$165.00$; $(2 \times \$4.50 \times 10) + (2 \times \$6.50 \times 10) = \$90.00 + \$130.00 = \$220.00$.
	2	Correct process, but uses incorrect number of weeks OR finds correct range of $82.50 − $110.00 for only one child
	1	Other partial correct process OR partial correct answer
	0	No response OR other response
4.	2	At least 3 tasks with reasonable amounts listed
	1	One or two tasks with reasonable amounts listed
	0	No response OR other response
Excursion	5	The number of hours of TV watched before and after 5:00 P.M.; multiplied by the appropriate rates; correct process and totals; logical explanations for comparing movies viewed on a television; accurate data display and written explanation
	4	Same as above, except 1 or 2 computational or estimating errors
	3	Same as above, except 3 or 4 errors
	2	Same as above, except 5 or 6 errors
	1	Partial correct process
	0	No response OR other response

Chapters 1–4 Answers (continued)

Chapter 1 Cumulative Review

1. A **2.** G **3.** A **4.** G **5.** D **6.** F **7.** B **8.** H **9.** A **10.** J
11. C **12.** J **13.** A **14.** H **15.** A **16.** F **17.** D **18.** F
19. −2m; 1m; 3m

Chapter 2

Practice (regular) 2-1

1. 3^5 **2.** 2.7^3 **3.** 11.6^4 **4.** 2^6 **5.** 8.3^5 **6.** 4^8 **7.** $0.5 \times 0.5 \times 0.5$;
0.125 **8.** $(-4) \times (-4) \times (-4) \times (-4) \times (-4)$; −1,024 **9.** $2.7 \times$
2.7; 7.29 **10.** $2 \times 2 \times 2$; 8 **11.** $(-5) \times (-5) \times (-5) \times (-5) \times$
$(-5) \times (-5)$; 15,625 **12.** $8.1 \times 8.1 \times 8.1$; 531.441 **13.** −64
14. −205 **15.** 270 **16.** 1,304 **17.** 5,625 **18.** 20 **19.** 42.592
20. 14 **21.** 26 **22.** 0.648 **23.** 180 **24.** 2.197 **25.** 79.507 **26.** 8 in.

Guided Problem Solving 2-1

1. Determine what number 10^5 is. **2.** the exponent **3.** the base
4. 100,000 **5.** 5 **6.** 100,000 **7.** Yes, because 10^2 has 2 zeros and
magnifies 100 times; 10^3 has 3 zeros and magnifies 1,000 times.
8. 9,000

Practice (adapted) 2-1

1. 3^5 **2.** 2.7^3 **3.** 11.6^4 **4.** 2^6 **5.** 8.3^5 **6.** 4^8 **7.** $0.5 \times 0.5 \times 0.5$;
0.125 **8.** $(-4) \times (-4) \times (-4) \times (-4)$; −1,024 **9.** 2.7×2.7;
7.29 **10.** $2 \times 2 \times 2$; 8 **11.** −64 **12.** −205 **13.** 270 **14.** 1,304
15. 5,625 **16.** 20 **17.** 42.592 **18.** 14 **19.** 26 **20.** 79.507 **21.** 8 in.

Activity Lab 2-1

1. 361 **2.** 1,681 **3.** 11,449 **4.** 1,419,857 **5.** 314,432 **6.** 2,097,152
7. 505,521 **8.** 3,905,738 **9.** 19,208

Reteaching 2-1

1. 6^5 **2.** 0.2^3 **3.** 12×12; 144 **4.** $8 \times 8 \times 8$; 512 **5.** $0.4 \times$
0.4×0.4; 0.064 **6.** 1.4×1.4; 1.96 **7.** 76 **8.** 5 **9.** 4 **10.** 40
11. 113 **12.** 48

Enrichment 2-1

1–30. Sample answers are given. **1.** $4 - 3$ **2.** $4 - 2$ **3.** $4 - 1$
4. $3 + 2 - 1$ **5.** $3 + 2$ **6.** $2 + 4$ **7.** $4 + 2 + 1$ **8.** $4 + 1 + 3$
9. $4 + 3 + 2$ **10.** $4 + 1 + 3 + 2$ **11.** $2 \times 4 + 3$ **12.** $4^2 - (3 + 1)$
13. $4^2 - 3$ **14.** $4^2 - 3 + 1$ **15.** $4^2 - 1$ **16.** 4^2 **17.** $4^2 + 1$
18. $4^2 + 3 - 1$ **19.** $4^2 + 3$ **20.** $4^2 + 3 + 1$ **21.** $4(2 + 3) + 1$
22. $24 - 3 + 1$ **23.** $4 \times 3 \times 2 - 1$ **24.** $4 \times 3 \times 2$
25. $4 \times 3 \times 2 + 1$ **26.** $24 + 3 - 1$ **27.** $(2 + 1)^3$ **28.** $23 + 4 + 1$
29. $4^2 + 13$ **30.** $13 \times 2 + 4$

Puzzle 2-1

1. 4 **2.** 3 **3.** 6 **4.** 8 **5.** 2 **6.** 1 **7.** 24 **8.** 0 Mystery number = 5

Practice (regular) 2-2

1. 55 **2.** 60 **3.** 84 **4.** 45 **5.** 90 **6.** 20 **7.** 70 **8.** 221 **9.** 56
10. 253 **11.** 70 **12.** 144 **13.** 18 necklaces **14.** at 1:30 pm
15. prime **16.** composite **17.** prime **18.** composite
19. $2 \times 3 \times 7$ **20.** $2 \times 5 \times 13$ **21.** $2 \times 3 \times 13$ **22.** $2 \times 3^2 \times 7$
23. 5^3 **24.** $2 \times 3^2 \times 5$ **25.** $2^2 \times 23$ **26.** $2^2 \times 3^2 \times 5$ **27.** 15
28. 6 **29.** 16 **30.** 5 **31.** 6 **32.** 17 **33.** 7 **34.** 3 **35.** 21

Guided Problem Solving 2-2

1. 125, 350, greatest number **2.** Find the greatest common
factor of 350 and 125. **3.** $2 \cdot 5 \cdot 5 \cdot 7$ **4.** $5 \cdot 5 \cdot 5$ **5.** $5 \cdot 5$
6. 25 **7.** 25 seats **8.** 14; 5; no **9.** 12 chairs

Practice (adapted) 2-2

1. 55 **2.** 60 **3.** 84 **4.** 45 **5.** 90 **6.** 20 **7.** 70 **8.** 221 **9.** 56
10. 18 necklaces **11.** prime **12.** composite **13.** prime
14. composite **15.** $2 \times 3 \times 7$ **16.** $2 \times 5 \times 13$ **17.** $2 \times 3 \times 13$
18. $2 \times 3^2 \times 7$ **19.** 5^3 **20.** $2 \times 3^2 \times 5$ **21.** 15 **22.** 6 **23.** 5
24. 6 **25.** 7 **26.** 3

Activity Lab 2-2

Check students' work.

Reteaching 2-2

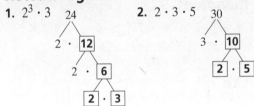

1. $2^3 \cdot 3$ **2.** $2 \cdot 3 \cdot 5$

3. 3^3

4. $2^2 \times 5$
5. 2×3^3
6. $2^3 \times 5$
7. $2^4 \times 3$
8. $2^3 \times 7$
9. $2 \times 3 \times 5^2$

Enrichment 2-2

1. 2 groups of 12, 3 of 8, 4 of 6, 6 of 4, 8 of 3, 12 of 2 **2.** Sample
answers: whether or not all students can see the chalkboard;
whether or not all group members can communicate; whether
or not there is enough aisle space **3.** Sample answers:

Chalkboard

Chalkboard

4. Sample answer: groups of eight, so that there will be
sufficient people to research the topic and write and act in the
skit **5.** Sample answer: It keeps the groups far enough apart.

Chapters 1–4 Answers (continued)

However, some students will have to move to see the chalkboard.

Chalkboard

Puzzle 2-2

1. 3 **2.** 19 **3.** 9 **4.** 9, 19, 3 **5.** Check students' answers.

Practice (regular) 2-3

1. $\frac{2}{3}$ **2.** $\frac{3}{5}$ **3.** $\frac{4}{5}$ **4.** $\frac{4}{5}$ **5.** $\frac{5}{6}$ **6.** $\frac{7}{15}$ **7.** $\frac{1}{4}$ **8.** $\frac{2}{3}$ **9.** $\frac{5}{8}$, 25 **10.** $\frac{9}{16}$, 4
11. $\frac{13}{18}$, 5 **12.** $\frac{5}{8}$, 9 **13.** $\frac{7}{17}$, 5 **14.** $\frac{5}{7}$, 6 **15.** $\frac{9}{20}$h **16.** $\frac{4}{5}$h **17.** $\frac{11}{12}$h
18–19. Check students' answers.

Guided Problem Solving 2-3

1. 75; out of; 365 **2.** Write the number of clear days out of a year in Houston as a fraction in simplest form. **3.** $\frac{90}{365}$ **4.** $2 \cdot 3 \cdot 3 \cdot 5$
5. $5 \cdot 73$ **6.** 5 **7.** 18; 73 **8.** $\frac{18}{73}$ **9.** yes; $365 \div 90 = (90 \times 5) \div (18 \times 5) = 73 \div 18$ **10.** $\frac{11}{12}$

Practice (adapted) 2-3

1. $\frac{2}{3}$ **2.** $\frac{3}{5}$ **3.** $\frac{4}{5}$ **4.** $\frac{5}{6}$ **5.** $\frac{7}{15}$ **6.** $\frac{1}{4}$ **7.** $\frac{5}{8}$, 25 **8.** $\frac{9}{16}$, 4 **9.** $\frac{5}{8}$, 9
10. $\frac{7}{17}$, 5 **11.** $\frac{4}{5}$ h **12.** $\frac{11}{12}$ h **13–14.** Check students' answers.

Activity Lab 2-3

1–5. Sample answers:

$\frac{2}{4} = \frac{4}{8}$

$\frac{1}{4} = \frac{4}{16}$

$\frac{2}{4} = \frac{6}{12}$

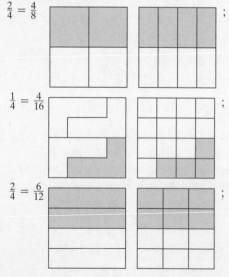

$\frac{3}{4} = \frac{6}{8}$

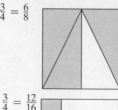

$\frac{3}{4} = \frac{12}{16}$

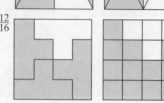

Reteaching 2-3

1. $\frac{10}{20} = \frac{10 \div 2}{20 \div 2} = \frac{5 \div 5}{10 \div 5} = \frac{1}{2}$
2. $\frac{24}{60} = \frac{24 \div 6}{60 \div 6} = \frac{4 \div 2}{10 \div 2} = \frac{2}{5}$ **3.** $\frac{6}{7}$; 2 **4.** $\frac{3}{5}$; 3 **5.** $\frac{5}{6}$; 7 **6.** $\frac{4}{5}$;
10 **7.** $\frac{7}{10}$ **8.** $\frac{5}{9}$ **9.** $\frac{9}{10}$ **10.** $\frac{1}{3}$ **11.** $\frac{1}{3}$ **12.** $\frac{13}{15}$ **13.** $\frac{2}{3}$ **14.** $\frac{10}{19}$

Enrichment 2-3

1–4. Sample answers are given. **1.** Ferdinand $9 and Rachel $6 so that each contributes as much as possible but still has a little left over **2.** Ferdinand would get $\frac{3}{5}$ of the grab bag and Rachel would get $\frac{2}{5}$; $\frac{9}{15} = \frac{3}{5}$ and $\frac{6}{15} = \frac{2}{5}$ **3.** Assign a value to each item and divide them with Ferdinand receiving about $\frac{3}{5}$ of the value and Rachel receiving about $\frac{2}{5}$ **4.** Ferdinand: $12 of the $20 value—2 tickets ($7), 2 combs ($1), 5 tokens ($3), and 1 button ($1); Rachel: $8 of $20 value—calculator ($5), 2 combs ($1), 3 pencils ($1), and 1 button ($1)

Puzzle 2-3

1. $\frac{3}{4}$ **2.** $\frac{5}{7}$ **3.** $\frac{15}{16}$ **4.** $\frac{1}{5}$ **5.** $\frac{3}{8}$ **6.** $\frac{3}{4}$ **7.** $\frac{5}{7}$ **8.** $\frac{15}{16}$ **9.** $\frac{3}{8}$ **10.** $\frac{1}{5}$

Practice (regular) 2-4

1. $\frac{4}{5}$; $\frac{5}{6}$, $\frac{4}{5} < \frac{5}{6}$ **2.** $\frac{7}{8}$; $\frac{2}{3}$, $\frac{7}{8} > \frac{2}{3}$ **3.** $\frac{9}{10}$, $\frac{7}{8}$; $\frac{9}{10} > \frac{7}{8}$ **4.** 24 **5.** 24 **6.** 10
7. 30 **8.** 60 **9.** 30 **10.** > **11.** = **12.** < **13.** > **14.** > **15.** =
16. < **17.** < **18.** < **19.** $\frac{1}{6}, \frac{1}{4}, \frac{1}{3}$ **20.** $\frac{1}{2}, \frac{5}{6}, \frac{7}{8}$ **21.** $\frac{1}{4}, \frac{3}{8}, \frac{2}{5}$
22. $\frac{5}{9}, \frac{2}{3}, \frac{7}{8}$ **23.** $\frac{3}{8}, \frac{1}{2}, \frac{5}{6}$ **24.** $\frac{9}{10}, \frac{11}{12}, \frac{15}{16}$ **25.** $\frac{1}{2}, \frac{3}{4}, \frac{7}{8}$ **26.** $\frac{5}{9}, \frac{7}{12}, \frac{2}{3}$
27. $\frac{1}{2}, \frac{7}{8}, \frac{15}{16}$ **28.** No; $\frac{1}{2}$ is less than $\frac{5}{8}$. **29.** No; $\frac{2}{3}$ is less than $\frac{3}{4}$.
30. Plant C, Plant A, Plant B **31.** Riverton; $\frac{5}{8}$ is greater than $\frac{7}{16}$.

Guided Problem Solving 2-4

1. $\frac{1}{2}$; $\frac{3}{8}$, $\frac{3}{4}$ **2.** Determine which nail is long enough to nail the board into the wall. **3.** Write each fraction with the same denominator. **4.** 8 **5.** $\frac{4}{8}$; $\frac{6}{8}$ **6.** $\frac{6}{8}$ **7.** the $\frac{3}{4}$ in. nail **8.** The $\frac{3}{8}$ in. nail is not long enough to go through the piece of wood. The only nail long enough is the $\frac{3}{4}$ in. nail. **9.** $\frac{1}{4}$; $-\frac{1}{8}$ **10.** $\frac{1}{2}$ in., $\frac{5}{8}$ in., $\frac{11}{16}$ in.

Chapters 1–4 Answers (continued)

Practice (adapted) 2-4

1. $\frac{4}{5}, \frac{5}{6}; \frac{4}{5} < \frac{5}{6}$ **2.** $\frac{7}{8}, \frac{2}{3}; \frac{7}{8} > \frac{2}{3}$ **3.** 24 **4.** 24 **5.** 10 **6.** 30 **7.** 60
8. 30 **9.** > **10.** = **11.** < **12.** > **13.** > **14.** = **15.** $\frac{1}{6}, \frac{1}{4}, \frac{1}{3}$
16. $\frac{1}{2}, \frac{5}{6}, \frac{7}{8}$ **17.** $\frac{1}{4}, \frac{3}{8}, \frac{2}{5}$ **18.** $\frac{5}{9}, \frac{2}{3}, \frac{7}{8}$ **19.** $\frac{3}{8}, \frac{1}{2}, \frac{5}{6}$ **20.** $\frac{1}{2}, \frac{3}{4}, \frac{7}{8}$
21. No; $\frac{1}{2}$ is less than $\frac{5}{8}$. **22.** No; $\frac{2}{3}$ is less than $\frac{3}{4}$.
23. Plant C, Plant A, Plant B

Activity Lab 2-4

1. −9 **2.** −0.057 **3.** 0.0952 **4a.** 0 **4b.** They are equivalent
fractions. **5.** > **6.** < **7.** < **8.** = **9.** > **10.** > **11.** > **12.** <
13. = **14.** <

Reteaching 2-4

1a. 10; 9 **1b.** > **2a.** 4; 5 **2b.** < **3a.** 9; 9 **3b.** = **4.** < **5.** <
6. = **7.** < **8.** > **9.** = **10.** > **11.** < **12.** $\frac{1}{4}, \frac{1}{2}, \frac{4}{5}$ **13.** $\frac{3}{8}, \frac{1}{2}, \frac{2}{3}$
14. $\frac{1}{4}, \frac{5}{6}, \frac{7}{8}$ **15.** $\frac{1}{2}, \frac{5}{8}, \frac{5}{6}$ **16.** $\frac{1}{5}, \frac{2}{3}, \frac{7}{10}$ **17.** $\frac{1}{4}, \frac{2}{3}, \frac{11}{12}$

Enrichment 2-4

1. $\frac{8}{11}, \frac{7}{9}$ **2.** smaller **3.** $\frac{4}{7}, \frac{8}{11}, \frac{7}{9}$ **4.** Sample answer: $\frac{13}{19} > \frac{4}{7}$;
$\frac{13}{19} < \frac{8}{11}$, so $\frac{13}{19}$ falls between these two fractions. **5.** $\frac{4}{7}, \frac{13}{19}, \frac{8}{11}, \frac{3}{4}, \frac{7}{9}$
6. Sample answer: If two fractions have large unlike
denominators, use cross products. **7.** Sample answer: Yes; list
common denominators for some common fractions. Cross
products can be used to determine the rest.

Puzzle 2-4

1. C **2.** A **3.** P **4.** Y **5.** B **6.** A **7.** R **8.** A
CAPYBARA

Practice (regular) 2-5

1. $2\frac{3}{4}; \frac{11}{4}$ **2.** $\frac{19}{8}$ **3.** $\frac{16}{3}$ **4.** $\frac{17}{10}$ **5.** $\frac{37}{8}$ **6.** $\frac{41}{12}$ **7.** $\frac{31}{16}$ **8.** $8\frac{1}{3}$ **9.** 6
10. $4\frac{1}{2}$ **11.** $2\frac{1}{4}$ **12.** $1\frac{5}{6}$ **13.** $6\frac{2}{3}$ **14.** 25 **15.** $4\frac{6}{7}$ **16.** $6\frac{2}{3}$ **17.** 3 mi
18. $2\frac{1}{4}$ mi **19.** $2\frac{2}{3}$ mi **20.** $3\frac{2}{3}$ mi **21.** 29

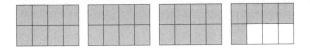

Guided Problem Solving 2-5

1. Find how many eighths of an inch are in $25\frac{1}{4}$ in. **2.** a fraction
in which the numerator is greater than the denominator **3.** 8
4. $25\frac{1}{4} \cdot 8$ **5.** Write $25\frac{1}{4}$ as an improper fraction. **6.** 202
7. 202 eighths of an inch **8.** $202 \div 8 = 25\frac{1}{4}$ **9.** $\frac{35}{24}$ cups

Practice (adapted) 2-5

1. $2\frac{3}{4}; \frac{11}{4}$ **2.** $\frac{19}{8}$ **3.** $\frac{16}{3}$ **4.** $\frac{37}{8}$ **5.** $\frac{41}{12}$ **6.** $8\frac{1}{3}$ **7.** 6 **8.** $2\frac{1}{4}$ **9.** $1\frac{5}{6}$
10. 3 mi **11.** $2\frac{1}{4}$ mi **12.** $2\frac{2}{3}$ mi **13.** $3\frac{2}{3}$ mi **14.** 29

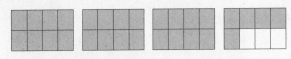

Activity Lab 2-5

1. $\frac{23}{3}$ **2.** $3\frac{1}{9}$ **3.** $\frac{79}{8}$ **4.** $1\frac{11}{20}$ **5.** $\frac{245}{16}$ **6.** $1\frac{11}{32}$ **7.** $\frac{263}{12}$ **8.** $1\frac{23}{27}$ **9.** $\frac{899}{25}$
10. $8\frac{3}{8}$ **11.** $\frac{2,353}{40}$ **12.** $28\frac{1}{3}$ **13.** $\frac{3,139}{63}$ **14.** $1\frac{81}{82}$ **15.** $\frac{8,941}{446}$ **16.** $146\frac{2}{7}$

Reteaching 2-5

1. $\frac{13}{4}$ **2.** $\frac{8}{3}$ **3.** $\frac{11}{4}$ **4.** $\frac{37}{7}$ **5.** $\frac{27}{4}$ **6.** $\frac{10}{9}$ **7.** $\frac{9}{2}$ **8.** $\frac{19}{5}$ **9.** $\frac{31}{6}$
10. $\frac{10}{3}$ **11.** $\frac{47}{8}$ **12.** $\frac{33}{8}$ **13.** $3\frac{1}{2}$ **14.** 6 **15.** $4\frac{2}{5}$ **16.** $5\frac{1}{3}$
17. $5\frac{7}{8}$ **18.** 8 **19.** $4\frac{1}{4}$ **20.** $3\frac{1}{2}$ **21.** $2\frac{3}{5}$ **22.** $5\frac{3}{4}$ **23.** $1\frac{4}{9}$
24. 7

Enrichment 2-5

1. $1\frac{2}{3}, \frac{5}{3}$ **2.** $1\frac{3}{5}, \frac{8}{5}$ **3.** $1\frac{5}{8}, \frac{13}{8}$ **4.** $1\frac{8}{13}, \frac{21}{13}$ **5.** Sample answer: The
numerator is the sum of the numerators of the two prior
fractions; the denominator is the sum of the two prior
denominators. **6.** $\frac{233}{144}$

Puzzle 2-5

1. $\frac{4}{3} = 1\frac{1}{3}$ **2.** $\frac{3}{2} = 1\frac{1}{2}$ **3.** $\frac{17}{5} = 3\frac{2}{5}$ **4.** $\frac{14}{6} = 2\frac{1}{3}$ **5.** $9\frac{7}{8} = \frac{79}{8}$
6. $2\frac{5}{8} = \frac{21}{8}$ **7.** $8\frac{4}{5} = \frac{44}{5}$ **8.** $11\frac{6}{7} = \frac{83}{7}$

Practice (regular) 2-6

1. 0.6 **2.** 0.875 **3.** $0.\overline{7}$ **4.** 0.3125 **5.** $0.1\overline{6}$ **6.** 0.625 **7.** $0.\overline{3}$
8. $0.\overline{6}$ **9.** 0.9 **10.** $0.\overline{63}$ **11.** 0.45 **12.** 0.75 **13.** $0.\overline{4}$ **14.** $0.\overline{81}$
15. 0.55 **16.** $\frac{3}{5}$ **17.** $\frac{9}{20}$ **18.** $\frac{31}{50}$ **19.** $\frac{4}{5}$ **20.** $\frac{13}{40}$ **21.** $\frac{29}{40}$ **22.** $4\frac{3}{4}$
23. $\frac{33}{100}$ **24.** $\frac{37}{40}$ **25.** $3\frac{4}{5}$ **26.** $4\frac{7}{10}$ **27.** $\frac{1}{20}$ **28.** $\frac{13}{20}$ **29.** $\frac{171}{200}$ **30.** $\frac{13}{125}$
31. $\frac{47}{100}$ **32.** $\frac{447}{500}$ **33.** $\frac{69}{250}$ **34.** 0.02, $\frac{1}{5}$, $0.\overline{2}$ **35.** $1\frac{1}{10}$, 1.101, $1.\overline{1}$
36. $\frac{6}{5}$, $1.\overline{3}$, $1\frac{5}{6}$ **37.** $4.\overline{3}$, $4\frac{3}{7}$, $\frac{9}{2}$ **38.** beam, vault, uneven parallel
bars; $\frac{4}{9}$, 0.33, $\frac{1}{7}$

Guided Problem Solving 2-6

1. Order the DNA contents of the organisms. **2.** Make all the
numbers fractions or make all the numbers decimals. **3.** 0.85
4. 0.76 **5.** mosquito **6.** sea star **7.** $\frac{17}{20}$ pg, $\frac{19}{25}$ pg, 0.19 pg,
0.024 pg **8.** $\frac{19}{100}$; $\frac{3}{125}$, $\frac{17}{20}$ pg, $\frac{19}{25}$ pg, 0.19 pg, 0.024 pg; yes
9. 0.25 oz, $\frac{9}{16}$ oz, 0.6 oz, $\frac{2}{3}$ oz

Chapters 1–4 Answers (continued)

Practice (adapted) 2-6

1. 0.6 **2.** 0.875 **3.** $0.\overline{7}$ **4.** 0.3125 **5.** $0.1\overline{6}$ **6.** 0.625 **7.** $0.\overline{3}$
8. $0.\overline{6}$ **9.** 0.9 **10.** $\frac{3}{5}$ **11.** $\frac{9}{20}$ **12.** $\frac{31}{50}$ **13.** $\frac{4}{5}$ **14.** $\frac{13}{40}$ **15.** $\frac{29}{40}$
16. $4\frac{3}{4}$ **17.** $\frac{33}{100}$ **18.** $\frac{37}{40}$ **19.** $3\frac{4}{5}$ **20.** $4\frac{7}{10}$ **21.** $\frac{1}{20}$ **22.** $0.02, \frac{1}{5},$
$0.\overline{2}$ **23.** $1\frac{1}{10}, 1.101, 1.\overline{1}$ **24.** $\frac{6}{5}, 1.\overline{3}, 1\frac{5}{6}$ **25.** $4.\overline{3}, 4\frac{3}{7}, \frac{9}{2}$
26. beam, vault, uneven parallel bars; $\frac{4}{9}, 0.33, \frac{1}{7}$

Activity Lab 2-6

1. 0.375 **2.** $0.8\overline{3}$ **3.** $0.58\overline{3}$ **4.** 0.8 **5.** $0.\overline{8}$ **6.** 0.3 **7.** $0.2\overline{6}$
8. 0.6875 **9.** 5, 8, 10, 16 **10.** 2s and 5s **11.** 6, 9, 12, 15 **12.** 2, 3,
5, 11 **13.** Denominators for terminating decimals have only 2s,
only 5s, or 2s and 5s as prime factors. **14a.** repeating
14b. terminating **14c.** terminating **14d.** terminating
14e. repeating **14f.** repeating **15.** Sample answer: $\frac{111}{160}$
16. Sample answer: $\frac{32}{231}$

Reteaching 2-6

1. 0.8 **2.** 0.75 **3.** $0.1\overline{6}$ **4.** 0.25 **5.** $0.\overline{6}$ **6.** 0.7 **7** $0.\overline{5}$
8. 0.2 **9.** 0.375 **10.** $\frac{2}{5}$ **11.** $\frac{3}{4}$ **12.** $1\frac{1}{2}$ **13.** $\frac{7}{20}$ **14.** $2\frac{7}{10}$
15. $1\frac{4}{5}$ **16.** $\frac{5}{8}$ **17.** $\frac{39}{50}$ **18.** $\frac{22}{25}$ **19.** $\frac{13}{6}, 2.\overline{6}, 2\frac{5}{6}$ **20.** $2\frac{1}{200}, 2.0202,$
$2.\overline{02}$ **21.** $\frac{5}{4}, 1.\overline{4}, 1\frac{4}{5}$

Enrichment 2-6

1. 0.375 **2.** $0.8\overline{3}$ **3.** $0.58\overline{3}$ **4.** 0.8 **5.** $0.\overline{8}$ **6.** 0.3 **7.** 5, 8, 10
8. 2, 5 **9.** 6, 9, 12 **10.** 2, 3 **11.** Sample answer: Denominators
for terminating decimals have only 2, only 5, or 2 and 5 as
prime factors. **12a.** repeating **12b.** terminating
12c. repeating **12d.** repeating **13.** Sample answer: $\frac{102}{160}$
14. Sample answer: $\frac{36}{101}$

Puzzle 2-6

1. 5 **2.** 19 **3.** 12 **4.** $8\frac{1}{2}$ **5.** 34 **6.** 92 **7.** 31

Practice (regular) 2-7

1. > **2.** > **3.** > **4.** > **5.** < **6.** > **7.** > **8.** = **9.** < **10.** $-\frac{3}{2},$
$-0.5, \frac{5}{4}, 1.5$ **11.** $-0.9, 0.09, \frac{1}{11}, \frac{1}{10}$ **12.** $-\frac{11}{12}, -\frac{1}{6}, -0.1, 0.1\overline{2}$
13. $-6.6, -\frac{5}{6}, 0.6, \frac{2}{3}$ **14.** $-1.33, -1\frac{3}{10}, 1.312, 1\frac{3}{8}$ **15.** $-1, -\frac{8}{9}, \frac{4}{5}, 1$
16. $\frac{3}{10}$ **17.** $-\frac{5}{6}$ **18.** $\frac{1}{4}$ **19.** $\frac{1}{2}$ **20.** noon **21.** Shelly

Guided Problem Solving 2-7

1. $\frac{1}{25}; 0.25; \frac{1}{5}$ **2.** Find which animal's eggs have the highest
survival rate. **3.** Change the fractions to decimals. **4.** 0.04
5. 0.2 **6.** 0.25 **7.** frog **8.** $\frac{1}{4}$; yes **9.** the 0.62 in. nail

Practice (adapted) 2-7

1. > **2.** > **3.** > **4.** > **5.** < **6.** > **7.** $-\frac{3}{2}, -0.5, \frac{5}{4}, 1.5$
8. $-0.9, 0.09, \frac{1}{11}, \frac{1}{10}$ **9.** $-\frac{11}{12}, -\frac{1}{6}, -0.1, 0.1\overline{2}$ **10.** $-6.6, -\frac{5}{6}, 0.6, \frac{2}{3}$
11. $\frac{3}{10}$ **12.** $-\frac{5}{6}$ **13.** $\frac{1}{4}$ **14.** noon **15.** Shelly

Activity Lab 2-7

1a. 2; 5 **1b.** 4; 5 **1c.** 8; 5 **1d.** 16; 5 **1e.** 32; 5 **1f.** 64; 5
2. Sample answer: Dividends stay the same, divisors are
divided by 2, quotients are multiplied by 2. **3.** Sample answer:
Dividends are divided by 10, divisors are divided by 10,
quotients stay the same. **4a.** 2; 2 **4b.** 4; 2 **4c.** 8; 2 **4d.** 16; 2
4e. 32; 2 **5.** Check students' answers.

Reteaching 2-7

1. > **2.** < **3.** < **4.** > **5.** < **6.** = **7.** $-0.35, -\frac{1}{3}, -\frac{3}{10}, 0.3$
8. $-0.25, \frac{1}{5}, 0.21, \frac{3}{10}$ **9.** Your brother's investment is worth
more.

Enrichment 2-7

1a. $-\frac{5}{8}, -\frac{1}{2}, 0.25$ **1b.** $-\frac{5}{6}, \frac{1}{3}, 0.7$ **1c.** $-\frac{14}{22}, -\frac{25}{41}, -0.516, \frac{13}{50}$
2. Sample answer: Use Beth's way for the first three; the
fractions can easily be shown on a number line. Use Leroy's
way for the others; the fractions are not as easily shown on a
number line.

Puzzle 2-7

1. VIRGINIA **2.** KENTUCKY **3.** WISCONSIN
4. CONNECTICUT

Practice (regular) 2-8

1. 7.3×10^7 **2.** 4.3×10^3 **3.** 5.1×10^2 **4.** 5.687×10^4
5. 6.89×10^4 **6.** 9.8×10^{10} **7.** 4.89×10^6 **8.** 3.8×10^1
9. 1.2×10^5 **10.** 5.43×10^5 **11.** 2.7×10^1 **12.** 5.4×10^4
13. 5,700,000 **14.** 245,000,000 **15.** 470,600,000,000 **16.** 80
17. 7,200 **18.** 1,630,000,000,000 **19.** 803,000,000,000,000
20. 32,600 **21.** 517,900 **22.** 2×10^5 **23.** 2.2×10^8 **24.** 1×10^{14}
25. 2.8×10^9 **26.** 1.06×10^7 **27.** 9.19263177×10^9

Guided Problem Solving 2-8

1. Write the number 350,000 in scientific notation.
2. A number in scientific notation is written as the product of
two factors. One factor is greater than or equal to 1 or less than
10, and the other is a power of 10. **3.** 5 places **4.** 5 **5.** 3.5 and
10^5 **6.** 3.5×10^5 **7.** 350,000; yes **8.** 2.87509286×10^8

Chapters 1–4 Answers (continued)

Practice (adapted) 2-8

1. 7.3×10^7 **2.** 4.3×10^3 **3.** 5.1×10^2 **4.** 5.687×10^4
5. 6.89×10^4 **6.** 9.8×10^{10} **7.** 4.89×10^6 **8.** 3.8×10^1
9. 5,700,000 **10.** 245,000,000 **11.** 470,600,000,000 **12.** 80
13. 7,200 **14.** 1,630,000,000,000 **15.** 2×10^5 **16.** 2.2×10^8
17. 2.8×10^9 **18.** 9.19263177×10^9

Activity Lab 2-8

1. Mercury: 5.709×10^7; Mercury: 1.082×10^8; Earth: 1.496×10^8; Mars: 2.2794×10^8; Jupiter: 7.784×10^8; Saturn: 1.4236×10^9; Uranus: 2.867×10^9; Neptune: 4.4484×10^9; Pluto: 5.9096×10^9 **2.** Check students' answers.

Reteaching 2-8

1. 3, left; 3.5, 10^3 **2.** 6, left; 1.4, 10^6 **3.** 9.3×10^7 **4.** 1.2×10^6
5. 1.7×10^4 **6.** 7.5×10^5 **7.** 5.6×10^{11} **8.** 3.48×10^7
9. 2,580 **10.** 8,000,000 **11.** 481,600 **12.** 811 **13.** 80.03
14. 5,660,000,000 **15.** 423 **16.** 99,920,000,000

Enrichment 2-8

1a.

343	49	7	1
4	5	0	3

1b. 1,620

2a.

4,096	512	64	8	1
7	1	4	6	2

2b. 29,490

3a.

128	64	32	16	8	4	2	1
1	0	1	1	0	1	1	1

3b. 183

Puzzle 2-8

1. 0.0002 **2.** 369,870,000 **3.** 0.00000063 **4.** 50,120,000
5. 301,650 **6.** 475,000,000 **7.** 561 **8.** 266,720 **9.** 9,602

Chapter 2A Graphic Organizer

1. Exponents, Factors, and Fractions **2.** 8 **3.** Writing Short Responses **4.** Check students' diagrams.

Chapter 2B Reading Comprehension

1. The geysers at Yellowstone National Park **2.** $1\frac{1}{4}$
3. $5 \text{ min} \times \frac{1 \text{ hr}}{60 \text{ min}} = \frac{5}{60} \text{ hr} = \frac{1}{12} \text{ hr}$ **4.** Steamboat Geyser
5. $\frac{5 \text{ min}}{10,000 \text{ gal}} = \frac{1 \text{ min}}{2,000 \text{ gal}}; \frac{5 \text{ min}}{12,000 \text{ gal}} = \frac{1 \text{ min}}{2,400 \text{ gal}}$; 2,000 to 2,400 gallons per minute **6.** a

Chapter 2C Reading/Writing Math Symbols

1. Negative seven is less than six. **2.** Four raised to the third power is sixty-four. **3.** Negative three is greater than negative five. **4.** The absolute value of negative five is five. **5.** Three squared is nine. **6.** Three and one hundredth is approximately equal to three. **7.** Eight divided by four is equal to two. **8.** One-third is less than three-fifths. **9.** Four point six repeating is greater than zero. **10.** Five raised to the fourth power is six hundred twenty-five. **11.** $3\frac{7}{10} < 4\frac{1}{2}$ **12.** $|2.6| = 2.6$ **13.** $-\frac{3}{4} > -10$ **14.** $4.3 \approx 4.\overline{3}$ **15.** $2^5 = 32$ **16.** $6^3 = 216$

Chapter 2D Visual Vocabulary Practice

1. improper fraction **2.** greatest common factor **3.** repeating decimal **4.** equivalent fractions **5.** least common denominator **6.** scientific notation **7.** least common multiple **8.** simplest form **9.** prime factorization

Chapter 2E Vocabulary Check

Check students' answers.

Chapter 2F Vocabulary Review Puzzle

NENPTEXO	EXPONENT
FECINCITSI NATNOOTI	SCIENTIFIC NOTATION
OPWER	POWER
LORNIATA RUNMEB	RATIONAL NUMBER
SIVIEBIDL	DIVISIBLE
TARTEEGS COOMNM RAOFTC	GREATEST COMMON FACTOR
MIEPLLUT	MULTIPLE
LESAT COOMNM METLULPI	LEAST COMMON MULTIPLE
RIPME MUNREB	PRIME NUMBER
MIEDX MUEBRN	MIXED NUMBER
ROMPIERP FRTAINOC	IMPROPER FRACTION

WHAT I TELL YOU

THREE TIMES IS TRUE

Chapter 2 Checkpoint Quiz 1

1. 11 **2.** 108 **3.** 49 **4.** –27 **5.** 2, prime; 14, composite; GCF 2 **6.** 15, composite; 18, composite; GCF 3 **7.** 20, composite; 35, composite; GCF 5 **8.** 7, prime; 13, prime; GCF 1 **9.** 18

Chapters 1–4 Answers (continued)

Chapter 2 Checkpoint Quiz 2

1. $\frac{7}{8}$ **2.** $5\frac{2}{3}$ **3.** $\frac{21}{5}$ **4.** $8\frac{1}{8}$ **5.** $\frac{13}{10}$ **6.** $\frac{27}{7}$ **7.** $\frac{3}{5}$ **8.** $\frac{5}{6}$ **9.** $\frac{2}{3}$ **10.** $\frac{3}{4}$
11. $\frac{5}{12}$

Chapter 2 Test (regular)

1. 66 **2.** 25 **3.** $\frac{7}{9}$ **4.** $\frac{5}{6}$ **5.** $\frac{7}{8}, \frac{7}{11}, \frac{5}{6}$ **6.** $-0.51, -\frac{1}{2}, \frac{1}{2}, 0.\overline{5}$
7. $2^2 \cdot 13$ or $2 \cdot 2 \cdot 13$ **8.** $2^2 \cdot 3 \cdot 5$ or $2 \cdot 2 \cdot 3 \cdot 5$ **9.** $\frac{33}{10}$ **10.** $8\frac{4}{6}$,
or $8\frac{2}{3}$ **11.** 1.325×10^6 **12.** 83,500 **13.** No; $9 + 8 + 2 = 19$,
and 19 is not divisible by 3. **14.** Sample answer: $\frac{2}{6}, \frac{3}{9}, \frac{4}{12}$
15. 1 and 3 **16.** 6^4 **17.** $>$ **18.** 9 **19.** Sample answer: 19, 23
20. Sample answer: 18, 20 **21.** 3 and 13, or 5 and 11 **22.** 121
23. 0.4 **24.** $\frac{14}{25}$ **25.** $\frac{13}{9}$ **26.** The 100th digit is 3.

Chapter 2 Test (below level)

1. 66 **2.** 25 **3.** $\frac{7}{9}$ **4.** $\frac{5}{6}$ **5.** $-0.51, -\frac{1}{2}, \frac{1}{2}, 0.\overline{5}$ **6.** $2^2 \cdot 13$ or $2 \cdot 2 \cdot 13$
7. $2^2 \cdot 3 \cdot 5$ or $2 \cdot 2 \cdot 3 \cdot 5$ **8.** $\frac{33}{10}$ **9.** $8\frac{4}{6}$, or $8\frac{2}{3}$ **10.** 1.325×10^6
11. 83,500 **12.** No; $9 + 8 + 2 = 19$, and 19 is not divisible by 3.
13. Sample answer: $\frac{2}{6}, \frac{3}{9}, \frac{4}{12}$ **14.** 1 and 3 **15.** 6^4 **16.** $>$ **17.** 9
18. Sample answer: 19, 23 **19.** 121 **20.** 0.4 **21.** $\frac{14}{25}$ **22.** $\frac{13}{9}$
23. The 100th digit is 3.

Chapter 2: Alternative Assessment

Exercise	Points	Explanation
1.	2	$\frac{1}{3}; \frac{19}{24}; \frac{11}{24}; \frac{3}{8}; \frac{1}{4}$
	1	Fractions listed but not in simplest terms OR with other error
	0	No response OR multiple incorrect fractions
2.	1	Reasonable answer with explanation
	0	No response OR unreasonable answer OR reasonable answer with no explanation
3.	3	Full set of reasonable answers and correctly expressed fractions
	2	As above but with some errors in expressing fractions
	1	Incomplete set of answers OR full set of answers, but with many errors in entries and fractions
	0	No response
4.	1	Reasonable answer expressed in hours with method shown
	0	No response OR weak response OR no method shown
5.	3	Full set of answers (at least 4) and correctly expressed fractions
	2	At least 3 answers OR 4 answers, but 1 mistake in fractions
	1	Fewer than 3 answers OR 4 answers with more than 1 mistake in fractions
	0	No response

Excursion	
5	Identification of person and reason for choosing; at least 2 tasks, and correct fractions expressed in simplest form; at least 3 activities, and fractions expressed in simplest form
4	Identification of person and reason, at least 1 task and correct fraction; at least 2 activities and fractions (Fractions need not be in simplest form.)
3	Identification of person and reason, at least 1 task and correct fraction; at least 1 activity and fraction
2	Same as above except no identification of person OR reason
1	Lacks major elements and contains no fractions
0	No response

Chapter 2 Cumulative Review

1. A **2.** H **3.** B **4.** H **5.** B **6.** C **7.** H **8.** A **9.** H
10. D **11.** D **12.** H **13.** D **14.** F **15.** C **16.** 60 dancers
17. Max rode farther because $1\frac{2}{3} > 1.6$. **18.** A prime number
has exactly two factors: 1 and itself. A composite number has at
least one factor other than 1 and itself. Sample answer: prime:
5; composite: 6

Chapter 3

Practice (regular) 3-1

1. $\frac{1}{2}$ **2.** 1 **3.** 2 **4.** 1 **5.** 1 **6.** $\frac{1}{2}$ **7.** 9 **8.** $1\frac{1}{2}$ **9.** 13 **10.** 25
11. $1\frac{1}{2}$ **12.** 1 **13.** 2 **14.** 45 **15.** 4 **16.** 7 **17.** 42 **18.** 3
19. 4 **20.** 3 **21.** 7 **22.** 45 **23.** 8 **24.** 40 **25.** about 42 yd
26. 20 pairs **27.** about 4 gal **28.** about \$35 **29.** 3 **30.** 1
31. 80 **32.** 3 **33.** 45 **34.** $\frac{1}{2}$ **35.** $\frac{1}{2}$ **36.** 4 **37.** $1\frac{1}{2}$

Guided Problem Solving 3-1

1. Determine how much chicken you should order. **2.** If the
numerator is bigger than half the denominator, you round to the
next whole number. If the numerator is smaller than half the
denominator, you keep the whole number. **3.** 9 **4.** 8 **5.** bigger
6. up **7.** about 10 pounds **8.** 20 packages **9.** 0.5625; 1; yes
10. 2 yards

Practice (adapted) 3-1

1. $\frac{1}{2}$ **2.** 1 **3.** 1 **4.** 1 **5.** 9 **6.** $1\frac{1}{2}$ **7.** 2 **8.** 45 **9.** 7 **10.** 42
11. 4 **12.** 3 **13.** about 42 yd **14.** about 4 gal **15.** 3 **16.** 1
17. 3 **18.** 45 **19.** $\frac{1}{2}$ **20.** 6

Activity Lab 3-1

1. $A \approx \frac{1}{2}$; $B \approx 1$; $C \approx 1$; $D \approx \frac{1}{2}$; $E \approx 1$ **2.** 4 km **3.** no **4.** Sample
answer: Measure the property in meters.

Chapters 1–4 Answers (continued)

Reteaching 3-1

1. 1 **2.** 0 **3.** 1 **4.** 1 **5.** $1\frac{1}{2}$ **6.** 2 **7.** 1 **8.** 0 **9.** 4
10. $11\frac{1}{2}$ **11.** $9\frac{1}{2}$ **12.** 7 **13.** $5 \cdot 2$ **14.** $12 \div 4$ **15.** $20 \div 4$
16. $5 \cdot 7$ **17.** 24 **18.** 3 **19.** 8 **20.** 50 **21.** 4 **22.** 33

Enrichment 3-1

1. 16 in. **2.** 24 cm **3.** 26 m **4.** 52 yd **5.** 113 in. **6.** 30 in.

Puzzle 3-1

1. $4\frac{1}{2}$ **2.** 2 **3.** 7 **4.** $\frac{1}{2}$ **5.** $7\frac{1}{2}$ **6.** $3\frac{1}{2}$ **7.** 3 **8.** $1\frac{1}{2}$ **9.** $2\frac{1}{2}$ **10.** 9 **11.**
$6\frac{1}{2}$ **12.** 5 **13.** $9\frac{1}{2}$ DIXON, ILLINOIS

Practice (regular) 3-2

1. $\frac{9}{10} - \frac{1}{2} = \frac{2}{5}$ **2.** $\frac{1}{3} + \frac{1}{4} = \frac{7}{12}$ **3.** $\frac{7}{8} - \frac{1}{4} = \frac{5}{8}$ **4.** $1\frac{1}{24}$ **5.** $\frac{11}{15}$
6. $\frac{1}{3}$ **7.** $\frac{1}{2}$ **8.** $\frac{11}{12}$ **9.** $\frac{1}{6}$ **10.** $\frac{4}{9}$ **11.** $\frac{1}{2}$ **12.** $\frac{19}{20}$ **13.** $\frac{5}{6}$ **14.** $\frac{5}{24}$
15. $\frac{11}{30}$ **16.** sesame sticks, dried apricots **17.** walnuts, almonds
18. pretzels, almonds **19.** raisins, sesame sticks **20.** walnuts,
pretzels **21.** pretzels, dried apricots; or almonds, sesame sticks
22. 0 **23.** $\frac{2}{5}$ **24.** 1 **25.** $\frac{1}{4}$ **26.** $\frac{1}{2}$ **27.** $\frac{1}{2}$

Guided Problem Solving 3-2

1. $\frac{2}{3}$ mi; $\frac{8}{10}$ mi **2.** Determine who rowed farther and by how
much. **3.** The denominators need to be the same. **4.** $\frac{2}{3}$ mi
5. $\frac{8}{10}$ mi **6.** 30 **7.** $\frac{20}{30}, \frac{24}{30}$ **8.** your friend **9.** $\frac{2}{15}$ of a mile
10. $\frac{2}{3} + \frac{2}{15} = \frac{8}{10}$ **11.** 6 pieces of cheesecake left, or $\frac{2}{5}$ of the
cheesecake.

Practice (adapted) 3-2

1. $\frac{7}{8} - \frac{1}{4} = \frac{5}{8}$ **2.** $\frac{1}{3} + \frac{1}{4} = \frac{7}{12}$ **3.** $1\frac{1}{24}$ **4.** $\frac{11}{15}$ **5.** $\frac{1}{2}$ **6.** $\frac{11}{12}$ **7.** $\frac{4}{9}$
8. $\frac{1}{2}$ **9.** $\frac{5}{6}$ **10.** $\frac{5}{24}$ **11.** walnuts, almonds **12.** pretzels, almonds
13. raisins, sesame sticks **14.** walnuts, pretzels **15.** almonds,
sesame sticks **16.** 0 **17.** $\frac{2}{5}$ **18.** $\frac{1}{4}$ **19.** $\frac{1}{2}$

Activity Lab 3-2

1a. $\frac{3}{9}$ **1b.** $\frac{1}{3}$ **1c.** Check students' work. **2a.** $\frac{3}{4} + \frac{4}{8} = \frac{7}{8}$
2b–c. Check students' work. **3–5.** Check students' work.
6a. $\frac{1}{6}$ **6b.** $\frac{3}{4}$ **6c.** 1 **6d.** $\frac{3}{10}$ **6e.** $\frac{4}{3}$ **6f.** $\frac{2}{5}$

Reteaching 3-2

1. $\frac{3}{10} + \frac{4}{10} = \frac{7}{10}$ **2.** $\frac{3}{12} + \frac{6}{12} = \frac{9}{12} = \frac{3}{4}$ **3.** $\frac{5}{8} + \frac{2}{8} = \frac{7}{8}$
4. $\frac{3}{4} - \frac{2}{4} = \frac{1}{4}$ **5.** $\frac{5}{9} - \frac{3}{9} = \frac{2}{9}$ **6.** $\frac{9}{15} - \frac{5}{15} = \frac{4}{15}$ **7.** $1\frac{3}{5}$ **8.** $\frac{1}{4}$
9. $\frac{1}{6}$ **10.** $\frac{1}{6}$ **11.** $1\frac{1}{8}$ **12.** $\frac{5}{8}$ **13.** $\frac{1}{2}$ **14.** $\frac{4}{1}$ **15.** $1\frac{2}{5}$ **16.** $\frac{7}{12}$
17. $1\frac{1}{8}$ **18.** $\frac{1}{10}$

Enrichment 3-2

1. A fraction with the numerator less than the denominator.
2. 2 fractions **3.** 4 digits **4.** $\frac{2}{4}, \frac{2}{6}; \frac{2}{8}, \frac{4}{6}; \frac{4}{8}, \frac{6}{8}$ **5.** $\frac{2}{4}, \frac{6}{6}; \frac{2}{8}, \frac{4}{8}, \frac{2}{6}$
6.

Fraction Pairs	Sum	Difference
$\frac{2}{4}, \frac{6}{8}$	$1\frac{1}{4}$	$\frac{1}{4}$
$\frac{2}{6}, \frac{4}{8}$	$\frac{5}{6}$	$\frac{1}{6}$
$\frac{2}{8}, \frac{4}{6}$	$\frac{11}{12}$	$\frac{5}{12}$

7a. $\frac{2}{4} + \frac{6}{8}$ **7b.** $\frac{4}{6} - \frac{2}{8}$ **7c.** $\frac{2}{6} + \frac{4}{8}$ **7d.** $\frac{4}{8} - \frac{2}{6}$ **8.** Estimate the
sums and differences. Use compensation to adjust for the
values of the fractions **9a.** $\frac{2}{3} + \frac{6}{8}$ **9b.** $\frac{3}{6} - \frac{2}{8}$ **9c.** $\frac{2}{6} + \frac{3}{8}$
9d. $\frac{3}{8} - \frac{2}{6}$

Puzzle 3-2

1. $2\frac{3}{4}$ **2.** $\frac{1}{2}$ **3.** $\frac{3}{8}$ **4.** 5 **5.** $\frac{1}{16}$
LOUISIANA

Practice (regular) 3-3

1. 9 **2.** $11\frac{5}{8}$ **3.** $8\frac{3}{4}$ **4.** $12\frac{1}{2}$ **5.** $15\frac{5}{12}$ **6.** $14\frac{1}{2}$ **7.** $2\frac{1}{2}$ **8.** $6\frac{7}{10}$
9. $7\frac{3}{10}$ **10.** $3\frac{1}{6}$ **11.** $3\frac{1}{4}$ **12.** $8\frac{3}{4}$ **13.** $\frac{5}{12}$ **14.** $1\frac{5}{8}$ **15.** $17\frac{5}{8}$ **16.** $\frac{7}{12}$
17. $20\frac{19}{20}$ **18.** $\frac{13}{30}$ **19.** $1\frac{1}{3}$ h **20.** $5\frac{3}{4}$ h **21.** $4\frac{11}{12}$ h **22.** $14\frac{1}{6}$ h

Guided Problem Solving 3-3

1. $4\frac{3}{8}$ mi; $3\frac{1}{2}$ mi **2.** Find the total distance you hiked. **3.** $4\frac{3}{8}$ is
about 4, $3\frac{1}{2}$ is about 4, so $4 + 4 = 8$. **4.** 7 **5.** a common
denominator **6.** 8 **7.** $\frac{7}{8}$ **8.** $7\frac{7}{8}$ **9.** $7\frac{7}{8}$ miles **10.** yes **11.** $4\frac{1}{8}$ mi

Practice (adapted) 3-3

1. 9 **2.** $11\frac{5}{8}$ **3.** $12\frac{1}{2}$ **4.** $15\frac{5}{12}$ **5.** $2\frac{1}{2}$ **6.** $6\frac{7}{10}$ **7.** $3\frac{1}{6}$ **8.** $3\frac{1}{4}$
9. $\frac{5}{12}$ **10.** $1\frac{5}{8}$ **11.** $\frac{7}{12}$ **12.** $20\frac{19}{20}$ **13.** $1\frac{1}{3}$ h **14.** $5\frac{3}{4}$ h **15.** $4\frac{11}{12}$ h
16. $14\frac{1}{6}$ h

Activity Lab 3-3

1–4. Check students' work. **5.** Sample answer: Less than; the
total height of the desk and the chair is less than the height of
the classroom. **6.** Sample answer: Yes, if the height of the chair
is greater than $2\frac{3}{4}$ ft.

Reteaching 3-3

1. $4\frac{6}{8} - 2\frac{3}{8} = 2\frac{3}{8}$ **2.** $4\frac{7}{12} - 2\frac{10}{12} = 6\frac{17}{12} = 7\frac{5}{12}$ **3.** $4\frac{5}{15} - 1\frac{9}{15} =$
$3\frac{20}{15} - 1\frac{9}{15} = 2\frac{11}{15}$ **4.** $3\frac{7}{10}$ **5.** $6\frac{5}{18}$ **6.** $1\frac{3}{10}$ **7.** $\frac{5}{6}$ **8.** $3\frac{1}{12}$ **9.** $7\frac{5}{6}$
10. $4\frac{9}{10}$ **11.** $13\frac{7}{12}$ **12.** $11\frac{3}{10}$ **13.** $5\frac{9}{16}$ **14.** $1\frac{7}{10}$ **15.** $8\frac{1}{10}$
16. $3\frac{13}{20}$ **17.** $11\frac{3}{10}$ **18.** $\frac{1}{6}$ **19.** $19\frac{1}{8}$ in.

Chapters 1–4 Answers (continued)

Enrichment 3-3

1. Areas of shapes A and B **2.** $4\frac{2}{3}$ m² **3.** $1\frac{1}{3}$ m²

4–5.

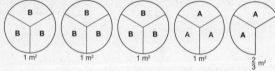

6. $1\frac{2}{3}$ m² **7.** 3 m² **8.** $1\frac{2}{3} + 3 = 4\frac{2}{3}$ **9.** Shape C: $3\frac{1}{4}$ in.²; Shape D: $5\frac{1}{2}$ in.²

Puzzle 3-3

1–5.

$2\frac{6}{11}$	$2\frac{7}{11}$	$2\frac{2}{11}$
$2\frac{1}{11}$	$2\frac{5}{11}$	$2\frac{9}{11}$
$2\frac{8}{11}$	$2\frac{3}{11}$	$2\frac{4}{11}$

$1\frac{1}{8}$	$1\frac{3}{16}$	$1\frac{3}{8}$
$1\frac{5}{16}$	$1\frac{5}{16}$	$1\frac{1}{16}$
$1\frac{1}{4}$	$1\frac{3}{16}$	$1\frac{1}{4}$

$3\frac{1}{3}$	$2\frac{17}{18}$	$1\frac{1}{9}$
$1\frac{1}{3}$	$\frac{17}{18}$	$4\frac{5}{9}$
$2\frac{1}{6}$	$3\frac{1}{2}$	$1\frac{1}{6}$

$2\frac{1}{5}$	$1\frac{9}{10}$	$\frac{2}{5}$
$\frac{7}{10}$	$2\frac{1}{2}$	$1\frac{3}{10}$
$1\frac{3}{5}$	$\frac{1}{10}$	$2\frac{4}{5}$

$3\frac{1}{4}$	$1\frac{3}{4}$	$5\frac{1}{8}$
$6\frac{1}{2}$	$2\frac{3}{4}$	$\frac{7}{8}$
$\frac{3}{8}$	$5\frac{5}{8}$	$4\frac{1}{8}$

6. Check students' work.

Practice (regular) 3-4

1. $\frac{1}{2}$ **2.** $\frac{7}{10}$ **3.** $\frac{3}{8}$ **4.** $\frac{3}{8}$ **5.** 6 **6.** 20 **7.** 27 **8.** $1\frac{4}{5}$ **9.** $7\frac{1}{5}$ **10.** $1\frac{1}{9}$
11. $1\frac{1}{3}$ **12.** $\frac{9}{40}$ **13.** $13\frac{1}{2}$ **14.** $11\frac{1}{4}$ **15.** 8 **16.** $5\frac{1}{2}$ **17.** 10 **18.** $7\frac{1}{24}$
19. $13\frac{1}{8}$ in. **20.** $22\frac{4}{5}$ cm **21.** $16\frac{9}{40}$ lb **22.** about 8,760,000

Guided Problem Solving 3-4

1. $\frac{1}{4}$ mi; $3\frac{1}{2}$ times **2.** Find how far you jogged. **3.** Multiplication
4. $\frac{1}{4}$ mi **5.** $3\frac{1}{2}$ times **6.** $\frac{1}{4} \cdot 3\frac{1}{2}$ **7.** $\frac{7}{8}$ mi **8.** 4 times; yes, because
$\frac{7}{8}$ mi is close to 1 mi and $3\frac{1}{2}$ is close to 4. **9.** $1\frac{7}{8}$ walls

Practice (adapted) 3-4

1. $\frac{1}{2}$ **2.** $\frac{7}{10}$ **3.** $\frac{3}{8}$ **4.** 6 **5.** 27 **6.** $1\frac{4}{5}$ **7.** $1\frac{1}{9}$ **8.** $1\frac{1}{3}$ **9.** 13.5
10. $11\frac{1}{4}$ **11.** $5\frac{1}{2}$ **12.** 10 **13.** $22\frac{4}{5}$ cm **14.** $16\frac{9}{40}$ lb
15. about 8,760,000

Activity Lab 3-4

1a. There are a total of 10 vertical columns, so five columns is one half of the total. **1b.** $\frac{1}{2}$ **1c.** 25 **1d.** $\frac{1}{4}$ **2a.** 1 **2b.** 4 **2c.** 4
2d. $\frac{4}{100} = \frac{1}{25}$ **3a.** You cannot divide 100 evenly by 3, so you cannot correctly represent either of these fractions using a decimal grid. **3b.** Make a grid with a total number of squares that is divisible by 3 and 6; for example, use 6 rows and 3 columns. $\frac{1}{18}$ **4.** The value of the solution is always less than the values of the two factors.

Reteaching 3-4

1. $\frac{1 \cdot 2}{5 \cdot 3} = \frac{\boxed{2}}{\boxed{15}}; \frac{2}{15}$ **2.** $\frac{1}{4} \cdot \frac{\boxed{33}}{8} = \frac{\boxed{33}}{32}; 1\frac{1}{32}$ **3.** $\frac{\boxed{11}}{4} \cdot \frac{\boxed{5}}{3} = \frac{\boxed{55}}{12}$;
$4\frac{7}{12}$ **4.** $\frac{1}{4}$ **5.** $\frac{1}{8}$ **6.** $2\frac{7}{12}$ **7.** $8\frac{1}{3}$ **8.** $\frac{13}{20}$ **9.** $2\frac{11}{40}$ **10.** 3
11. $1\frac{1}{16}$ **12.** $8\frac{5}{8}$ **13.** $3\frac{13}{21}$ **14.** $16\frac{3}{7}$ **15.** $14\frac{2}{3}$ **16.** 3 **17.** $15\frac{1}{2}$

Enrichment 3-4

1. $\frac{11}{48}$ yd² **2.** $\frac{1}{16}$ in.² **3.** $\frac{1}{6}$ ft² **4.** $\frac{3}{32}$ mi² **5.** $\frac{5}{18}$ yd² **6.** $\frac{1}{6}$ in.²

Puzzle 3-4

1–4.

$3\frac{1}{8}$	•	$\frac{1}{4}$	=	$\frac{25}{32}$
•		•		•
$\frac{3}{8}$	•	$2\frac{3}{4}$	=	$1\frac{1}{32}$
=		=		=
$1\frac{11}{64}$	•	$\frac{11}{16}$	=	$\frac{825}{1,024}$

$2\frac{1}{3}$	•	$1\frac{5}{6}$	=	$4\frac{5}{18}$
•		•		•
3	•	$\frac{2}{9}$	=	$\frac{2}{3}$
=		=		=
7	•	$\frac{11}{27}$	=	$2\frac{33}{27}$

Chapters 1–4 Answers (continued)

$2\frac{1}{8}$	·	$\frac{14}{17}$	=	$1\frac{3}{4}$
·		·		·
$3\frac{1}{4}$	·	$\frac{1}{2}$	=	$1\frac{5}{8}$
=		=		=
$6\frac{29}{32}$	·	$\frac{7}{17}$	=	$2\frac{27}{32}$

$3\frac{1}{4}$	·	$\frac{10}{13}$	=	$2\frac{1}{2}$
·		·		·
$\frac{3}{13}$	·	$\frac{15}{5}$	=	$\frac{3}{5}$
=		=		=
$\frac{3}{4}$	·	2	=	$1\frac{1}{2}$

5. Check students' work.

Practice (regular) 3-5

1. 2 **2.** $\frac{16}{9}$ **3.** $\frac{5}{4}$ **4.** $\frac{4}{5}$ **5.** $\frac{10}{29}$ **6.** $\frac{6}{19}$ **7.** 3 **8.** 10 **9.** $\frac{1}{10}$ **10.** 8
11. $5\frac{5}{9}$ **12.** $\frac{2}{5}$ **13.** $\frac{7}{24}$ **14.** $\frac{1}{18}$ **15.** $2\frac{1}{4}$ **16.** $\frac{9}{16}$ **17.** 2 **18.** $2\frac{1}{3}$
19. $3\frac{2}{5}$ **20.** $1\frac{4}{5}$ **21.** $1\frac{11}{19}$ **22.** $5\frac{3}{7}$ **23.** $4\frac{3}{8}$ **24.** $2\frac{7}{10}$ **25.** $4\frac{1}{3}$ **26.** $1\frac{23}{35}$
27. $2\frac{7}{16}$ **28.** $7\frac{1}{2}$ servings **29.** 40 times **30.** 24 min **31.** $1\frac{1}{4}$ h

Guided Problem Solving 3-5

1. 5 miles; $1\frac{1}{4}$ h; 1 h **2.** Find the distance the manatee can swim in 1 hour. **3.** $\frac{5}{1\frac{1}{4}}$ **4.** $\frac{x}{1}$ **5.** $\frac{5}{1\frac{1}{4}} = \frac{x}{1}$ **6.** 4 mi **7.** Less; yes, the manatee can swim 4 miles in 1 hour. **8.** $3\frac{1}{5}$ miles

Practice (adapted) 3-5

1. 2 **2.** $\frac{16}{9}$ **3.** $\frac{5}{4}$ **4.** $\frac{4}{5}$ **5.** $\frac{10}{29}$ **6.** $\frac{6}{19}$ **7.** 3 **8.** 10 **9.** $\frac{1}{10}$ **10.** 8
11. $5\frac{5}{9}$ **12.** $\frac{2}{5}$ **13.** $\frac{7}{24}$ **14.** $\frac{1}{18}$ **15.** $2\frac{1}{4}$ **16.** $\frac{9}{16}$ **17.** 2 **18.** $2\frac{1}{3}$
19. $3\frac{2}{5}$ **20.** $1\frac{4}{5}$ **21.** $7\frac{1}{2}$ servings **22.** 40 times **23.** $1\frac{1}{4}$ h

Activity Lab 3-5

1–8. Check students' work. **9.** The solutions in each row are the same. **10.** Multiply the dividend by the reciprocal of the divisor.

Reteaching 3-5

1. $\frac{8}{7}$ **2.** $\frac{3}{8}$ **3.** $\frac{10}{9}$ **4.** $\frac{3}{2}, \frac{2}{3}$ **5.** $\frac{9}{5}, \frac{5}{9}$ **6.** $\frac{11}{4}; \frac{4}{11}$ **7.** $\frac{2}{3} \cdot \frac{8}{3} = \frac{16}{9}; 1\frac{7}{9}$
8. $\frac{10}{1} \div \frac{7}{8} = \frac{10}{1} \cdot \frac{8}{7} = \frac{80}{7}; 11\frac{3}{7}$ **9.** $\frac{18}{5} \div \frac{6}{5} = \frac{18}{5} \cdot \frac{5}{6} = \frac{90}{30}; 3$
10. $\frac{2}{5}$ **11.** $\frac{9}{16}$ **12.** 10 **13.** 8 **14.** $\frac{15}{32}$ **15.** $1\frac{1}{5}$

Enrichment 3-5

1–7. Sample answers are given. **1.** $\frac{7}{8}, \frac{3}{8}, 2\frac{1}{3}, \frac{7}{8} \div \frac{3}{8} = 2\frac{1}{3}$
2. $\frac{1}{5}, \frac{1}{5}, 1, \frac{1}{5} \div \frac{1}{5} = 1$ **3.** $\frac{5}{6}, \frac{1}{20}, 16\frac{2}{3}, \frac{5}{6} \div \frac{1}{20} = 16\frac{2}{3}$
4. $\frac{7}{8}, \frac{6}{7}, 1\frac{1}{48}, \frac{7}{8} \div \frac{6}{7} = 1\frac{1}{48}$ **5.** $\frac{3}{4}, \frac{1}{8}, 6, \frac{3}{4} \div \frac{1}{8} = 6$
6. $4\frac{1}{9}, 1\frac{2}{3}, 2\frac{7}{15}, 4\frac{1}{9} \div 1\frac{2}{3} = 2\frac{7}{15}$ **7.** $\frac{3}{7}, \frac{2}{3}, \frac{9}{14}, \frac{3}{7} \div \frac{2}{3} = \frac{9}{14}$

Puzzle 3-5

1. $\frac{2}{3}$ **2.** $\frac{1}{2}$ **3.** $\frac{1}{2}$ **4.** $\frac{1}{3}$ **5.** $\frac{1}{2}$ **6.** $\frac{2}{3}$ **7.** $\frac{1}{6}$ **8.** $\frac{2}{3}$ **9.** $\frac{1}{3}$ **10.** $\frac{1}{2}$ **11.** $\frac{1}{6}$
12. $\frac{2}{3}$

Practice (regular) 3-6

1. multiply **2.** divide **3.** divide **4.** multiply **5.** divide
6. multiply **7.** $2\frac{1}{4}$ **8.** 4,500 **9.** 126 **10.** 12 **11.** 15 **12.** $20\frac{1}{2}$
13. $109\frac{3}{8}$ **14.** 28 **15.** $5\frac{1}{2}$ **16.** 30 **17.** 32 **18.** 2,640 **19.** 6,336
20. $2\frac{3}{8}$ **21.** $2\frac{1}{4}$ **22.** 78,720,000,000 quarts **23.** 188 in. **24.** fluid ounces **25.** feet **26.** miles **27.** fluid ounces

Guided Problem Solving 3-6

1. 4,000 miles; feet **2.** Convert 4,000 mi. into feet. **3.** 5,280 feet
4. multiply **5.** 4,000 miles · 5,280 $\frac{ft}{mi}$ **6.** 21,120,000 feet
7. more **8.** 475,200 ft

Practice (adapted) 3-6

1. multiply **2.** divide **3.** divide **4.** multiply **5.** divide
6. multiply **7.** $2\frac{1}{4}$ **8.** 4,500 **9.** 126 **10.** 12 **11.** 15 **12.** $20\frac{1}{2}$
13. $109\frac{3}{8}$ **14.** 28 **15.** $5\frac{1}{2}$ **16.** 78,720,000,000 quarts
17. 188 in. **18.** fluid ounces **19.** miles **20.** fluid ounces

Activity Lab 3-6

1. sec **2.** 1 **3.** 24 **4.** min **5.** min **6.** day **7.** 5,280 **8.** yd **9.** in.
10. 365 **11.** 6,000 **12.** 33 **13.** 1 **14.** 63,360 **15.** 5 **16.** 2
17. 140 times **18.** 4,800 times **19.** 897,600 ft **20.** $20\frac{5}{6}$ ft

Reteaching 3-6

1. 42 in.; 1 ft = 12 in. **2.** 12 oz; 1 c = 8 fl oz **3.** 80oz; 1 lb = 16 oz **4.** 11pt; 1 qt = 2 pt **5.** 13 qt; 1 gal = 4 qt **6.** 8 c; 1 pt = 2 c **7.** 10,560 ft; 1 mi = 5,280 ft **8.** 12 pt; 1 qt = 2 pt
9. 3,000 lb; 1 t = 2,000 lb **10.** 3 c; 1 c = 8 fl oz **11.** 2 lb; 1 lb = 16 oz **12.** $1\frac{1}{2}$ pt; 1 pt = 2 c **13.** 2 t; 1 t = 2,000 lb
14. $3\frac{1}{2}$ qt; 1 qt = 2 pt **15.** 9 yd; 1 yd = 3 ft **16.** 2,540 miles

Chapters 1–4 Answers (continued)

Enrichment 3-6

1. $\frac{324 \text{ words}}{1} \times \frac{1 \text{ pal}}{3 \text{ words}} = 108$ pals **2.** $\frac{108 \text{ pals}}{1} \times \frac{1 \text{ mut}}{9 \text{ pals}} = 12$ muts

3. $\frac{12 \text{ muts}}{1} \times \frac{1 \text{ lap}}{6 \text{ muts}} = 2$ laps **4.** word **5.** lap **6.** As you convert

a quantity into a larger measure, the number of units decreases.

7. $\frac{8 \text{ laps}}{1} \times \frac{6 \text{ muts}}{1 \text{ lap}} = 48$ muts **8.** $\frac{48 \text{ muts}}{1} \times \frac{9 \text{ pals}}{1 \text{ mut}} = 432$ pals

9. $\frac{432 \text{ pals}}{1} \times \frac{3 \text{ words}}{1 \text{ pal}} = 1{,}296$ words **10.** As you convert a

quantity into a smaller measure, the number of units increases.

11. The larger the unit, the smaller the quantity and vice versa.

Puzzle 3-6

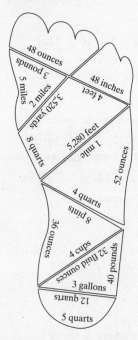

Practice (regular) 3-7

1. 20.7 oz **2.** 1,830 g **3.** 63.70 L **4.** 5,610 lb **5.** 58.3 cm
6. 1,735 mL **7.** 0.95 pt **8.** 516 sec **9.** 2.7 mL **10.** 8.39 cm
11. 3,106 in. **12.** 6.123 lb **13.** 10.6 oz **14.** 81 g **15.** 12.84 yd
16. 75 cm **17.** 13 m **18.** 4,306 ft **19.** 11.1 mL **20.** 45 lb
21. 17.1 km **22.** 4,250 ft **23.** Brother's measurement; since a
foot is a shorter unit than a yard, the measurement in feet is
more precise.

Guided Problem Solving 3-7

1. 2,458.75 ft; 3,000 - ft; How much farther **2.** Find the distance
the climber still has to climb. **3.** 3,000 ft, because it has fewer
decimal places **4.** the nearest whole number **5.** 2,485.75 ft
6. 3,000 ft **7.** 541.25 ft **8.** 541 ft **9.** 2,459; 541 ft; yes
10. 3.8 oz

Practice (adapted) 3-7

1. 20.7 oz **2.** 1,830 g **3.** 63.70 L **4.** 5,610 lb **5.** 58.3 cm
6. 1,735 mL **7.** 0.95 pt **8.** 516 sec **9.** 2.7 mL **10.** 10.6 oz
11. 81 g **12.** 75 cm **13.** 13 m **14.** 11.1 mL **15.** 45 lb
16. 4,250 ft **17.** Brother's measurement; since a foot is a
shorter unit than a yard, the measurement in feet is more
precise.

Activity Lab 3-7

1.

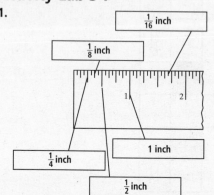

2. Check students' work. **3.** sixteenth inch; inch
4. Check students' work.

Reteaching 3-7

1. 8,448 ft **2.** 8.87 km **3.** 13 in. **4.** 5.64 cm **5.** 4.3 yd
6. 17.33 mm **7.** 8.6 in **8.** 86 cm^2 **9.** 31 cm^2 **10.** 15.4 ft
11. 8 mm **12.** 14 yd^2

Enrichment 3-7

1. 1 mm, 0.5 mm, 18.5 mm − 19.5 mm **2.** 0.1 m, 0.05 m, 20.75 m
− 20.85 m **3.** 0.01 m, 0.005 m, 54.745 m − 54.755 m **4.** 1 in.,
0.5 in., 24.5 in. − 25.5 in. **5.** 1 g, 0.5 g, 29.5 g − 30.5 g **6.** 0.1 mg,
0.05 mg, 54.75 mg − 54.85 mg **7.** ±5 cm **8.** 10.575 g **9.** 0.5 mL

Puzzle 3-7

1. 3 **2.** 5 **3.** 7 **4.** 9 **5.** 2 **6.** 4 **7.** 6 **8.** 8 **9.** 1

Chapter 3A Graphic Organizer

1. Operations with Fractions **2.** 7 **3.** Reading for Understanding
4. Check students' diagrams.

Chapter 3B Reading Comprehension

1. ancient measurements **2.** a foot, which is about $11\frac{1}{42}$ inches
3. 3, 4, 5, 9, $11\frac{1}{42}$ **4.** 12 inches − $11\frac{1}{42}$ inches = $\frac{41}{42}$ inch **5.** 11 inches
$\times \frac{3 \text{ grains}}{\text{inch}} = 33$ grains **6.** 12 inches $\times \frac{3 \text{ grains}}{\text{inch}} = 36$ grains **7.** a

Chapters 1–4 Answers (continued)

Chapter 3C Reading/Writing Math Symbols

1. C **2.** H **3.** A **4.** F **5.** D **6.** G **7.** B **8.** E **9.** 100 km
10. 47 lb **11.** 3.7 oz **12.** 2.5 mL **13.** 5.33 g **14.** $4\frac{3}{4}$ in.
15. 13 m **16.** $5\frac{1}{3}$ t

Chapter 3D Visual Vocabulary Practice

1. convert **2.** sum **3.** define **4.** figure **5.** compare
6. equivalent **7.** order **8.** estimate **9.** table

Chapter 3E Vocabulary Check

Check students' answers.

Chapter 3F Vocabulary Review Puzzle

Chapter 3 Checkpoint Quiz 1

1. 8 **2.** 5 **3.** 3 **4.** 6 **5.** 2 in. **6.** $\frac{7}{10}$ **7.** $5\frac{1}{15}$ **8.** $\frac{1}{9}$ **9.** $5\frac{11}{30}$

Chapter 3 Checkpoint Quiz 2

1. 2 **2.** 76 **3.** 2.5 **4.** 8 **5.** $11\frac{11}{24}$ **6.** $\frac{1}{4}$ **7.** $\frac{9}{10}$ **8.** $4\frac{5}{12}$ **9.** $\frac{4}{17}$
10. $\frac{9}{26}$ **11.** $2\frac{1}{4}$ **12.** $4\frac{12}{13}$ **13.** 7 photographs

Chapter 3 Test (regular)

1. 3 **2.** 10 **3.** 80 **4.** 12 **5.** 2 **6.** 2 **7.** $\frac{1}{4}$ **8.** $\frac{1}{4}$ **9.** $6\frac{14}{15}$ **10.** $12\frac{3}{4}$
11. $\frac{6}{17}$ **12.** $\frac{11}{40}$ **13.** $25\frac{7}{8}$ dollars a share **14.** $\frac{1}{6}$ **15.** $1\frac{2}{5}$ **16.** $11\frac{2}{5}$
17. $\frac{4}{7}$ **18.** $19\frac{1}{2}$ **19.** $1\frac{2}{5}$ **20.** 6 tiles **21.** $8\frac{3}{4}$ yd **22.** $\frac{1}{4}$ **23.** 66
24. 8,800 **25.** 6,800 **26.** 6 oz **27.** 12 ft **28.** 3 pt **29.** 15 min
30. 12 oz **31.** 35 lb **32.** No; divide a circle into two equal
parts. Then divide each of these into three equal parts. You now
have six, not five, equal parts.

Chapter 3 Test (below level)

1. 3 **2.** 10 **3.** 12 **4.** 2 **5.** $\frac{1}{4}$ **6.** $\frac{1}{4}$ **7.** $12\frac{3}{4}$ **8.** $\frac{6}{17}$ **9.** $25\frac{7}{8}$ dollars
a share **10.** 6 tiles **11.** $\frac{1}{6}$ **12.** $1\frac{2}{7}$ **13.** $11\frac{2}{5}$ **14.** $\frac{4}{7}$ **15.** $19\frac{1}{2}$
16. $1\frac{2}{5}$ **17.** $\frac{1}{4}$ **18.** 66 **19.** 6,800 **20.** 6 oz **21.** 3 p **22.** 15 min
23. 12 oz **24.** 35 lb

Chapter 3: Alternative Assessment

Exercise	Points	Explanation
1.	2	$4\frac{1}{3}$ h; $21\frac{2}{3}$ h
	1	One incorrect answer
	0	Both answers incorrect
2.	2	Two routes with appropriate explanation (Possible routes include $E\rightarrow D\rightarrow A\rightarrow$Home and $E\rightarrow A\rightarrow B\rightarrow$Home$\rightarrow A\rightarrow E$)
	1	Two routes with no explanation OR one route with appropriate explanation
	0	No reasonable response OR incorrect routes without explanation
3.	2	$7\frac{9}{10}$ h; 447 min
	1	One correct answer
	0	Both answers incorrect
4.	2	Route starts at Home (or Point B) and ends at Point B (or Home); $15\frac{1}{2}$ h (Home$\rightarrow D\rightarrow E\rightarrow A\rightarrow B\rightarrow C\rightarrow D\rightarrow A\rightarrow$Home$\rightarrow B$)
	1	Incorrect route with correct time OR incorrect time with correct route
	0	No reasonable response OR incorrect route with incorrect time
5.	2	17 mi $(2\frac{5}{6} \div \frac{1}{6})$ with appropriate explanation
	1	Incorrect answer with appropriate explanation OR correct answer with inappropriate explanation
	0	No reasonable response OR incorrect answer with inappropriate explanation
Excursion	5	Map showing routes with estimated running times. Appropriate practice schedule coordinates with map so that total time is about 3 h daily. Explanation complete.
	4	Complete map and explanation as above; incorrect practice schedule due to computation error(s)
	3	Incomplete map OR incomplete explanation OR incomplete schedule
	2	2 of the 3 items above incomplete
	1	All 3 items above incomplete showing partial map, schedule, and explanation
	0	No reasonable response

Chapter 3 Cumulative Review

1. B **2.** J **3.** B **4.** F **5.** C **6.** G **7.** B **8.** J **9.** B **10.** H
11. A **12.** D **13.** F **14.** D **15.** G **16.** A **17.** J **18.** C
19. J **20.** B **21.** J **22.** C **23.** Sample answer: $\frac{6}{14}, \frac{9}{21}, \frac{12}{28}$

Chapters 1–4 Answers (continued)

Chapter 4

Practice (regular) 4-1

1. 29 **2.** 30 **3.** 4 **4.** 14 **5.** 24 **6.** 56 **7.** 11 **8.** 28 **9.** 112
10. $2n + 3$ **11.** 16 more than n **12.** 3.2 times n
13. $25.6n$ less than **14.** n divided by 24 **15.** 45 divided by n
16. $15.4n$ less than **17.** $m + 12$ **18.** $6f$ **19.** $a - 25$
20. $\frac{s}{10}$ **21a.** $5m$ **21b.** \$26.25

Guided Problem Solving 4-1

1. Write an algebraic expression for the approximate number of names in p pages of the directory. **2.** a mathematical phrase with at least one variable **3.** the number of pages in the directory **4.** 11 names **5.** 110 names **6.** 440 names **7.** 440 names **8.** $440p$ names **9.** $440p$ names **10.** 440; 880; 1,320; yes **11.** $48p$

Practice (adapted) 4-1

1. 29 **2.** 30 **3.** 4 **4.** 14 **5.** 24 **6.** 56 **7.** $2n + 3$ **8.** 16 more than n **9.** 3.2 times n **10.** n divided by 24 **11.** n divided by 45 **12.** $m + 12$ **13.** $6f$ **14a.** $5m$ **14b.** \$26.25

Activity Lab 4-1

1. $y + 15 = 20$ **2.** $4n = 48$; $12 \div n = 1$ **3.** $t \times 6 = 60$
4. $p + \frac{7}{12} = 1$; $p - \frac{4}{12} = \frac{1}{12}$ **5.** $r + \frac{1}{8} = \frac{1}{4}$ **6.** $10 - s = 6$
7. $s - 2 = 8$ **8.** $s - \frac{2}{10} = \frac{1}{2}$

Reteaching 4-1

1. 3; 12; 21 **2.** 8; 32; 25 **3.** 8; 8; 40; 8; 48 **4.** 8; 3; 8; 6; 14
5. 18 **6.** 30 **7.** 30 **8.** 192 **9.** 9 plus a number **10.** 6 times a number **11.** 8 less than a number **12.** a number divided by 5
13. $x + 10$ **14.** $x - 4$ **15.** $x + 3$ **16.** $6x$

Enrichment 4-1

1a. $2c$ **1b.** $2c - 6$ **1c.** $\frac{1}{2}c$ **1d.** $2c + 8$ **2.** $c + 2c + 2c - 6 + \frac{1}{2}c + 2c + 8$ **3a.** 200 calendars **3b.** 194 calendars
3c. 50 calendars **3d.** 208 calendars **4.** 752 calendars
5. \$1,504 **6a.** 20 calendars **6b.** 34 calendars **6c.** 10 calendars
6d. 48 calendars **7.** 152 calendars **8.** \$304

Puzzle 4-1

1. $b + 7$ **2.** $4c$ **3.** $q - 5$ **4.** $3a + 2$ **5.** $c - 4$ **6.** $5q$ **7.** $2a - 3$
8. $d + 4$ **9.** $4d$
A VARIABLE

Practice (regular) 4-2

1. 30 **2.** 99 **3.** 29.6 **4.** 57 **5.** $t = 5$ **6.** $w = 8$ **7.** $p = 7$ **8.** $a = 13$
9. $h = 24$ **10.** $g = 128$ **11.** $y = 39$ **12.** $d = 16$ **13.** $w = 25$
14. $t = 4$ **15.** $y = 10.64$ **16.** $x = 104.97$ **17.** $210 + x = 520$; about 300 cans **18.** $\$25.30x = \$227.70$; about 10 bolts of fabric **19.** $\$.79x = \$11.85$; 15 balloons

Guided Problem Solving 4-2

1. 2,000 lb; 55-lb boxes **2.** Write an equation to estimate the number of boxes you can safely place on the elevator at one time. **3.** the number of boxes **4.** 2,000 lb **5.** 55 lb
6. $55x = 2,000$ **7.** 36 boxes **8.** yes; 36 boxes × 55 lb/box = 1,980 lb **9.** $65x = 5,000$; x is about 77 minutes or 1 hour 17 minutes

Practice (adapted) 4-2

1. 30 **2.** 99 **3.** $t = 5$ **4.** $w = 8$ **5.** $p = 7$ **6.** $a = 13$ **7.** $h = 24$
8. $g = 128$ **9.** $y = 39$ **10.** $d = 16$ **11.** $w = 25$ **12.** $210 + x = 520$; about 300 cans **13.** $\$25.30x = \$227.70$; about 10 bolts of fabric **14.** $\$.79x = \$11.85$; 15 balloons

Activity Lab 4-2

Check students' work.

Reteaching 4-2

1. $t = 6$ **2.** $p = 8$ **3.** $h = 21$ **4.** $g = 28$ **5.** $y = 22$ **6.** $d = 20$
7. $d = 14$ **8.** $c = 25$ **9.** $a = 41$ **10.** $q = 444$ **11.** $b = -9$
12. $r = 9$

Enrichment 4-2

1a. $w = 2.4$
1b. $e = 4.5$
1c. $r = 10.5$
1d. $m = 10$
1e. $y = 8.4$
1f. $t = 10.2$
1g. $q = 12.1$
1h. $c = 8.1$

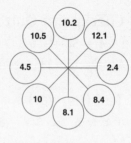

2a. $s = 4$
2b. $d = 6$
2c. $a = 0.5$
2d. $z = 3$
2e. $v = 5$
2f. $n = 6.5$
2g. $g = 2$
2h. $u = 1$

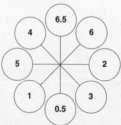

Puzzle 4-2

1. 15 **2.** 3 **3.** –10 **4.** –7 **5.** –8 **6.** 125 **7.** 25 **8.** 103

Chapters 1–4 Answers (continued)

Practice (regular) 4-3

1. 3 **2.** −2 **3.** 5 **4.** −8 **5.** −5 **6.** −4 **7.** 4 **8.** 11 **9.** −10
10. 21 **11.** −6 **12.** 22 **13.** −15 **14.** −25 **15.** 18 **16.** −11
17. −27 **18.** −45 **19.** 65 **20.** 55 **21.** $m + 62.3 = 20{,}186.7$;
20,124.4 miles **22.** $g − \$25.00 = \$176.89$; $\$201.89$ **23.** $x − 3$
$= 11.5$; 14.5 inches

Guided Problem Solving 4-3

1. 12 ladybugs; 9 fewer **2.** Find the number of ladybugs the
student collected yesterday. **3.** the number of ladybugs the
student collected yesterday **4.** 12 **5.** Sample: b **6.** $b − 9$
7. $12 = b − 9$ **8.** $b = 21$ **9.** 21 ladybugs **10.** $12 = b − 9$; $12 =$
$21 − 9$; $12 = 12$ **11.** $72 = k + 15$; 57 in. tall

Practice (adapted) 4-3

1. 3 **2.** −2 **3.** 5 **4.** −5 **5.** −4 **6.** 4 **7.** −10 **8.** 21 **9.** −6
10. −15 **11.** −25 **12.** 18 **13.** −27 **14.** −45 **15.** 65
16. $m + 62.3 = 20{,}186.7$; 20,124.4 miles **17.** $g − \$25.00 = \$176.89$;
$\$201.89$ **18.** $x − 3 = 11.5$; 14.5 inches

Activity Lab 4-3

1. $x − 48 = 300$; $x = 348$ **2.** $x + 4 = 6$; $x = 2$ **3.** $x − 3 = 12$;
$x = 9$ **4.** $x − 13 = 22$; $x = 35$ **5.** $x + 2 = 5$; $x = 3$
6. $x + 16 = 36$; $x = 20$

Reteaching 4-3

1. 6; 2 **2.** 3; 23 **3.** $(−3)$; $(−3)$; −4 **4.** 5; 5; −7 **5.** $(−4)$;
$(−4)$; −6 **6.** 16; 16; −7 **7.** 16 **8.** 1 **9.** −4 **10.** 32 **11.** 47
12. −22 **13.** $j + 2.5 = m$; $m = 9.5$ min

Enrichment 4-3

1. Don's Sports, Economy Sports, and Hockey Shop **2.** League
installment fee and a lesson cost $135. $500 − $135 leaves $365
for equipment. Economy Sports equipment costs $225. Others
cost more than $365. **3.** Yes; he will have $1,060 ($914 for
equipment, $125 for fee installment, and $10 for first lesson).
4. Sample answer: Economy Sports so he has money for the
league fee and can begin playing immediately. He can buy
better equipment when he is sure he enjoys the sport.

Puzzle 4-3

Diagram with connected dots forms the inequality $7 < 17$.

Practice (regular) 4-4

1. 14 **2.** −243 **3.** −28 **4.** −18 **5.** 36 **6.** 48 **7.** −7 **8.** −7
9. 16 **10.** −52 **11.** −7 **12.** −126 **13.** −96 **14.** −5 **15.** 4
16. 288 **17.** −399 **18.** 1,386 **19.** −4 **20.** −8,918 **21.** −113
22. −50 **23.** $15n = 240$, $n = 16$; 16 flowers **24.** $\frac{10{,}500}{n} = 1{,}500$,
$n = 7$; 7 gal

Guided Problem Solving 4-4

1. 26 lb; 390 lb **2.** Find the number of years it will take for a
tree to absorb 390 lb of carbon dioxide. **3.** Multiplication; the
number of years times the amount of carbon dioxide a tree
absorbs each year equals the total amount of carbon dioxide
absorbed. **4.** 26 lb **5.** $26y$ lb **6.** $26y = 390$ **7.** $y = 15$
8. 15 years **9.** $26y = 390$; $26 \times 15 = 390$; $390 = 390$
10. $8x = 1{,}000$; $x = 125$ days

Practice (adapted) 4-4

1. 14 **2.** −243 **3.** −28 **4.** 36 **5.** 48 **6.** −7 **7.** 16 **8.** −52
9. −7 **10.** −399 **11.** 1,386 **12.** −4 **13.** −8,918 **14.** −113
15. −50 **16.** $15n = 240$, $n = 16$; 16 flowers

Activity Lab 4-4

1A. 46 mpg **1B.** 32 mpg **1C.** 33 mpg **1D.** 29 mpg **1E.** 30 mpg
1F. 28 mpg **1G.** 27 mpg **2.** Model A **3.** Check students'
answers.

Reteaching 4-4

1. −5; −5; −6 **2.** 2; 2; −32 **3.** −2; −2; 2 **4.** 8; 8; 4 **5.** 6; 6; 30
6. −3; −3; 15 **7.** −4 **8.** −25 **9.** −80 **10.** 8 **11.** −48
12. −7 **13.** 24 **14.** 35 **15.** 19 **16.** −1 **17.** −18 **18.** 5

Enrichment 4-4

1. $d = 55 \times t$
2.

Rate (in mi/h)	40	55	60	65	70
Time (in hours)	$12\frac{1}{2}$	9	$8\frac{1}{4}$	$7\frac{3}{4}$	$7\frac{1}{4}$
Distance (in miles)	500	500	500	500	500

3. division; $t = \frac{d}{r}$ **4.** $r = \frac{d}{t}$; Sample answer: To find the rate,
divide the distance by the time. **5.** You use inverse operations to
isolate the variable. **6.** Sample answer: If you needed to find
many solutions using the same equation, it would be faster to
have the variable isolated before doing each calculation. **7.** $s = \frac{P}{n}$

Puzzle 4-4

1. $2n = −44$; −22 **2.** $n + 87 = −98$; −185 **3.** $n − 7 = 15$; 22
4. $−6n = 102$; −17 **5.** $n + 10 = −66$; −76 **6.** $n − 17 = −80$; −63
7. $n \div (−9) = 54$; −486 **8.** $3n = −204$; −68 **9.** $n − (−29) = 128$; 99
10. $−19n = −152$; 8 **11.** $n + 43 = −2$; −45 **12.** $−4n = 344$; −86

Practice (regular) 4-5

1. Let g = the price of gas; $6g − 20$ **2.** Let d = the distance
from Boston to New York; $\frac{1}{2}d − 25$ **3.** Let e = the number of
eggs needed in the recipe; $5e − 2$ **4.** Let m = the number of
megabytes in a computer; $\frac{m − 10}{6}$ **5.** $h = 3$ **6.** $s = 9$ **7.** $y = 1$
8. $g = 4$ **9.** $j = 2$ **10.** $w = 4$ **11.** $h = 6$ **12.** $g = 32$
13. $b = 7$ **14.** $\$5 + \$2m$; $\$45$

Chapters 1–4 Answers (continued)

Guided Problem Solving 4-5

1. 2 zucchini per minute; 30 sliced zucchini; already sliced 12 zucchini **2.** Find how long it will take to finish slicing the zucchini. **3.** the number of minutes it will take to finish slicing the zucchini **4.** 30 **5.** 12 **6.** $30 - 12 = 18$ **7.** 2 minutes **8.** $2t = 18$ **9.** 9 minutes **10.** $9 \times 2 = 18$; yes **11.** $t = 2$ hours

Practice (adapted) 4-5

1. Let g = the price of gas; $6g - 20$ **2.** Let d = the distance from Boston to New York; $\frac{1}{2}d - 25$ **3.** $h = 3$ **4.** $s = 9$ **5.** $y = 1$ **6.** $g = 4$ **7.** $j = 2$ **8.** $w = 4$ **9.** $h = 6$ **10.** $g = 32$ **11.** $\$5 + \$2m$; $\$45$

Activity Lab 4-5

1. 32 **2.** 30.2 **3.** 28.4 **4.** 23 **5.** 14 **6.** 5 **7.** –4 **8.** –13 **9.** Some are negative and some are positive. All are less than 32°F. **10.** 4.4 **11.** 1.1 **12.** 0.6 **13.** 0 **14.** –0.6 **15.** –1.1 **16.** –17.8 **17.** –20.6 **18.** –23.3 **19.** They are all negative. **20.** Sample answer: Since 32°F = 0°C, Celsius temperatures below freezing are negative.

Reteaching 4-5

1. $4h + 3$ **2.** $6t - 4$ **3.** $\frac{1}{2}m + 8$ **4.** $4h + 5$; $\$13$ **5.** $10 + 15h$; $\$70$ **6.** $x = 10$ **7.** $n = 10$ **8.** $s = 6$

Enrichment 4-5

1. 11, 12 **2.** –54, –55 **3.** –7, –8, –9 **4.** 64, 65, 66 **5.** 21, 22, 23, 24 **6.** –106, –107, –108, –109 **7.** $40 + 42 = 82$; 41

Puzzle 4-5

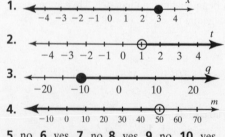

Practice (regular) 4-6

1. $m = 9$ **2.** $y = 35$ **3.** $y = 12$ **4.** $m = 342$ **5.** $y = -60$ **6.** $a = 10$ **7.** $c = 225$ **8.** $t = -2$ **9.** $b = -4$ **10.** $d = -1$ **11.** $z = 153$ **12.** $e = 175$ **13.** $f = 18$ **14.** $y = 3$ **15.** $w = 27$ **16.** $j = -57$ **17.** $(4 + 8) \div 3 = 4$ **18.** $(11 + 4) \times 5 = 75$ **19.** $(9 + 3) \div 2 = 6$ **20.** $(9 - 1) \times 4 = 32$ **21.** C **22.** A **23.** D **24.** B

Guided Problem Solving 4-6

1. $\$20$ per hour; $\$1.50$; $\$117$ **2.** Find the number of hours you need to work to earn $\$117$. **3.** $\$3$ **4.** $20h$ **5.** $20h - 3$ **6.** $\$117$ **7.** $20h - 3 = 117$ **8.** $h = 6$ **9.** 6 hours **10.** $20h - 3 = 117$; $20 \times 6 - 3 = 117$; $117 = 117$ **11.** 7 hours

Practice (adapted) 4-6

1. $m = 9$ **2.** $y = 35$ **3.** $y = 12$ **4.** $y = -60$ **5.** $a = 10$ **6.** $c = 225$ **7.** $b = -4$ **8.** $d = -1$ **9.** $z = 153$ **10.** $n = 4$ **11.** $n = 75$ **12.** $n = 6$ **13.** C **14.** A **15.** B

Activity Lab 4-6

1. 13 **2.** –1.2 **3.** –6 **4.** –1.2 **5.** –6 **6.** 13 **7.** 1 and 6; 2 and 4; 3 and 5 **8.** 1, 2, 4, 5, 6 **9.** 3 **10.** Check students' answers.

Reteaching 4-6

1. $2x$; 3; 9; 3 **2.** $3x$; 4; 7; 1 **3.** 7; 7; 5; 5; -1 **4.** 1; 1; 2; 2; 5 **5.** 2 **6.** 6 **7.** -3

Enrichment 4-6

1. yes **2.** Sample answer: Jane's method, because she did not have to work with fractions.

3.

Jane's method:	John's method:
$3x - 9 + 9 = 24 + 9$	$\frac{3x}{3} - \frac{9}{3} = \frac{24}{3}$
$3x = 33$	$x - 3 = 8$
$\frac{3x}{3} = \frac{33}{3}$	$x - 3 + 3 = 8 + 3$
$x = 11$	$x = 11$

4. Sample answer: When all coefficients and constant terms are divisible by the coefficient of x.

Puzzle 4-6

1. 5 **2.** 3 **3.** 7 **4.** 15 **5.** 6 **6.** 5 **7.** 20 **8.** 2 **9.** 8
Unshaded region is the shape of Nevada.

Practice (regular) 4-7

1.
```
  ←——————————●——————→ x
  -4 -3 -2 -1 0 1 2 3 4
```

2.
```
  ←————————————⊕————————→ t
  -4 -3 -2 -1 0 1 2 3 4
```

3.
```
  ←————●————————————————→ q
  -20   -10   0   10   20
```

4.
```
  ←————————————————⊕————→ m
  -10 0 10 20 30 40 50 60 70
```

5. no **6.** yes **7.** no **8.** yes **9.** no **10.** yes **11.** $x > -2$ **12.** $z \leq 30$

13. $t \leq 20$
```
  ←————————————●————————→ t
  0 5 10 15 20 25 30 35 40
```

Chapters 1–4 Answers (continued)

14. $v > 150$

15. $e \leq 350$

Guided Problem Solving 4-7

1. Explain why -17 is greater than -22. **2.** a number line

3–4.

5. -17 **6.** -17 is farther to the right on the number line. **7.** the definition of ordering numbers **8.** -8 is farther to the left on the number line.

Practice (adapted) 4-7

1.

2.

3.

4. no **5.** yes **6.** no **7.** yes **8.** $x > -2$ **9.** $z \leq 30$

10. $t \leq 20$

11. $v > 150$

12a. $e \leq 350$ **12b.**

Activity Lab 4-7

1.

2.

3.

4.

5.

6.

7. Sample answer: shading and/or arrows

Reteaching 4-7

1a. x is less than or equal to -3. **1b.** closed

1c.

2a. x is less than 3. **2b.** open

2c.

Enrichment 4-7

1. 13 years $\leq x \leq$ 14 years; 90 lb $\leq x <$ 95 lb **2.** Midget; two 90-second periods **3.** 15 years $\leq x \leq$ 16 years **4.** Bantam division

Puzzle 4-7

1. T **2.** O **3.** S **4.** M **5.** A **6.** L
TOO SMALL

Practice (regular) 4-8

1. $w < -6$

2. $a \geq 4$

3. $a > -6$

4. $x \leq 5$

5. $a > -5$

6. $t < 9$

7. $r \leq 6$

8. $a \geq -8$

9. $h > 4$

10. $y < -8$

11. $x + 44 > 85; x > 41$; Lawrence needs to score more than 41 points. **12.** $x + 12,500 \leq 16,000; x \leq 3,500$; you can not load more than 3,500 pounds on the truck.

Guided Problem Solving 4-8

1. give you $35; $100 **2.** Find how much money you need to save to buy the scooter. **3.** $\geq$ 100 **4.** $s + 35$ **5.** at least $100 **6.** $s + 35 \geq 100$ **7.** $s \geq 65$ **8.** at least $65 **9.** $100 **10.** $h + 36 \geq 42; h \geq 6$ in.

Practice (adapted) 4-8

1. $w < -6$

2. $a \geq 4$

3. $a > -6$

4. $x \leq 5$

Chapters 1–4 Answers (continued)

5. $a > -5$

6. $t < 9$

7. $r \leq 6$

8. $a \geq -8$

9. $x + 44 > 85; x > 41$; Lawrence needs to score more than 41 points.

Activity Lab 4-8

1. $x \geq 2$ **2.** $x \geq 2$ **3.** $x \geq 1$ **4.** $x \leq -5$ **5.** $x \geq -3$ **6.** $x \leq -5$
7. Check students' graphs and answers.

Reteaching 4-8

1. $a > 4$

2. $w \leq 4$

3. $a \geq 5$

4. $w \leq 3$

5. $y < 2$

6. $g \geq 6$

7. $x > 5$

8. $r < 6$

Enrichment 4-8

1–5. Sample answers are given. **1.** $6 + 6 \geq 12$ **2.** $-2 + 4 < 3$
3. $6 - 4 < 3$ **4.** $3 + 3 > 4$
5.

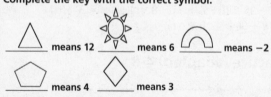

Complete the key with the correct symbol.

△ _____ means 12   ☼ _____ means 6   ⌒ _____ means −2

⬠ _____ means 4   ◇ _____ means 3

Puzzle 4-8

1. $160 + x \leq 500$ **2.** $x + 1 > 3$ **3.** $x + 14 \leq 25$ **4.** $x + 57 \leq 160$
5. $9{,}400 + x > 15{,}000$ **6.** $273 - x \leq 250$

Practice (regular) 4-9

1. $w \leq 6$

2. $a \geq 4$

3. $f \leq -6$

4. $v > 8$

5. $a > -4$

6. $c \leq -9$

7. $f > -2$

8. $a \leq 7$

9. $w \geq -3$

10. $h \leq 10$

11. $5b \leq \$35; b \leq \$7$; Each baseball cannot cost more than \$7. **12.** $4b \leq \$25; b \leq 6.25$; Melinda cannot babysit for more than 6 hours.

Guided Problem Solving 4-9

1. 36 people per run; At least 10,000 people **2.** Find how many times the roller coaster needs to run. **3.** $\geq 10{,}000$ **4.** $36r$
5. 10,000 **6.** $36r \geq 10{,}000$ **7.** $r \geq 277.\overline{7}$ **8.** 278 times **9.** 10,008 people **10.** up to 10 pounds

Practice (adapted) 4-9

1. $w \leq 6$

2. $a \geq 4$

3. $f \leq -6$

4. $v > 8$

5. $a > -4$

6. $c \leq -9$

7. $f > -2$

8. $a \leq 7$

9. $4b \leq \$25; b \leq 6.25$; Melinda cannot babysit for more than 6 hours.

Chapters 1–4 Answers (continued)

Activity Lab 4-9

1. no errors **2.** Step 3: arrow should point to the right.
3. Step 2: adding instead of subtracting 4; $y + 4 - 4 > 6 - 4$;
$y > 2$ **4.** no errors **5.** Step 1: not changing inequality sign;
change $\leq$ to $\geq$; $y \geq -5$ **6.** Step 2: incorrect change of inequality
sign; sign should be $>$; $x > -4$ **7.** Step 2: incorrect
multiplication; $5 \leq x$ **8.** no errors **9.** "at most" means "less
than or equal to"; $2x \leq 40$ **10.** incorrect sign; $30n < 30$ **11.** no
errors **12.** no errors **13.** incorrect coefficient for variable;
$3y < 9$ **14.** no errors

Reteaching 4-9

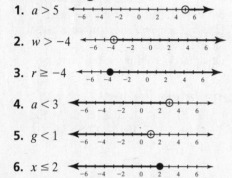

1. $a > 5$

2. $w > -4$

3. $r \geq -4$

4. $a < 3$

5. $g < 1$

6. $x \leq 2$

7. $m < 0$

Enrichment 4-9

1. average score > 40 **2.** addition and division
3. $\frac{x + 49 + 32 + 52}{4} > 40$ **4.** $x > 27$ **5.** Sample answer: Yes;
all of the other averages listed in the table are well above 27.
So it does not appear that the company should have much
trouble achieving their goal. **6a.** $\frac{x + 49 + 32 + 52}{4} \geq 51$; $x \geq 71$
6b. Sample answer: No; the averages listed in the table are
well below 71. It does not appear that the company will achieve
the certificate.

Puzzle 4-9

1. A **2.** C **3.** E **4.** O **5.** L **6.** B **7.** R **8.** U **9.** N **10.** Y
YOUR BALANCE

Chapter 4A Graphic Organizer

1. Equations and Inequalities **2.** 9 **3.** Writing Extended
Responses **4.** Check students' diagrams.

Chapter 4B Reading Comprehension

1. Sample answer: American Indian and Alaska Native population
in the United States **2.** 4 million **3.** 1.5% **4.** California
5. 133,000 **6.** Sample answer: The California population is
much larger. **7.** b

Chapter 4C Reading/Writing Math Symbols

1. C **2.** E **3.** D **4.** A **5.** B **6.** $11x - 9$ **7.** $x + 4 = 13$
8. $x \div 4$ **9.** $|x|$ **10.** a number decreased by ten; ten less than x
11. the product of five and a number; five times a number
12. the sum of a number and three squared; a number
increased by the quantity three squared

Chapter 4D Visual Vocabulary Practice

1. Addition Property of Equality **2.** inequality **3.** solution of
an equation **4.** variable **5.** Subtraction Property of Inequality
6. open sentence **7.** Division Property of Equality **8.** solution
of an inequality **9.** Multiplication Property of Inequality

Chapter 4E Vocabulary Check

Check students' answers.

Chapter 4F Vocabulary Review

1. variable **2.** equation **3.** solution **4.** inverse **5.** inequality
6. Associative Property of Addition **7.** opposite **8.** median
9. commutative **10.** Identity Property of Zero **11.** absolute value
12. integers **13.** additive **14.** outlier **15.** order of operations

Chapter 4 Checkpoint Quiz 1

1. $n - 5$ **2.** $7n$ **3.** $2 \div n$ **4.** $n + 8$ **5.** $h = -4$ **6.** $y = 7$
7. $x = -6$ **8.** $y = 12$ **9.** $m - 12 = 1973$; 1985 **10.** $3x = 27$; 9 hrs

Chapter 4 Checkpoint Quiz 2

1. $h = 6$ **2.** $y = 39$ **3.** $x = 1$ **4.** $3n + 4 = 19$; $n = 5$
5. $2n - 15 = 78$; $n = \$46.50$

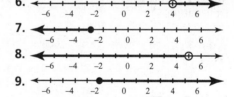

6.

7.

8.

9.

Chapters 1–4 Answers (continued)

Chapter 4 Test (regular)

1. 6 **2.** 13 **3.** 2 **4.** 28 **5.** 27 **6.** 24 **7.** $x = 5$ **8.** $m = 30$ **9.** $a = 11$
10. $y = 9$ **11.** $n = 14$ **12.** $y = 32$ **13.** $y = 45$ **14.** $n = -3$
15. Sample answer: $210p = 1,155$; $5.50 **16.** Sample answer:
$p \div 11 = 15$; 165 players **17.** $t \le 85$ **18.** $h \ge 48$ **19.** $t < 200$
20. $n \ge 6$;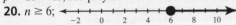
21. $y > 28$;
22. $x < -5$;
23. $p \ge 8$;
24. $x > 2$;
25. $y \ge -14$;
26. $34 + p > 175$; $p > \$141$ **27.** $50b \ge 25,000$; $b \ge 500$

Chapter 4 Test (below level)

1. 6 **2.** 13 **3.** 2 **4.** 28 **5.** 27 **6.** 24 **7.** $x = 5$ **8.** $m = 30$ **9.** $a = 11$
10. $n = 14$ **11.** $y = 32$ **12.** $y = 45$ **13.** Sample answer:
$210p = 1,155$; $5.50 **14.** Sample answer: $p \div 11 = 15$; 165 players
15. $t \le 85$ **16.** $t < 200$
17. $n \ge 6$;
18. $y > 28$;
19. $x < -5$;
20. $p \ge 8$;
21. $34 + p > 175$; $p > \$141$ **22.** $50b \ge 25,000$; $b \ge 500$

Chapter 4: Alternative Assessment

Exercise	Points	Explanation
1.	2	$15; 2($1.50) + 3($2) + 2($3)
	1	Correct process with one computational error
	0	Incorrect process
2.	1	Any six, with the correct class on at least five of the six
	0	No response OR other reponse
3. a.	1	Correct expression for six identified in Question 2
	0	Incorrect expression
b.	1	Correct total cost for six identified in Question 2
	0	Incorrect response
4.	1	Simplified sum of the two expressions
	0	Incorrect response
5.	1	Acceptable response, which meets requirements
	0	Incorrect response
6.	2	Mini Pack saves $6; $21 − $15 Regular Pack saves $10; $35 − $25 Giant Pack saves $22.50; $87.50 − $65

	1	One incorrect amount
	0	Two or three incorrect amounts OR no response
7.	1	Any two Class A, three Class B, and four Class C
	0	Incorrect number of any class
Excursion	5	3 Regular Packs + 2A = 3($25) + 2($1.50) = $78; $21 saved
	4	3 Regular Packs + 2A; no flaws in reasoning, partially complete
	3	3 Regular Packs + 2A; flaws in reasoning; partially complete
	2	Incorrect response due to computational error(s) OR partial correct reasoning
	1	Incorrect response due to process; partial incorrect reasoning
	0	Other incorrect response OR no response

Chapter 4 Cumulative Review

1. D **2.** H **3.** D **4.** F **5.** D **6.** G **7.** B **8.** H **9.** A **10.** H
11. A **12.** G **13.** C **14.** J **15.** C **16.** G **17.** C **18.** H
19. D **20.** $(9.5 + 2.5h) - 1.85$